FRANÇOIS MAGENDIE

Bas-relief portrait in marble of François Magendie, David d'Angers (1789-1856) sculptor, in possession of Dr. Hauriot, Paris, who has kindly permitted its photographic reproduction here for the first time.

François Magendie

PIONEER IN EXPERIMENTAL PHYSIOLOGY AND SCIENTIFIC MEDICINE IN XIX CENTURY FRANCE

By

J. M. D. Olmsted

PROFESSOR OF PHYSIOLOGY, UNIVERSITY OF CALIFORNIA

With a Preface by

JOHN F. FULTON

Illustrated

SCHUMAN'S · NEW YORK
1944

COPYRIGHT 1945 BY
SCHUMAN'S, NEW YORK

This book has been manufactured in
accordance with the regulations of
the War Production Board

PRINTED IN THE UNITED STATES OF AMERICA
BY J. J. LITTLE & IVES COMPANY, NEW YORK

CONTENTS

		PAGE
Preface		vii
Foreword		xi
1. Son of the Revolution		3
2. Revolt from Bichat. 1809		19
3. Pioneer in Experimental Pharmacology. 1809		35
4. The "Volte-Face" from Anatomy and Surgery to Physiology. 1813-1815		45
5. The Publication of the Précis and Experiments on Nutrition, Circulation and Emetics. 1816-1817		62
6. Beginnings of Official Recognition and Interest in Medical Practice. 1818-1822		74
7. The Bell-Magendie Controversy. 1822		93
8. Experiments on the Central Nervous System, Work on Hydrophobia and the First English Visit. 1823-1824		123
9. Medical Practice, Repercussion of Political Affiliations, Work on Cerebrospinal Fluid. 1825-1828		146
10. Marriage, Appointment to Professorship at the Collège de France, the Cholera Epidemic. 1830-1832		172
11. Professional Activities, Published Lectures, Recurrent Sensitivity. 1833-1840		195

PAGE

12. Government Committees and Collaboration with Claude Bernard. 1840-1845   220

13. Semi-Retirement, Committee on Public Hygiene, Last Year's. 1845-1855   243

References   263

Index   281

PREFACE

A DISTINGUISHED historian recently remarked that few nations
which have achieved ascendency in medicine retain that
pre-eminence for more than fifty years. French medicine
gained a commanding influence in the Western world during the time of François Magendie; soon after he died,
leadership passed largely to Germany; now it has come to
England and the United States. Magendie's life coincided
with the most critical period of French history: the chaos
of the late 18th century, the French Revolution, and the
subsequent rise of democratic government and the appearance of physicians such as Corvisart, Bichat, Laennec, Louis
and Cruveilhier. Then came the rise of scientific medicine
associated so intimately with the names of Flourens and
LeGallois, but more particularly with the positive leadership of Magendie.

In the early 19th century American medicine was profoundly influenced by the clinics and experimental schools
of France. Older physicians as well as students who had
recently graduated from our medical schools flocked to Paris
—men such as W. W. Gerhard, Alfred Stillé, George C.
Shattuck, Jr., Oliver Wendell Holmes, James Jackson and
his son, James Jackson, Jr.,—these and many others * so-

---

* Stillé gives the following list of American physicians in Paris in 1836:
"From *Boston:* James Jackson, jun., H. I. Bowditch, O. W. Holmes, George
C. Shattuck, jun., John C. Warren (then past middle age), John Mason
Warren, and John D. Fisher. From *Philadelphia:* George W. Norris, William
W. Gerhard, Caspar W. Pennock, Thomas Stewardson, Alfred Stillé, Thomas
D. Mütter, E. Campbell Stewart, Charles Bell Gibson, John B. Biddle,
David H. Tucker. *Baltimore:* William Power. *Charleston:* G. S. Gibbes,
Peter C. Gaillard, Peyre Porcher. *Virginia:* J. L. Cabell, L. S. Joynes, Ran-

journed there and brought back to this country rich gleanings in new spheres of medical thought. The influence of
the French upon early medicine in this country is a theme
upon which many have dwelt, no one more effectively than
the late Sir William Osler in his essays on Louis, Elisha
Bartlett, and John Y. Bassett in the *Alabama Student*.

At a time when American physicians are once more
returning in large numbers to the soil of France, it is important that they should know something of the scientific
roots from which they themselves have sprung. To understand the gallant co-operation they have received from
Frenchmen in areas liberated during the summer of 1944,
they must know of her history and traditions. The life of
Magendie epitomizes the very essence of the freedom-loving
and enquiring spirit of France, the France which created
Claude Bernard, Pasteur, Lavaran, Roux, and many others
to whom the world looks in deep reverence.

Magendie's life also illustrates some of the qualities
peculiar to men of science in any country—universal curiosity, tenacity of purpose, unceasing industry, willingness
to admit error—and in addition he exhibited personal qualities of restlessness and a certain impetuousness which sometimes brought him into conflict with his contemporaries.
These after all are human qualities which one somehow
expects in men of commanding genius. To neurologists
Magendie's experimental studies have peculiar significance.
Not only did he for the first time satisfactorily distinguish
between the functions of the dorsal and the ventral nerve
roots of the spinal cord, but he also studied elementary
reflexes, the functions of the soft palate (his thesis), and
late in life he published an important monograph—one of
the great rarities of neurological literature—on the cerebro-

dolph. *New York:* John A. Swett, Abraham Dubois, Alonzo Clark, Charles
L. Mitchell, Punnett, Charles D. Smith, Valentine Mott, sen. *In addition:*
Edward Peace, Meredith, Clymer, William P. Johnston, W. S. W. Ruschen-
berger, and John T. Metcalfe."

spinal fluid. In addition to all this he issued a textbook of physiology which was a standard work for many years in many languages, and later a two-volume monograph on the functions of the central nervous system. These were all pioneer endeavors, and through the personal influence which he exerted Magendie attracted many distinguished followers, the best known of whom was Claude Bernard.

We are especially fortunate, therefore, that Professor Olmsted, whose *Claude Bernard, Physiologist* has been so well received, should have undertaken a life of Magendie, for few in this country have a more intimate knowledge than he of French medicine in the nineteenth century. May one not ask that others—perhaps Brown-Séquard—also receive attention from Dr. Olmsted's talented pen?

It is to be hoped that all physicians who have the good fortune to find themselves in France at this time will have the opportunity to scrutinize Professor Olmsted's timely introduction to a phase of the life and thought of the nation which it has been their privilege to assist at a time of supreme national crisis. May they give their assistance in the spirit of repaying an old debt—the debt that all American physicians owe to French medicine of the early 19th century.

J. F. FULTON

Yale University
15 September 1944

FOREWORD

A BIOGRAPHER who attempts to portray a character out of
the past in one sense makes his own picture from bits of
direct evidence which have survived—published works, letters, verbatim reports of speeches. He may also have access
to contemporary portraits, which he will compare with his
own; for he will probably find that these portraits are not
only different in their details from the one which he has
made for himself, but vary one with another according to
the points of view, prejudices, or sympathies of their authors. No matter how his faith is shaken by discrepancies,
he will feel unable to ignore contemporary judgments of
his subject, since they rest upon what a scientist might be
allowed to describe as "immediate sense data."

It happens that in the case of François Magendie we have
three contemporary estimates of him as a man and a scientist from three quite different points of view. In their
chronological order these are (i) the tribute paid by his
pupil and collaborator, Claude Bernard, in his opening
lecture as Magendie's successor at the Collège de France,
February 29, 1856; (ii) the eulogy read by his medical
colleague, F. Dubois, at the Paris Academy of Medicine,
December 15, 1857; (iii) and, finally, the eulogy read by
his scientific confrère, P. Flourens, at the Paris Academy
of Sciences, February 8, 1858. Each of these men knew
Magendie, each seems to have wished to do him justice, but
it is clear that each saw him from his own angle of vision.

Bernard's personal interest was to establish the experimental method for the medical sciences, and his interest in

Magendie was the latter's contribution to that end. He says
here unexpectedly little about Magendie's actual contributions to physiology; for instance, in regard to the Bell-
Magendie controversy he acquiesces in a division of the
credit between the two men, while upholding Magendie's
claim to have been the first to give experimental proof of
the difference in function of the dorsal and ventral roots
of the spinal nerves. Although here, in 1856, Bernard credits
Bell with the establishment of this principle "by admirable
anatomico-physiological considerations," it is to be remembered that ten years later, after he had actually obtained a
copy of Bell's 1811 pamphlet, he revised his opinion and
stoutly maintained in his *Rapport sur les progrès et la
marche de la physiologie générale en France* (1867) that
Bell had entirely missed the point, and that the honor of
the discovery belonged unequivocally to Magendie and to
France. In the lecture to which we have referred he praises
Magendie for his complete exploitation of the experimental
method, a praise which he later qualified by the admission
that Magendie's empiricism had led to lack of plan in his
work; he also praises the service Magendie had rendered
in accustoming the public to the necessity for experimentation on living animals, and he approves Magendie's opposition to the vitalistic doctrines of Bichat and his recognition
of the part played by physical and chemical processes in
the animal economy. He refers to the disconcerting mannerisms of Magendie in his relations with his students, but
makes it clear that in his own case all other considerations
were outweighed by a sincere admiration for the integrity
and real generosity of his master.

Dubois represents the attitude toward Magendie of the
medical profession of the day. He therefore disapproves
equally of his anti-vitalistic approach and of his substitution of experimental physiology for clinical observation in
the teaching of medicine. He reviews Magendie's principal

fields of research—absorption, circulation, the nervous system—and in each case minimizes the value of the work on the grounds (i) that it was all mere verification and control of earlier experimentation, and (ii) that solution of physiological problems was impossible from Magendie's anti-vitalistic point of view. In regard to the controversy with Bell, he granted Magendie only demonstration of Bell's prior discovery, bolstering up his case with a quotation spuriously attributed to Bell's 1811 pamphlet. Although most of his criticism of Magendie's scientific work is merely the reflection of his own general prejudices, nevertheless he is right in one or two specific cases, viz., in repudiating Magendie's deductions from his experiments on cutting certain cranial nerves. His discussion of Magendie's teaching at the Collège de France develops into an attack on animal experimentation as a means of discovering the nature of living phenomena. As a fellow-physician he indulges in mild approval of Magendie's early hospital work and the medical handbooks on drugs and urinary calculi, but condemns him for neglect of his hospital services after he became involved in experimental medicine. He praises the vigor and intelligence which Magendie displayed in public health assignments, but adds that insistence on personal prejudices prevented him from being a good chairman of committees. His summary is that the cult of experimentation "misled the physiologist, effaced the teacher, and suppressed the doctor" in Magendie. Nevertheless, since Dubois apparently wished to maintain a well-established reputation for impartiality, as well as elegance, in his "eulogies," he is careful to credit Magendie with complete honesty as a scientist. He considers much of his work to have been unnecessary, but the activity was not sterile, for the final influence on science was salutary and would be transmitted through the pupils who would carry on the tradition established at the Collège de France. His estimate of Magendie as a person is very kindly.

He admits that after his reputation was established the elderly scientist was not unjustly accused of churlish manners in his professional relations, but he apologizes for him by saying that his natural good temper had been spoiled by the flattery of admirers.

Flourens sees Magendie with the eyes of an experimental physiologist and fellow member of the Academy of Sciences. In his official capacity as Permanent Secretary of this Academy he collects and preserves all the little anecdotes of Magendie's youth and personal life which were remembered by his contemporaries, and he is betrayed into a few of the slight inaccuracies which are characteristic of this kind of evidence. He has high praise for Magendie as an experimenter and appreciates fully the value of his contributions to physiology, with the exception that he takes what seems to have been the conventional view at the time, sharpened by a note of personal rivalry, regarding the Bell-Magendie controversy. He considers that the discovery was Bell's "intellectuellement," if not "expérimentalement." He refers in his text to the 1811 pamphlet, but the supporting references and quotations in his notes are taken, not directly from the pamphlet, but from a French translation, made in 1825, of Bell's "Exposition of the Natural System of the Nerves of the Human Body" (1824), and from the third edition of Bell's "The Nervous System of the Human Body," published in 1836. Some of the passages quoted reproduce the actual wording of the pamphlet, but the general impression of Bell's work to be gained from these later sources is not the same as that which would be derived from Bell's writings previous to Magendie's article of 1822. Flourens rather gives his own case away when he remarks that the enthusiasm over Bell in England was derived from French enthusiasm over Magendie. He regards Magendie as having been a most successful physician, with a larger private practice than he really wanted, and the anecdotes cited in this

connection attest satisfaction, at least on the part of the
patients, with Magendie's administration of his hospital
services. Flourens joins in the general verdict as regards
Magendie's absolute scientific probity, but condemns his
intolerance and unwillingness to recognize the possibility of
other investigators beside himself occasionally being right.
He uses the strongest terms to express his disapprobation
of Magendie's lack of restraint, especially in debate. He
recognizes, however, the difference between Magendie's
public and private manners, and comments on his domestic
mellowness in old age. As a fellow physiologist he completely absolves him from the charges of cruelty which had
been made in connection with his experimentation on living
animals.

These are the three principal contemporary portraits of
Magendie, and in spite, or perhaps because, of the discrepancies which they contain, a composite picture emerges
of the man whom Bernard, Dubois and Flourens had known.
There are other brief surviving personal impressions of
Magendie in his lifetime—those of a French medical student,
less brilliant than Bernard; even those of a young American
finishing his medical education abroad. The documentary
evidence, although not bulky, covers a considerable range,
from the few private records and letters which Magendie
himself thought worth preserving in an old portfolio, to the
original papers and pamphlets which make an independent
judgment of the Bell-Magendie controversy still possible.
The method of dealing with all this material has been a
process less mathematical than the one described by Aldous
Huxley in his "Grey Eminence" as adding "the flattery, the
calumny, and refutation" together and dividing by three.
The author, influenced, no doubt, by his own sympathies
and prejudices, human frailties from which he does not
claim to be more completely exempt than other people, has
made his own portrait of the pioneer of experimental physi-

ology in France, and herewith presents it for the reader's judgment.

I wish to thank Dr. Maurice Genty, Librarian of the Paris Academy of Medicine, Dr. Raymond Neveu of the Musée Gilbert, and Dr. Hauriot for their courtesies to me in my search for Magendie "réliques." I am happy also to acknowledge the critical cooperation of my wife who, as she herself says, always takes great pleasure in representing the unscientific point of view.

J. M. D. OLMSTED.

Berkeley, California.
July 6, 1944.

1

SON OF THE REVOLUTION
1783-1808

"À mon père. Amitié, reconnaissance." [1]

THE most authentic data regarding François Magendie's birth and parentage have been preserved in a document available for consultation, at least before the recent German occupation of Paris, in the Musée Gilbert of the Paris Faculty of Medicine. This document, which records the exemption of Magendie from military service, was signed by the Empress Marie-Louise on August 25, 1805, while she was acting in the absence of Napoleon, who had gone to Boulogne to distribute with his own hand to his soldiers the second award of the coveted crosses of his newly established Legion of Honor. It is here stated that François Magendie was born in Bordeaux, October 6, 1783, the son of Antoine Magendie and his wife, Marie Nichole Deperey Delaunay.[2]

At the time of François' birth, his father was a surgeon in the seaport city. He is said to have been well thought of by his patients, although his reputation was purely local.[3] He had come to Bordeaux from a small town, Pontacq, in

---

[1] Dedication of thesis presented for doctorate of medicine, 1808.

[2] Flourens (1794-1867) in his official eulogy of Magendie written for the Paris Academy of Sciences in 1858 is the authority for biographers who give the day of Magendie's birth as October 15. Claude Bernard (1813-1878), perhaps in a confused recollection of the date of Magendie's death certificate, gives October 8 (*Substances toxiques*, 1857, p. 1).

[3] Dubois, F., *Mém. Acad. Imp. de Méd.*, 22:1, 1858.

3

the lower Pyrenees, near Pau, and was an ardent republican. His wife was Parisian, and her double "place" name, which, when it appears in documents relating to her son, François, is nearly always written "de Perey de Launay," suggests that she laid claim to a rank somewhat above that of her husband, or at least that she may have been less antagonistic to the *ancien régime* than he.

The tradition that the young François remained undisciplined and without schooling until he was over ten years old has led one of his biographers to invent the death of his mother while he was still in infancy and a fictitious stepmother who was supposed to have neglected the offspring of her predecessor.[4] His own mother, however, did not die until François was in his ninth year, and she must at least have acquiesced in the early stages of her husband's educational plan of allowing the child to do whatever he wished without let or hindrance. This policy was in conformity with Antoine Magendie's political principles and with the approved contemporary theory of education. The prime mover of revolutionary thought, Jean-Jacques Rousseau, had laid down the principles not only of government but also of education. In his "Social Contract" he had outlined the ideal state; in "Éloise" he had shown the place of the family in society; and, finally, in "Émile" he had described the proper procedure for educating young citizens. Antoine Magendie, proud of being a member of the third estate, carried his admiration of Rousseau to the point of naming his second son Jean-Jacques, and he rigidly applied to the education of both sons the directions for bringing up the imaginary Émile between the ages of five and twelve. Rousseau had said:

"The first education ought to be purely negative and ought to consist not at all in teaching virtue or truth, but in shielding the heart from vice and the mind from error. If you could do nothing

4 *London Med. Times and Gaz.*, 11:558, 1855.

and allow nothing to be done; if you could bring your pupil
sound and robust to the age of twelve years without his being
able to distinguish his right hand from his left, from your very
first lessons the eyes of his understanding would be open to reason; being without prejudice, without habit, he would have
nothing in him which could counteract the effects of your endeavors. Soon he would become in your hands the wisest of men;
and although you would begin by doing nothing, you would
finally have produced a prodigy of education. . . . Leave your
pupil to himself in perfect liberty, and observe what he does
without saying anything to him." [5]

The chief events of François' boyhood were the removal
of the family to Paris in 1791 when he was eight years old
and the death there, in May of the next year, of his mother,
who had suffered from long-standing illness. This left the
two small boys, François and Jean-Jacques, in the care of a
father whose predominant interest was in the stirring political events then taking place in the capital. The year 1792
was one of the most turbulent in the history of France.
Open insurrection broke out in Paris the month after the
death of the children's mother. Thirty thousand ill-clad
inhabitants of the Faubourg Saint-Antoine stormed the
Assembly Hall and then invaded the Tuileries, some of them
boisterously penetrating to the very room where the king,
the queen and the little dauphin were waiting. In July Paris
streets first rang to the stirring strains of

> "Allons, enfants de la Patrie,
> Le jour de gloire est arrivé."

In August there occurred another attack on the Tuileries,
but this time the crowd was in no playful mood and the
royal family was taken away to be imprisoned in the
Temple. Then came the terrible days of the Commune when

[5] Rousseau, J.-J., *Émile*, 1762, v. i, p. 130.

the streets echoed to wild voices and dancing feet as the madness of the Carmagnole swept over the frenzied populace. With the proclamation of the Republic, September 21, the monarchy fell and the third estate came into its own.

It was no wonder that a zealous republican like Antoine Magendie thought that the provinces were too tame while such events were taking place in the capital. He seems not to have tried to establish in Paris a surgical practice to replace the apparently successful one which he had abandoned in Bordeaux, but to have devoted himself to a career of municipal politics. Citizen Magendie was made surgeon of one of the Paris districts by the Revolutionary Committee, became a member of the Commune late in 1793, and in March of the next year was appointed an "administrator of public establishments." These were, however, the days of Robespierre, when a merely whispered denouncement led to imprisonment. Just three months after the last-mentioned appointment, Antoine Magendie was thrown into prison on the charge of neglect in his supervision of the foundlings' asylum, euphemistically called "Maison des Enfants de la Patrie." May we hazard a guess that some unenlightened citizen had objected to the application of Rousseau's principles to the education of foundlings? At all events, Magendie was released in a fortnight through the intervention of the members of the district for which he was surgeon.[6] His political career evidently suffered no check from this episode, for later he became mayor of the 10th arrondissement and a member of the Board of Administration of Hospitals.

These political appointments seem not to have been very remunerative and François' father, having little income for the support of his children, was obliged to adopt the simpler and more "natural" life so urgently advocated by his mentor,

[6] Genty, M., *Biogr. Méd.*, 9:113, 1935.

Rousseau. François' education continued along the prescribed lines and he passed his tenth birthday without being
able to read or write, but he probably had surreptitiously
learned his right hand from his left. Then the subject of
the noble experiment rebelled. To foster his spirit of inde-
pendence and inculcate the "back to nature" principle firmly
in his young mind, his father had said that if the boy
wanted shoes to wear he should make his own. This was
too much for young François. He declared that he preferred
to be well-shod, even if it did make him dependent, and,
furthermore, he wanted to go to school. The father, still
acting on Rousseau's principle of allowing children perfect
liberty, permitted his son to attend the infant school where,
naturally, the beginners were much younger than François.
As luck would have it, educational theory was in this case
vindicated, for the boy soon outstripped his classmates and
when fourteen, at the annual *concours* in which all the best
pupils in the schools of Paris competed, won the grand
prize for his essay entitled, "On the knowledge of the rights
of man and the constitution."

It is, of course, to the prominence in local politics of his
father that we owe a reference in a contemporary news-
paper to the boy at this time. The republican *Journal des
hommes libres*, of the date "5 germinal an VI" (March 25,
1798), stated:

"There is still hope for the tenderest age when the corrupting
poisons of reaction have not blasted it in its first bloom, since
the son of citizen Magendie, municipal officer, elector, member
of the Commune, etc., having met a child who was weeping and
did not dare to put in an appearance before his father, com-
forted him, encouraged him and restored him to the bosom of
his family."

The anecdote gives an impression of the young François'
temperament which is borne out by what we know of the

grown man's tendency to impulsive kindness. The incident resulted in the award of a prize for "republican virtue," which Magendie was proud enough of having won for the story to become one of his favorites in later life.

Antoine Magendie now felt that his son had come to the age when his education could safely be directed. He decided that François owed a duty to family tradition and must gain the right to enter the medical profession. The connections of Magendie *père* with the Paris hospitals made it possible for him to enter his elder son as a medical student at the early age of sixteen. The younger son, Jean-Jacques, presently chose a naval career, in which he seems to have prospered.[7]

François Magendie began his medical studies at a time when change was the order of the day in France, not only in government but in education, and the teaching of medicine came in for its full share of innovation. The year before the Magendie family had come to Paris, the Constitutional Assembly had decreed that there should be created a system of public instruction open to all citizens. There were to be no privileged classes; all citizens were to have equal opportunities for the acquisition of knowledge. The ideas of those who framed these sweeping decrees were so vague that their first move consisted merely in the thorough scrapping of the existing order. The decrees of March 8 and September 15, 1793, ordered the sale of all possessions of universities, colleges, etc., in France, and the suppression of the old faculties of Theology, Medicine, Law and Arts. Education must be free, and it was so free that for two years there was no formal medical instruction whatsoever. Those who wished to become physicians learned wherever they could. They either picked up practical knowledge by apprenticing

---

[7] In 1830 Jean-Jacques Magendie had the rank of captain and had been made Officer of the Legion of Honor and Chevalier of the Royal Military Order of St. Louis.

themselves to a practitioner or entered a hospital. This lack of system, however, was too haphazard in its results. War had been declared on England, Holland and Spain in the early months of 1793 and trained physicians were needed. In 1794 Fourcroy was charged by the Convention to reintroduce system into medical instruction and reestablish the medical schools. Chaussier [8] (1746-1826) professor of anatomy at Dijon, was called to Paris to look over the situation and make recommendations. His famous report was read before the Convention November 27, 1794, and adopted a week later. The resulting law established three Écoles de Santé, one in Paris, one in Montpellier, one in Strasbourg, the three cities where in pre-revolutionary days had been located the medical centres of France. The attempt was made to organize medicine and surgery on a scale unexampled in any country up to that time.

One of Antoine Magendie's friends was Citizen Boyer [9] (1757-1833) who had already won fame as a surgeon and who before long was to accompany Napoleon as the Emperor's personal surgeon on his German campaign and return to Paris a baron. In 1795 he had been made associate professor of operative medicine in the newly established École de Santé of Paris and at the same time had been appointed second surgeon at the Hôtel-Dieu. He already held the post of second surgeon at the Charité and gave his private courses there. It was therefore at the busiest time of his life that the elder Magendie prevailed upon him to accept François for instruction. In a very short time the youth became the surgeon's favorite pupil and his prosector in anatomy. Moreover, although he was very young and a mere beginner in the science of anatomy and dissection, François Magendie had the knack of teaching other young people what he himself was in process of learning. Soon he

[8] Busquet, P., *Biogr. méd.*, 1:41, 1927.
[9] Busquet, P., *Biogr. méd.*, 3:171, 1929.

was conducting his own classes, where he lectured in anatomy and demonstrated the art of dissection. That this procedure was by no means an unusual one at this time, particularly in the cases of the more talented students, is shown by the similarity in the early careers of two men, only slightly older than Magendie, who were to have considerable influence upon his development, Bichat and Dupuytren.

Marie François Xavier Bichat [10] (1771-1802) had come from Lyons to Paris at the age of twenty-two in order to complete his medical studies. He had attached himself to Dessault (1744-1795), the foremost surgeon at the largest hospital in the capital, the Hôtel-Dieu, and he began almost at once to give lectures there in anatomy. At the time Magendie was giving his first lectures Bichat was only twenty-seven, but he had already become the most popular professor of anatomy in all France. Students flocked to his lectures, which were a stimulating rapid-fire of question and comment, an interchange of ideas between professor and student, rather than a set exposition of established facts. It is almost unthinkable that Magendie did not attend some of Bichat's lectures, although the only reference in Magendie's writings which might lead one to believe that he had done so is a passing mention of these lectures in the first article which he published in a scientific journal.[11] Bichat's doctrines were already beginning to permeate medicine in France, and after the publication of his "Treatise on Membranes" in 1800 they were spread throughout the civilised world. Unfortunately, this brilliant young teacher was destined for an early death, victim of the combined results of accident and the lowered physical resistance consequent upon his incessant zeal for work.

[10] Busquet, P., *Biogr. méd.*, 3:33, 1929; Genty, M., *Méd. internat.*, p. 101, 1934-35.
[11] *Bull. de la Soc. méd. d'émulation*, 4:145, 1809.

The second contemporary of Magendie who, like him, began lecturing early in his career was Guillaume Dupuytren [12] (1777-1835). He had come to Paris to study medicine from a small town near Limoges, had entered the service of Boyer at the Charité and at the age of eighteen became prosector in anatomy in the Paris École de Santé. When only twenty-four he was made head of the anatomical laboratory and in the next year, 1802, rose to be assistant surgeon at the Hôtel-Dieu, attached to the service of Boyer. His lectures also, on anatomy, physiology and pathological anatomy, were extremely successful, but in his case the approach was a more strictly practical one and his teaching was less thought-provoking than that of Bichat.

It was thus from a very early age that Magendie was able to support himself by teaching, although not in great luxury. Speaking of this part of his life in later years, he would point out that after his necessary expenses were discharged there remained only five sous a day—and he kept a dog. "We shared with each other," said Magendie, "and if he was not fat, neither was I." Since he was independent of his father's help, he felt that his time was his own and he need not devote himself exclusively to his medical studies. He was conscious of the gaps in his education resulting from his having been brought up in the "natural" or "Émile" school; not only had he been delayed in learning to read and write his own language until an age when other boys were studying Latin and Greek, but he had been plunged into medicine very early. He therefore began to apportion his time carefully so that he might have some hours for the pursuit of other than medical studies, although he still reserved the major part of his day for dissection and for giving lectures in anatomy. He managed to attend an excellent course in the classics given by M. Lemare (1767-1832), who before the Revolution had been a well-known professor

[12] Busquet, P., *Biogr. méd.*, 3:1, 1929; Delhoume, L., *Dupuytren*, 1934.

of rhetoric. We are told that Magendie stood as high in his Latin class as he did in his medical studies.

Although his interest in anatomy and dissection was leading him in the direction of surgery, his attitude was not narrowly professional. Not all his dissections were performed on human cadavers; comparative anatomy claimed a share of his attention. He seems to have come under the influence of Cuvier (1769-1832), for he afterwards [13] referred to Cuvier's having given him the head of a large blind goat from the zoo at the Jardin des Plantes to dissect. He took pains to inform himself in branches of medical science other than surgery. For example, his intimate friendship with Ferrus (1784-1861), a physician at the Salpetrière, who had already begun to enjoy a reputation for his views on mental diseases, dates from his student days.

Another aspect of his character began to make its appearance when he was about eighteen. Up to this time he would seem to have been entirely the son of his father, a good republican, his position firmly established as an emancipated member of the third estate, enjoying to the full his hard-won liberty and equality. However, he had perhaps inherited from his mother leanings toward a more cultured and refined mode of existence than that advocated and practised by his father. With the return of a measure of tranquillity after the violences of the Revolution had subsided, the salons, that aspect of culture so typically French, again came into fashion.[14] Poor though he was, Magendie took time off from his studies, both classical and medical, to frequent some of these gatherings, deriving, if possible, more pleasure from them on the principle that stolen fruit is the sweeter. He even managed to make a good appearance in spite of lack of means. We are told that he was received as a "young man of elegance and distinction, for he dis-

[13] *Syst. nerv.*, 1839, ii, 316.
[14] Guizot, F., *Mélanges biographiques et littéraires*, 1816, p. 49.

sembled with truly Roman stoicism the real distress of his situation." [15]

Almost in the manner of a fairy tale, Magendie presently acquired the means for a period of indulgence in the luxury for which he was developing a taste. Like the proverbial poor but noble-minded youth, slowly starving in his miserable garret, François began to grow melancholy and to long for a release from his struggles. As a budding physician he of course attributed his mental anguish to some deep-seated and incurable malady. He was sure that he was on the point of death and said so to all his friends. One morning a representative of the law knocked at his door, much to the surprise of the despondent but virtuous student, who was not conscious of having been guilty of any transgression. Instead of being the bearer of disagreeable news, the official brought notice that young Magendie had come into a legacy of 20,000 francs, of which he could take possession at once. The incurable disease was forgotten in an instant and the windfall turned to account. Magendie purchased some fine horses and dogs, hired a smart groom, fitted him out in a neat livery and rented a stable near the hospital to house the lot. So proud and pleased was the young owner of these new possessions that, by his own account, he used to dash out of the hospital at every leisure moment to have a look at them and now took all his recreation in the stable. Needless to say, the 20,000 francs were soon gone, but so was the melancholy. It may well have been at this time that the artist Guérin was commissioned to paint the engaging portrait now hanging on the walls of the Collège de France. It is not difficult to believe that the curly hair in becoming disarray, the clever and humorous eyes, the boyishly full lips about to break into a smile, the rounded chin with the hint of a cleft, would easily have earned their possessor a

[15] Flourens, M., *Éloge historique de François Magendie*, 1858, p. 5.

modest place in post-revolutionary drawing-rooms, to which birth and rank were no longer the only passports of admission. We can supplement the portrait with the details mentioned in the document exempting Magendie from military service at the age of twenty-two: "Height, 5 ft., 5½ in.; hair and eyebrows brown; forehead high; chin round; face oval."

The system of medical education under which Magendie had begun his studies as an apprentice to the surgeon Boyer in 1799 was almost immediately subjected to drastic revision. This time it was Napoleon who interfered. As early as 1801 the future Emperor had announced his intention of reforming public instruction and it was not long before the liberal, if vague, ideas of the Revolution were utterly abandoned.[16] The first step consisted of removing all control over education from the hands of local authorities and placing it in those of agents who were directly responsible to the First Consul himself. Another provision, aimed particularly at the medical schools,[17] with a view to reducing the sums demanded of the government for their maintenance, was the revival of the custom, practised by the universities of the *ancien régime*, of demanding certificates of all those engaged in the different professions. A statute was passed forbidding anyone to practise medicine without a diploma certifying that he was a doctor of medicine. For this diploma there was a fee of 1000 francs, part of which was to pay for registration and part for the necessary examination. Every professor's salary was cut in half and the difference was supposed to be made up from fees paid by the successful candidates for their diplomas. Guizot's comment on this scheme is that it reestablished one of the greatest abuses of pre-revolutionary public instruction, since it concentrated the interest of the professor on letting as many students as

[16] Guizot, F., *Essai sur l'histoire et sur l'état actuel de l'instruction publique en France*, 1816, p. 54.
[17] Guizot, F., *Op. cit.*, 1816, p. 67.

possible pass, rather than on giving them the best possible teaching; and this state of affairs was further aggravated by the fact that the fees were divided equally among all the professors whether their lectures were so bad that no one attended them or so good that all the students flocked to hear them.

There was no escaping the new law. None of the middle-aged and younger practitioners had formal medical degrees. Bichat, the most brilliant of them all, who had left a lasting imprint on medicine, had died without one. Dupuytren had to write a thesis and defend it, and even the great Boyer himself, although nearly fifty at the time, had to submit to an examination by his less illustrious colleagues and pay for his diploma.

Finally, five years after the initial changes, on May 10, 1806, Napoleon created his great Imperial University, which, although it was to be composed of different faculties under different heads, was to bring public instruction even more directly than before under his own control, since he was to be the one central and dominant figure of every phase of French life. Five faculties were created, theology, law, medicine, including pharmacy, sciences and finally, as a concession, letters; for, in Napoleon's opinion, letters were a mere pastime, fit only for women and idlers. It was his belief that education must be practical; his university must turn out capable doctors, engineers, lawyers, even theologians, all of whom must be serviceable to the state. Above all, they should be docile, well-disciplined and disposed to devote their energies to the execution of his will. Whether or not the system gave rise to the desired discipline and docility, at least the tendency towards practicality introduced into education by Napoleon is still dominant in France, particularly in the medical schools.[18]

The transitional conditions in French medical education

[18] Final Report of the Commission on Medical Education, 1932.

which have been described probably account for the lapse of eight years which occurred between the beginning of Magendie's studies under the informal curriculum of the Paris École de Santé and their completion under the rigid Napoleonic system. The first three years passed without formal examination. In May, 1803 (7 floreal, an XI, according to the contemporary calendar), at the age of nineteen, he passed "brilliantly" his first competitive examination, that for his interneship in the Paris hospitals. He was seventh on the list and in the autumn was placed as interne at the hospital Saint-Louis, which was in the arondissement of which his father was mayor and at which Richerand (1779-1840), the avowed enemy of Dupuytren and the author of the best-known text-book of physiology of the day,[19] had only the year before been appointed surgeon-in-chief.[20] Here Magendie remained until February, 1804, when he was transferred to the Vénériens. He now began to encounter the series of examinations which has not undergone any marked change since his day. First came anatomy and physiology in December, 1804. In 1805, however, there is no record of his attendance at the hospitals. It is to be presumed that he was ill, since the document exempting him from military service in 1805 was issued on the ground that he was suffering from "visceral obstruction." The second examination of the regular series covered pathology and nosology. Unfortunately, the certificate preserved in the Muséé Gilbert is defaced by worm holes, so that the years in which Magendie passed his second and third examinations are wanting. The second, however, occurred in the month of June, and the third, which included materia medica and chemical pharmacology, was in September, both presumably in 1806. In April, 1807, he came out first in a competitive examination which won for him the post of aide in

19 Richerand, A. B., *Nouveaux Eléments de Physiologie*, 1801.
20 Menetrier, M., *Bull. Soc. fr. d'hist. de la méd.*, 20:251, 1926.

anatomy at the Faculty of Medicine. On May 30, 1807, he passed his examinations in hygiene and legal medicine, and finally, February 22, 1808, his clinical examination.

The fact that his examination in this subject took place in this particular year will have significance for members of the medical profession. The National Convention had designated Corvisart (1755-1821) as the senior of the two professors of Internal Clinical Medicine in the Paris École de Santé. Corvisart had for years practised percussion, which he had learned from the Viennese school and the use of which he had developed and taught his students. This invaluable method of tapping the surface of the body to elicit sounds indicative of diseased tissue within was not at this time known to the world at large, in spite of the fact that Auenbrugger (1722-1809) had published an account of his discovery in 1760 and a French translation of it had appeared ten years later. Magendie must, therefore, have become proficient in the use of this method under the direction of Corvisart himself, and in the very year in which Magendie passed his examination in Corvisart's subject, the latter published a new translation of Auenbrugger's "Inventum Novum," expanding the work to more than fourfold its original number of pages with comments and illustrations from his own wide clinical experience. The prestige he had gained through his appointment the year before as first physician to Napoleon made for a favorable reception of this book and the method of diagnosis which it advocated soon came into universal use. The year 1808, in which the publication of Corvisart's translation of Auenbrugger took place and in which, incidentally, Magendie took his examination in Corvisart's subject, has become a landmark in medical practice.

To complete the requirements for a medical degree it remained that Magendie should write, present and defend an acceptable thesis. He chose as his subject "The uses of the soft palate, with some remarks on the fracture of the cartilage of the ribs," the first part of the paper being physiological anatomy, the second surgery.[21] A quotation on the title page prepares us for a short thesis: "We must be sparing of our reader's time, never can we be too miserly with it." The dedication is "To my father. Affection, gratitude." Having paid the necessary fees, François Magendie received on March 24, 1808, the parchment certifying him to be a doctor of medicine. This document is entirely handwritten, the title of the thesis is given and appended are the signatures of the council of administration of the Paris school of medicine, of which Magendie's first master, Boyer, was then president.

The year 1808 was also the year of the founding of the present Paris Faculty of Medicine, so that with the end of Magendie's student days came the end of radical change in French medical education. He was in a very special sense a child of the Revolution. The freedom from restraint and the lack of discipline of his early years, together with the informal character of his first medical education, all of which was a legacy from the great social and political upheaval, developed almost to a fault the impulsive frankness and vigorous self-reliance which were his by nature.

[21] Essai sur les usages du voile du palais, 1808.

Unsigned early portrait in oil of Magendie, attributed to Guérin (1774-
1833), in the Collège de France, Paris.

2

REVOLT FROM BICHAT
1809

"Bichat a eu malheureusement l'esprit imbu du préjugé que la condition de la vie excluait les phénomènes physiques; cette erreur a exercé une très fâcheuse influence sur tous ses écrits." [1]

MAGENDIE felt no immediate necessity for practising medicine. He was twenty-four years old when he obtained his medical degree and the income from his post as aide in anatomy at the Faculty of Medicine, combined with what he received in the way of fees from his private lectures, sufficed his needs. His lectures now began to deal with operative surgery as well as with descriptive anatomy and both subjects proved equally popular. Eager to be in touch with the newest scientific discoveries, he attended the meetings of the Paris Academy of Sciences, where he was able to listen to the reports of the original researches of France's greatest scientists. Laplace (1749-1827), the astronomer, was nearly always present, and if not himself making a contribution, often commented on the work of others. He had retained a lively interest in physiology ever since he collaborated in his youth with Lavoisier (1743-1794) in a memoir on the respiration of animals.[2] On one occasion Magendie heard him say that the two sciences most worthy of the attention of superior intellects were physiology and astron-

---

[1] Notes to Bichat's *Traité des Membranes*, 1827, p. 267.
[2] Bernard, C., *Substances toxiques*, 1857, p. 7.

19

omy, and if he placed physiology first, he did so not merely because it lacked its Newton.

It was a fashion of the time to make a distinction between the so-called "exact" sciences, like physics and astronomy, and the seemingly less perfect biological sciences. Newton's formulation of the laws of motion and gravitation had set a standard of "natural law" and placed both physics and astronomy on a stable foundation. Magendie shared the contemporary dissatisfaction with an un-Newtonian physiology, and, stimulated by Laplace's pronouncement, he began his own investigation of the causes contributory to the existing state of the science. The result was the publication in 1809 of an article entitled "Some general ideas on phenomena peculiar to living bodies," in the Bulletin of the Société Médicale d'Émulation de Paris.[3]

Although too young and too obscure to be more than a listener at the Academy of Sciences, Magendie had the year before been elected to membership in the Société Médicale d'Émulation, one of the many medical societies which sprang into existence when the medical faculties were dissolved during the Revolution. Xavier Bichat (1771-1802) had been the best known of the three founders of this society in 1796, and had continued to be its leading spirit as long as he lived. He contributed the most important scientific papers which it published, among them the memoirs which were the first statement of his views regarding "tissues" and "vital properties." [4] When he died in 1802, the succeeding volume of the society's journal was devoted to a eulogy of him. Even after his death, the chief purpose of the existence of the society seems to have been to keep green the memory of Bichat, a circumstance which did not prevent the continued membership of Barthez (1734-1806) of Montpellier, sponsor of the interpretation of vitalism

[3] Bull. de la Soc. méd. d'émulation, 4:145, 1809.
[4] Bichat, X., Mém. de la Soc. méd. d'émulation, 2:350, 371, 477, 1799.

which had preceded and which continued to rival Bichat's theories.

There is an apparent rashness, thoroughly characteristic of the Magendie whom we shall come to know as being incapable of caution when he was convinced that he was right, in this choice of a journal almost piously dedicated to the preservation of Bichat's influence for the publication of a paper which turned out to be a direct attack upon that influence. It is always said that Magendie made his "scientific début" by attacking Bichat's theory of "vital properties," and the paper of 1809 does in fact place the blame for the unsatisfactory state of physiology upon the misguided efforts of Bichat's followers to put his theory into practice in their physiological investigations.

It is not uncommon for the vitalism of the eighteenth and early nineteenth centuries to be regarded as having been altogether grounded in philosophical and religious prejudice, but this view involves a disregard of historical perspective, as well as some unfairness to men like Barthez and Bichat. The legacy of seventeenth century materialism during the early eighteen hundreds was in the custody of Lamarck (1744-1829), who was admired by his contemporaries rather as a systematist in biology than as the proponent of a mechanistic conception of life as motion, and the verdict was not without justice, for Lamarck's speculations on the nature of life rested on a basis of fantasy, an ubiquitous ethereal-electrical fluid, and they were not derived from the acute observations of form which supported his evolutionary theory. Cuvier (1769-1832) wielded a much more potent influence among biologists with an exposition of the problem of life based partly on his study of Kant and partly on his interpretation of the chemical processes occurring in organisms before and after death. It was, in fact, the progress of chemistry and discoveries in electricity and magnetism which had temporarily blurred the former sharp distinction between mechanism and vitalism, and it was only as the nineteenth century unfolded that biology was able to rebuild a mechanistic conception of life on a revised basis.[5] In the medical schools of France two types of vitalism were in vogue at the beginning of the century, the views of Bichat dominating the Paris medical Faculty, while in the rival centre at Montpellier Barthez had been so influential that his interpretation of vitalism virtually constituted the celebrated "doctrine of Montpellier." Both systems were considered to be based on scientific observation, and both were thought by their proposers to be consistent with the use of experimental method. "Vital principle" and "vital properties" alike served as symbols for what was regarded as a necessary margin of error for experimenters dealing with biological material.

Barthez considered that his account of the "vital principle" brought about a unification of the phenomena of life comparable to Newton's establishment of the reign of law in the kingdom of physics, and he chose the term "vital principle" because he thought it freer from psychological and other prejudicial associations than terms like "soul," "archaeus" or "nature," which had been used before. What he really offered was a doctrine of causation inside of which he thought it would be possible to carry on experimental investigation in biology. He held that first causes are unknowable and that an account of them need not be included in an hypothesis explanatory of the nature of life. He defined the "vital principle" as "the cause which produces all the phenomena of life in the human body." [6] He was convinced that life exhibits one unifying principle underlying all its forms and that in this sense vital phenomena have a single cause. He held that the laws of chemistry and mechanics cannot account for life since the dead body is still subject to these

[5] Nordenskiöld, E., *The history of biology*, 1935, p. 344.
[6] Barthez, P.-J., *Nouveaux élémens*, 3° éd., 1858, v. i, pp. 47, 94.

laws. His refusal to carry the account of the vital principle
beyond its function as a cause was held to be a virtue by
his followers. One of them,[7] in a discussion of the doctrine
of Montpellier, said:

"Barthez is the only one . . . who would present the living
principle as an abstract idea, indefinable, the nature and mode
of action of which one must guard oneself from attempting to
penetrate, because one can do so only by hypotheses which
destroy the whole of physiological science."

Bichat's interpretation of vitalism differed from that of
Barthez by breaking down the unity of the principle underlying the phenomena of life. His name for us is indissolubly
linked with the concept of tissues, but to his contemporaries
and immediate successors his theory of "vital properties"
was of at least equal importance. The two aspects of his
doctrine appear side by side in his first book, published in
1800, the "Treatise on Membranes." Here he established his
division of membranes (tissues) into three classes, mucous,
serous and fibrous. His examination of the tissues was carried further before the publication in 1801 of his "General
Anatomy," in which he made a more complete classification,
distinguishing twenty-two "systems," each with its characteristic type of tissue (e. g., cellular, nervous, vascular, absorbent, fibrous, mucous, etc.). To arrive at this analysis he
submitted all the various parts of the body to "dessication,
putrefaction, maceration, boiling, decoction, and the action
of acids, alkalis, etc." He pointed out that these methods
were not directed at discovering the "composition" (i.e.,
anything resembling a chemical analysis) of the tissues, but
were meant only to "supplement the inadequacy of the
scalpel." His analytical studies were accompanied by the
performance of a great number of autopsies, the traditional
count being six hundred in the course of a single winter.

[7] Bérard, F.-J., *Doctrine médicale de l'école de Montpellier*, 1819, p. 91.

What Bichat achieved was a new anatomy, that of the tissues composing the body and its organs, as opposed to the old gross anatomy of the form and topography of the bodily parts.

His doctrine of "vital properties" was not in any sense a conclusion from his studies of the bodily tissues. Rather it was his basic hypothesis that sensibility is the characteristic quality of the nervous system and contractility of the muscular system, and he used the degrees and peculiarities of the manifestations of these two qualities, or, as he came to call them "vital properties," to support the classification of types of tissue at which he was able to arrive independently on grounds of structure and function.[8] In fact, just as his analysis of the tissues was his contribution to anatomy, so his doctrine of "vital properties" was meant to lay the foundations of physiology and medicine. He said in his preface to the "General Anatomy" that he wished to substitute for the doctrine of "a single abstract principle, ideal and altogether imaginary," a new doctrine which would teach physiologists and physicians "to analyse precisely the properties of living bodies; to show that every physiological phenomenon is in the last analysis derived from these properties in their natural state, that every pathological phenomenon is the result of their augmentation, their diminution or their alteration, that every therapeutic measure depends in principle on their restoration to the natural state from which they have been diverted."

This has a very modern sound until Bichat's exact definitions of his "vital properties" are filled in. To begin with, the vital properties resident in the tissues were quite distinct from all physical properties. Physical forces outside and

---

[8] Bichat always describes separately the *vital properties* of a given kind of tissue and the *properties* of the tissue, e.g., its elasticity. In his preface to the "General Anatomy" (1801) he remarks that each tissue "has its characteristic organization just as it has its own peculiar life," but he does not undertake to establish a dependence of the one on the other.

vital forces within the organism were opposed to each other. He said:

"The measure of life is in general the difference which exists between the effort of outside forces and that of the interior resistance; the excess of one means feebleness, predominance of the other is an index to its strength."

His definition of life, so often quoted, was "the sum total of functions which resist death." [9]

He saw nothing in the inorganic world comparable to sensibility and contractility in the organic, and life was manifest only when these properties were exhibited. He therefore accepted these two properties as those most generally characteristic of life, but to arrive at his complete doctrine he made use of a distinction between animal and merely organic life. The latter included the life of the vegetable world and the unconscious life of animals. Such a classification is, of course, as old as Aristotle, and we still hear an echo of it when we speak of the functions of man's viscera as vegetative functions. By animal life Bichat meant those functions of animals which come under the control of the common centre, those, in fact, of which we can be conscious.[10] Each of the two fundamental properties, sensibility and contractility, were considered to bear a different character in the two "lives." The list of "vital properties" therefore came to include: (i) animal sensibility, (ii) organic sensibility, (iii) animal contractility, (iv) sensible organic contractility and (v) insensible organic contractility.[11]

[9] Bichat, X., *Recherches physiologiques sur la vie et la mort,* 1800.

[10] Bichat also thought that he could characterise animal life (i) by a direct relationship of this life to the outside physical world and (ii) by the symmetry of its organs, e.g., two eyes, two hands, etc. Organic life, on the contrary, he held to be characteristic of single or asymmetrical organs, e.g., the heart and liver. He wasted much effort in trying to prove that lungs and kidneys are in reality unpaired.

[11] Bichat held that animal and organic sensibility were separated only by degree, resting this conclusion on his observation that inflammation of

Bichat's most general conclusion from his investigation of vital properties was that a remarkable difference distinguished the operation of vital and physical laws. He said that vital properties were unceasingly variable in their intensity, energy and development; they passed rapidly from the last degree of prostration to the highest degree of exaltation and underwent, under the influence of the most insignificant causes, a thousand diverse modifications. Especially in regard to organic life he observed that "the vital forces and the excitants which set them in play, since they

tissue might so increase organic sensibility that it would pass into animal sensibility, i.e., pain was *felt*. On the other hand, he was not able to observe that animal contractility resulted from concentration of organic contractility, although he said that the two organic contractilities, sensible and insensible, were separated only by degree. The characteristic of animal sensibility was that it gives rise to sensation; organic, or unconscious, sensibility belonged to such organs as the stomach or intestines, and was present wherever nutritive processes of any kind occurred; animal contractility was the contractility of voluntary muscle; sensible organic contractility covered the movements of the heart, large arteries, stomach, intestines, etc., i.e., cardiac and smooth muscle contraction; insensible organic contractility referred to fibrillary movements occurring in the processes of nutrition, excretion and secretion, and in the smallest blood vessels. An attempt was made to elucidate the distinction between the two kinds of organic contractility by comparing sensible organic contractility with physical attraction between large aggregates of matter, and insensible organic contractility with chemical affinity occurring between the molecules of substances. It was also stated that the former was the equivalent of "irritability" and the latter of "tonicity." This is not very helpful unless the historical connotation of these terms is taken into consideration. In Bichat's day the term "irritability," originally employed by Glisson to denote the fundamental property in virtue of which all living things were capable of responding to a stimulus, was used in the special sense given it by Haller to mean shortening of a muscle during contraction. "Tonicity" likewise had no reference to what the physiologist now means by 'tone' of either voluntary or involuntary muscle. It was a vague term designating the property by which living tissues kept in circulation the nutritive fluids bathing them. Moreover, Bichat included under insensible organic contractility, as Magendie pointed out, certain movements of excretory ducts, of the ducts of glands and of the smallest blood vessels which were as much cases of smooth muscle contraction as were movements of the stomach and intestines.

are incessantly changing in the stomach, kidneys, liver, lungs, heart, etc., result in perpetual instability in the phenomena." All this and much more *could* be read as an acknowledgment merely of the baffling complexity of vital phenomena, but Bichat made his position quite clear. He said:

"One calculates the return of a comet, the speed of a projectile; but to calculate with Borelli the strength of a muscle, with Keil the speed of blood, with Lavoisier the quantity of air entering the lung is to build on shifting sand an edifice solid itself but which soon falls for lack of an assured base. This instability of the vital forces marks all vital phenomena with an irregularity which distinguishes them from physical phenomena remarkable for their uniformity. It is easy to see that the science of organized bodies should be treated in a manner quite different from those which have unorganized bodies for object." [12]

It was instability which came to be regarded by Bichat's followers as the special mark of vital phenomena and it was against belief in this characteristic that Magendie's initial attack and the later concerted revolt of the determinists was to be directed.

Magendie began his article of 1809 by expressing dissatisfaction with the existing state of physiology. He pointed out that it was the mark of a perfected science to have a small number of principles under which a large number of facts might be readily grouped, and the physical sciences, chemistry, physics and astronomy, were the models of what science ought to be. In the case of physiology there was no dearth of facts, nor did Magendie believe that the available facts were of such a nature as to be incapable of reduction to order. He admitted that some of the supposed facts might have been badly observed, but his fundamental criticism of the science was that it embodied too much hypothesis

[12] Bichat, X., *Recherches physiologiques sur la vie et la mort*, 1800, pp. 37, 93-98.

and that its special observations had been insufficiently generalized.

The first property of living things which impressed Magendie was their ability to assimilate food and eliminate waste. Nutrition was one of the general phenomena which characterized organized bodies during the whole of their existence. He was ready to grant that "as no analogy had as yet been discovered between the ordinary interplay of chemical affinities and the nutritive process," the latter must be regarded as dependent on a special cause, comparable to planetary or molecular attraction in that it was unknown in its nature but manifested in its effects. He was therefore willing to accept the contemporary doctrine of a vital force, but he was opposed to those physiologists who were working on the hypothesis that the properties of the vital force could best be investigated in small units of the organism. Proceeding on very scant experimental data these investigators had assumed, Magendie said, that "in each molecule the vital force is manifested in two properties, sensibility and motility." [13]

A second phenomenon, as universally characteristic of life as nutrition, Magendie recognized in "action" or activity. By this he meant nothing more than that muscles contract, the liver secretes, nerves convey sensation, etc. Again he points out that, "even if vital activity is due to insensible molecular movement," this movement is not "comparable to those which occur in inert bodies," and we must explain activity in muscles, secretory organs, nerves, etc., as we explain nutrition, by the hypothesis of the vital force manifesting itself in the general properties of organic sensibility and motility.

[13] The concept of the molecule was being made popular through its application to chemistry by Dalton and Gay-Lussac, and Magendie himself did not hesitate upon occasion to use the word in a physiological context to mean small particles. v. *Précis*, 4ᵉ éd., 1836, pp. 29-30.

Up to this point Magendie spoke as a vitalist of his day and he was, moreover, willing to accept as a working hypothesis Bichat's analysis in its most generalized form, i.e., that sensibility and contractility are properties universally characteristic of living things. He proceeded (without, however, mentioning Bichat by name) to examine the aspects of the latter's theory to which he was opposed. He questioned the necessity of endowing certain organs with special vital properties so that the list of those properties was enlarged to include terms like "sensible organic contractility," "animal sensibility" and "voluntary contractility." He admitted that certain parts of an animal seem to have an action peculiar to them and that it was proper to ask why the actions of living parts can be so different if they all depend on the same cause, vital force.

The theoretical basis of his case now made its appearance. He had grasped the chemist's view that "molecular movements regulate chemical affinity," and he apparently was willing to accept as an hypothesis the extension of the idea of the molecule for the explanation of physiological phenomena. That he did not equate chemical and physiological "molecules" is clear from his statement that physiological "molecules" could be "viewed under the microscope" and that their dimensions were to be estimated at "about $\frac{1}{7620}$ of an inch." [14] He held that the most general observation to be made about organized bodies was that "the nature, the disposition, the mode of union of living molecules, in a

[14] *Elementary Compendium of Physiology* (English tr. of 2nd ed. of *Précis* by E. Milligan), 1826, p. 5. Cf. 1er éd., 1816, p. 22; 2e éd., 1825, v. i, p. 8. In the fourth edition (1836) Magendie stated that, examined under the microscope, solids of the body look like "assemblages divers de petites molecules dont les dimensions ont été estimés approximativement un 300e de millimètre," with the note: "One must not confuse these visible molecules with the atoms or particles which according to physicists and chemists form all bodies. The latter are merely useful abstractions for explaining physical and chemical phenomena." *Précis,* 4e éd., p. 8.

word, organization, modifies vital force in such a way that
the phenomena by which it is manifested in living bodies
are always directly due to organization;" and he believed,
"even in the existing state of science," that "whenever the
vital force animates a body of a given organization it will
produce given phenomena." It was therefore Bichat's willingness to accept instability or undependability of reaction
as characteristics of organic life which was one of the two
chief grounds for Magendie's attack. Already at the outset
of his career Magendie was a scientific determinist in the
sense understood and stated by Claude Bernard when he
said that in the organic as well as in the inorganic world
under given conditions given phenomena will appear. On
the other hand, Magendie was still a vitalist, since he thought
that the assumption of a vital force was necessary to explain
the causation of vital phenomena. Nevertheless, he believed
that the laws according to which this vital force operated
could be investigated directly.

The remainder of the article was devoted to criticism of
three in particular of Bichat's "vital properties." Magendie
denied that there was any real meaning in distinguishing a
property called "sensible organic contractility" as characteristic of the movements of organs like the heart, large arteries,
stomach, etc. He said that such a property was "nothing
but the action of the organ in which one supposes it to
exist, this action being the result of the internal movement
occurring among the molecules of the organ." The two
general properties of sensibility and contractility, in which
the vital force was universally manifest, were adequate
hypothetical material for an explanation of the action of the
organs in question. A similar criticism was made of the
concepts of "animal sensibility" and "animal contractility"
and the localization of these properties in particular tissues.
With an air of convicting the enemy out of the mouth of
its own prophet, Magendie allowed himself for the first time

actually to use the name of Bichat, who had recognized that "animal sensibility" pervades (i) the sense which receives (ii) the nerve which transmits and (iii) the brain which perceives. "Animal sensibility," therefore, should be regarded not as a vital property peculiar to certain local parts, but as "a function, i.e., the common end of the action of a certain number of organs." "Animal contractility" was similarly defined as a "function" of brain, nerve and muscle, in which the brain initiates the contraction which the nerve transmits and the muscle produces. According to Magendie, all these various structures, viz, sense organs, nerves, brain and muscles, have two movements, (i) the nutritive movement and (ii) a movement having for result an action "in relation with the organization of the organ"; the molecular movements of the organ, in cooperation with the vital force, will produce both the nutritive movement and the characteristic activity of the organ, and no "vital properties" need be assumed except sensibility and contractility, which are universally characteristic of all forms of life.

It may be that these particular strictures of Magendie against Bichat, or Bichat's followers, are an expression of the difference in the points of view of a physiologist and a pathologist. When Bichat contended that the tissues rather than organs were the seat of vital properties, he was perhaps influenced by the observation that diseases, in so far as they attack individual organs, are localized in their tissues. We must not forget that appalling procession of autopsies. In spite of the praise which has been allotted to Bichat for directing attention to the tissues, Magendie's conception of function maps more accurately the method which physiological investigation throughout the century was to follow. To take his own example of the cooperation of sense organs, nerves, brain and muscles, the history of the discovery of the integrative action of the nervous system bears him out as it proceeds from his own discovery of the pathways in and out of the central nervous system, through Marshall Hall's (1790-1857) demonstration of the centres for reflexes in the spinal cord, on to Sir Charles Sherrington's (b. 1857) final and most illuminating synthesis. Even granting the contention of the modern histologist that a knowledge of function must be based on a knowledge of structure, Magendie's criticism of the concentration of attention on tissues rather than organs by contemporary physiologists may have the justification that their efforts were not likely to bear fruit before the enunciation of the cell theory, which did not take place for more than a quarter of a century. It was conceivably a well-founded impatience with the quality of investigations with which he was acquainted which drove Magendie to the attack.

At all events, he evidently considered that he had achieved a more complete degree of generalization for physiological theory than Bichat. All the phenomena peculiar to organized beings were described as either nutrition or action, and the number of vital properties required as hypothetical material for the explanation of these phenomena had been reduced to two of Bichat's five, viz, organic sensibility and insensible organic contractility. Even these two Magendie regarded with caution "since they do not designate any appreciable phenomenon." At the end of his paper he showed an inclination to discount even his own theoretical position and he revealed himself as the thorough-going empiricist of his later years when he said:

"It would perhaps be better to begin the study of physiology at the moment when the phenomena of living bodies become appreciable by our senses. The part of the science which explains interior molecular movements of the organs is not at the moment and probably will not be for some time more than a collection of conjectures more or less close to the truth: it offers few useful applications and has always given rise to discussions, of which the least inconvenience has been to cause loss of time better devoted to making experiments and describing important phenomena exactly."

It is plain that Magendie was none too sure of his hypothesis of organized molecular movement, and his views as to the nature of the cooperation of the "vital force" in this process were completely vague. His case rests very much on his faith in the scientific dependability of vital phenomena. It is interesting that we should have so clearly indicated in his first independent paper the two principles which guided him throughout his whole scientific life, distrust of theory and firm faith in experiment.

Since for the previous decade the ideas of Bichat had dominated physiology in France, Magendie's attack enjoyed a certain notoriety and must be taken as marking the beginning of a new period of development for the science, which had not yet established itself as a separate field of investigation in the other countries of Europe. Although he did not formally repudiate the vitalism of his contemporaries, he nevertheless took the first step towards making it an unnecessary hypothesis by announcing the principle of scientific determinism. If vital phenomena were no longer to be regarded as unstable, the practical ground for insisting upon the distinction between physical and vital phenomena no longer existed.

Hostility to Bichat's theoretical views was a recurrent motif in Magendie's speaking and writing for the rest of his life. He was to repeat the gist of the paper of 1809 seven years later in the early pages of his text book of physiology, and in subsequent editions was to re-write and expand the passages dealing with vital properties and the causes of vital phenomena. When he eventually became president of the Société Médicale d'Émulation, he combined the homage to Bichat suitable in a holder of this office with his own critical attitude to Bichat's doctrines by bringing out an annotated edition of the "Physiological Researches on Life and Death." It was later reissued with an even greater number of footnotes, and a similarly annotated edition of the "Treatise on Membranes" was also published. As late as 1837 Magendie was still combatting the influence of Bichat on the rising medical generation, and said to his students:

"Gentlemen, do not forget that this is a romance which we are analyzing, and that if you despoil it of its illusory prestige, instead of a clever invention, you have nothing more than an absurd piece of writing. Yes, an absurd piece of writing." [15]

It is curious that one who in later life was so scornful of everything which he could label as theoretical or abstract should have made his entrance into the scientific world with a paper announcing so clearly the general principles to which he was to adhere for the whole of his career. The paper is unique in being the only one which Magendie ever wrote which did not involve an account of some experimental investigation or at least a description of some observed state.

[15] *Phén. phys.*, 1842, v. ii, p. 121.

3

PIONEER IN EXPERIMENTAL
PHARMACOLOGY
1809

*"Il n'est donné qu'à l'observation d'établir un fait sur
des bases irrécusables."* [1]

HAVING thus achieved a certain notoriety by his criticism of
Bichat, Magendie made his maiden speech before the Paris
Academy of Sciences, April 24, 1809,[2] on the results of his
first experimental work. Among those present to hear this
first effort were Laplace, Cuvier, Lamarck, Berthollet (1749-
1822), Gay-Lussac (1778-1850), Geoffroy Saint Hilaire
(1772-1844) and Pinel (1745-1826), names now familiar to
students of biology and chemistry. The results upon which
Magendie was reporting had followed from the joint endeavor of himself and a young medical student, Delille, to
describe the action on living animals of certain vegetable
poisons from Java and Borneo. They had attempted to
combine the methods of biology and chemistry in a way
which the members of the distinguished audience were well
qualified to judge. The investigators had divided their results into two parts: the first was read by Magendie and the
second by Delille, and the latter was soon to present the
whole as a thesis for his doctor's degree.

Scientific exploration to uncivilized parts of the world

---

[1] *Phén. phys.*, 1842, v. ii, p. 79.
[2] *Bull. de la Soc. philomat.*, 1:368, 1809.

was popular at the beginning of the nineteenth century. In one journal an abstract of Magendie's memoir was printed next to the report of the journey to New Spain of the famous naturalist and explorer, Alexander von Humboldt (1769-1859). The experiments on poisons of Magendie and Delille were the outcome of an expedition of Captain Baudin in 1803. The chief naturalist on this expedition, Leschenault (1773-1826), was taken ill and had to remain in Java for some time to recover his health. While there he became curious about the poison with which the natives tip their arrows, and he persuaded one of them, for a consideration, to show him how to prepare this poison. The essential ingredient proved to be the root of a plant which was pointed out to the naturalist. Scrapings of the bark of the root were put into water and boiled, the liquor decanted off and more scrapings added. This was done three times and the final mixture was boiled down until it was of the consistency of thick molasses. There were now added, as if to make a more savory concoction, two onions, a clove of garlic, a pinch of pepper, a little ginger root, some galanga and a grain of allspice. Sharp slivers of bamboo were dipped in the mixture and shot into a hen. The hen died in two minutes.

Leschenault brought back to Paris samples of this gummy substance and Magendie and Delille made their first experiments by coating with it the point of a piece of wood shaped like a pen and thrusting this improvised arrow into the buttocks of a dog. For a few moments there appeared to be no effect; then, suddenly, the dog was thrown into a violent convulsion, all its muscles contracting vigorously. A period of calm followed this seizure, then there was another period of convulsion, and the chest muscles were now held so rigidly tight that breathing was suspended and the animal passed into a state of asphyxia. Again there was a period of calm, which was followed by such intense stiffening of the body that it was impossible to feel the heart through the wall of the chest. Death occurred in five minutes and at autopsy the blood was black as if the animal had died from asphyxiation. This experiment was followed by others on six dogs, a horse and three rabbits. The experimenters concluded that there was little effect on the brain, the chief action being on the spinal cord. When the cord was severed from the brain there were still convulsions of the limbs on administering the drug, but if the spinal cord had been destroyed there were no convulsions.

The problem of how the poison got to the spinal cord was of particular interest to the experimenters. To see if it was truly absorbed they injected it intraperitoneally, intravenously, gave it in food and placed it through an opening directly in the stomach. The results were the same for all methods of administration with the exception that when the substance had to traverse the wall of the stomach its action was sometimes delayed for as long as half an hour. The conclusion arrived at was that the poison was absorbed into the blood stream and thus conveyed to the spinal cord where it produced its characteristic effect. The young men suggested that this drug might be of use in medicine, particularly in the case of diseases having their seat in the central nervous system, a dose of 2-3 centigrams having the power to alter its functions profoundly.

It was the custom of the Academy of Sciences to appoint a committee to go to see for themselves the experiments reported in the papers read in the formal sessions, the committee making its own report at a later meeting. Two members of the committee to see the experiments of Magendie and Delille were particularly interested in the work now submitted to their judgment: Pinel as medical director of the Salpetrière had known Magendie from the very beginning of his medical studies, and Jussieu (1784-1836) as a botanist wished to identify the plant which exhibited these remarkable properties. Leschenault had brought back from Java only a few branches of the plant without either flowers or fruit, but Jussieu was able to identify it as "upas tieute" belonging to the group strychnos, and to show its relation to the St. Ignatius bean and particularly to nux vomica, the extract of which had been known since 1683 to produce vomiting and convulsions. The committee found that the results of administering the drug were those which the young authors had described, and they reported promptly within the month to the Academy in very complimentary and encouraging terms, remarking that they were particularly interested in this novel method of showing relationships in plants by establishing similarities in their action upon living animals. Today we recognize at once that the symptoms which Magendie was describing are typical of strychnine poisoning. It was not, however, until nine years later (1818) that the chemical substance responsible for these symptoms, the alkaloid strychnine, was isolated by Pelletier (1788-1842) and Caventou (1795-1877) from the three plants, strychnos tieute, nux vomica and the St. Ignatius bean.[3]

The question of the method of absorption of the poison still held Magendie's interest, perhaps because he was once more engaged in a refutation of Bichat; and in August he read a second memoir before the Academy with the title, "On the organs of absorption in mammals."[4] At the time he and Delille began their experiments it was the current belief, originated by John and William Hunter[5] in England and sponsored in France by Bichat, that the only mode of absorption of foreign materials into the mammalian body was

[3] *Procès-verb. Acad. d. Sc.,* 6:392, 1818; 412, 1819.

[4] *J. de physiol. expér.,* 1:1, 1821.

[5] William Hunter claimed for himself the discovery of the function of the lymphatics as absorbents and stated in his lectures that it was only second in importance to Harvey's discovery of the circulation of the blood. (MS. in the Sutro branch of the California state library, San Francisco, California.)

by way of the lymphatic system. This theory was held to be incontrovertible, first because it was easy to see fat after a meal being absorbed from the intestine not into blood vessels but into the lacteals (i.e., lymphatics) as white milky chyme, whence it could be traced to the thoracic duct which emptied into the blood of the subclavian vein; secondly, because upon injection the lymphatic vessels were found to be distinct from veins and arteries throughout the body. Death of animals whose thoracic duct had been tied off was supposed to have furnished the final proof that this was the only mode of entry of substances into the body. Dupuytren, "that skilful surgeon," to quote Magendie, had repeated in the latter's presence the older experiments on tying the thoracic duct, using the horse as the experimental animal, but while some of the animals died, others lived. Dupuytren's inconclusive results spurred Magendie to try to settle the question whether the lymphatics were or were not the sole organs of absorption in mammals.

The rate at which the poison from *upas tieute* was absorbed in his experimental animals had been so rapid that he did not see how it could possibly be carried to the spinal cord by way of the lymphatic system alone. He now tried injecting the poison into a series of dogs with the thoracic duct tied as he had seen Dupuytren tie it in horses, but again the results were not clear cut. Finally, he isolated a loop of the dog's intestine, cutting all arteries and veins except one of each and entirely destroying the lymphatics. *Upas tieute* introduced into this isolated intestinal loop produced the characteristic convulsions. In a still more drastic experiment he cut off the hind leg of a dog, leaving it attached to the body by the crural artery and vein only. He scraped these blood vessels with care in order to remove all trace of lymphatics and then inserted the poison into a cut in the foot of the detached leg. In ten minutes the animal died in convulsions. In a refinement of this last procedure he again prepared a dog with an isolated leg, but this time he divided both artery and vein. He then linked together the cut ends of each vessel by means of feather shafts. The circulation was now maintained between the limb and the body through these artificial connections. The result was the same as before. A few grains of poison inserted into the isolated foot brought on convulsions within four minutes. The poison had reached the spinal cord in spite of there being no possible connection between the lymphatic vessels of the isolated leg and the body.

Magendie now proceeded to employ a technique which has recently become highly developed in certain physiological laboratories at the present time, viz, crossed circulation. By means of his feather shaft he connected the peripheral end of a vein in the leg of one dog with the central end of the same vein in another animal. The poison was introduced into the foot of the first dog and it was to be expected that the blood from this limb would convey the poison to the second animal and convulse it. Magendie saw no signs of convulsion in the second dog. He could offer no satisfactory explanation of this result and without looking further into the matter inferred that no poison had passed from one animal to the other. Why it should have been able to pass from an isolated leg to the body of the same animal but not from the leg of one animal to the body of another did not sufficiently excite his curiosity to make him push the investigation further. He was evidently less disturbed when inconsistencies occurred in his own work than when he observed them in that of other people, as he had in this case in the experiments of Dupuytren.

Years later, Magendie's pupil, Claude Bernard, repeated his master's experiments on absorption before his own classes and included in his published lectures a drawing of the dog's isolated leg.[6] Bernard was always dissatisfied with

[6] Bernard, C., *Physiologie opératoire*, 1879, p. 337.

Magendie's practice of leaving tag ends dangling, and he felt it his duty to bring unfinished experiments to some sort of satisfactory conclusion. Here in Magendie's very first experimental work was an isolated observation left without explanation, a situation which not only disturbed Bernard but makes any physiologist who reads the 1809 memoir wonder why Magendie should have been content to leave the matter in this unsatisfactory state. The point was, as Bernard found out, that Magendie simply had not waited long enough for the poison to act in his second experiment. In the first experiment it had taken only four minutes for the poison to be absorbed and pass from the isolated leg to the spinal cord of the same animal. Magendie lacked either the patience or the analytical quality of mind which would have enabled him to solve the question of what was happening in those four minutes. Absorption into the blood and transport to the spinal cord were, of course, taking place; but accumulation of a sufficient amount of poison to act on the nervous centers and render them sensitive was also necessary before convulsions could appear. In the crossed circulation experiment the second animal had its full quota of blood, for there had been no hemorrhage during the operation which involved no amputation; the transfused blood containing the poison would be greatly diluted by mixture with the unpoisoned blood of the second animal, and it would take much longer for the accumulation of sufficient poison to induce convulsions. The explanation of Magendie's failure to produce convulsions in the transfused animal is a simple one. His observations were correct as far as they went, but he did not continue his experiment long enough.

The committee chosen to report on this second memoir dealing with the absorption of poisons again included Pinel, who this time was chairman. Strangely enough, nearly four years were to elapse before the committee got around to making its report, and then it was unfavorable in the sense that the ruling was that Magendie and Delille—for it was evident that the two young men were still working together, although the paper bore only Magendie's name—had not proved their point; but it was at the same time favorable because the committee, in spite of having had to suspend judgment on the conclusions drawn, wished to encourage the author "in his natural sagacity and manner of proceeding in experimentation with extreme reserve." It was recommended that the memoir be given a place among those presented by non-members of the Academy.

Magendie had evidently assumed in these experiments that a foreign substance introduced into the foot and appearing in blood leaving the leg must have entered directly through the blood vessels, and that if it entered the lymphatics it would have to be conveyed clear to the subclavian vein before it reached the blood. Pinel, who had a reputation for precision of mind and for conservatism amounting almost to timidity, had decided, after prolonged consideration, that the authors had not shown the actual seat of absorption. He thought their "conclusion a little premature and the facts not directed exactly enough toward the end aimed at, namely proof that the lymphatics are not always the route followed by foreign matter to reach the blood stream." In spite of this adverse verdict, Magendie reprinted the memoir more than a decade after it was first read without altering a word in it, and he stoutly affirmed: "Although this memoir is eleven years old, I see with satisfaction that there is nothing to change in it. Such is the advantage of the experimental method in science; facts are immutable."

At the end of the same month, August 28, 1809, Delille read his part of the paper before the Academy.[7] He dealt with experiments similar to those reported by Magendie in April, except that the poison this time was from *upas antiar,*

[7] Delille, R., *Procès-verb. Acad. d. Sc.*, 4:242, 1809.

a plant newly described and named by Leschenault. The results of administering extracts of this plant to dogs were similar to those obtained by administering its relative, *upas tieute, viz,* convulsions and death, with the distinguishing feature, however, that violent vomiting was an accompaniment of poisoning by *upas antiar.* The authors were curious to learn what effect this drug would have upon a horse, for in this animal the disposition of its alimentary apparatus is such that substances introduced into its true stomach cannot return through its oesophagus—in other words, the horse cannot vomit. They injected 25 drops of a solution of the poison into the jugular vein of a horse as it was held down on the floor on its side. The horse got on its legs, defecated with violence, fell on its side, made retching movements, extended all its limbs in convulsion, trembled and died in a very few minutes with its head thrown back and the muscles of the face contracted. Still with the idea of showing the method of absorption of the drug, the experimenters shut off the circulation of the hind leg of a dog by compression and injected the drug below the ligature. So long as the circulation was shut off there were no symptoms of convulsions, but as soon as the ligature was loosened and circulation restored so that the poison could reach the spinal cord, convulsions followed. Tartar emetic had long been known to cause vomiting, but although injection of this substance into the jugular vein of an animal first caused convulsions and vomiting, death occurred quietly without the violent spasms so characteristic of the vegetable poisons under investigation. It was therefore concluded that the emetic agent from *upas antiar* and that in tartar emetic could not be the same substance.

Once more Pinel was chosen chairman of the committee to report on the memoir, and this time he brought in a most favorable verdict within two months, complimenting the authors on having pursued so severe an experimental procedure and on having avoided "all gratuitous and frivolous explanations, limiting themselves to simple results and the relationship of the facts observed."

These three memoirs mark the beginning of experimental pharmacology. They were the first records of attempts to administer chemical substances to living organisms in a systematic way so that the effects of similar chemical agents from different sources might be compared. There was even an attempt to assess dosage, but until strychnine had been isolated in pure form this could not be thoroughly successful. After the effects of these substances had been tested out on the lower animals, their probable use as a medicament for man and the type of disease in which they might be helpful were indicated. These are the lines along which experimental pharmacology has proceeded from the year 1809 to the present time, and Magendie may rightly be called the father of this branch of medicine. Usually the name of Claude Bernard is linked with that of his master, the two being regarded as the pioneers of experimental pharmacology; but Bernard was not born until 1813, four years after these three memoirs were read before the Academy of Sciences.

There was immediate recognition of the value of the work on the poisons from Java and Borneo. Cuvier, permanent secretary of the Academy of Sciences, in his yearly summary of the chief discoveries of French scientists, quoted in detail the experiments of Magendie and Delille, not only in 1809, but again in 1811 and 1814. Text-books, such as the celebrated one by Orfila on Toxicology (1813), repeated in full Magendie's description of the symptoms of poisoning by these drugs. The work was indeed a triumph for a young man of twenty-five, who had only the year before obtained the diploma making him doctor of medicine.

4

THE "VOLTE-FACE" FROM ANATOMY AND SURGERY TO PHYSIOLOGY
1813-1815

*"Moi-même je vais me livrer à de nouvelles re-
cherches, pénétré que je suis que c'est dans cette étude
de la physique vitale que repose l'avenir de la médecine."* [1]

MAGENDIE in his twenties met with very little encouragement for his career in terms of appointments. Since 1807
he had continued to hold the post of aide in the anatomical
laboratories of the Faculty of Medicine, having been appointed before he was granted his medical degree. After his
brilliant beginning in experimental pharmacology there was
a lull even in his activity in research. For two years there
were no publications and a solitary paper which was read
before the Academy of Sciences, January 14, 1811, was of
little importance.[2]

This isolated piece of work, a memoir on loss of water
from the lungs, was apparently suggested by observations
on a patient in a clinic. It may stand as an unsuccessful
attempt to draw valid conclusions from unsuitable data.
The paper began with measurements over mercury of the
carbon dioxide exhaled by a man during a normal and
during a forced expiration. The conclusion arrived at was
that in either case the carbon dioxide present corresponded
exactly to the oxygen which disappeared. Any of our mod-

[1] Phén. phys., 1842, v. i, p. 310.
[2] *Bull. de la Soc. philomat.*, 2:252, 1811.

45

ern, more delicate methods would show that this could not be true for the conditions under which Magendie was experimenting. This, however, was not his main point. The question which he was trying to answer was, does the oxygen used by the body combine in the lungs with hydrogen to form water, and is this the water vapor we see in our breath on a cold day. He was inclined to answer in the negative on the following grounds: he observed that when a patient who had a tracheal fistula just below the thyroid cartilage breathed through the fistula in cold weather there was no cloud of vapor in his breath; but if the fistula were closed and the breath came through the mouth or nose, the cloud was visible. Magendie made a similar fistula in an animal and obtained similar results. From this he decided that there was no combination of hydrogen and oxygen in the lungs, and that the water vapor must come from the mucous membrane of the respiratory passages, particularly from the mouth and throat. It did not occur to him that the presence of water vapor in the air coming from the mouth and its absence when the air issued from the fistula might be explained by the consideration that the air in passing along the respiratory passages when the fistula was closed became warmer and would therefore take up much more water than air passing almost directly into and out of the lungs through the fistula; upon coming into contact with the cold air on expiration this warmed air would lose its water vapor through condensation. Magendie here showed a tendency to attach importance to rather obvious observable phenomena without a sufficient scrutiny of their direct bearing on the problem in hand. He had contributed nothing to the solution of the vexed question of the seat of oxidation in the animal body, the source of animal heat, a question which was first raised by Lavoisier and Laplace in 1784, and which was to occupy the attention of Claude Bernard for nearly his whole lifetime.

Magendie tried to support his conclusions about the source of water vapor in expired air by experiments on the mode of elimination (other than that through the more usual channels of perspiration, urine and faeces) of different substances injected into the animal body. He began with the injection of water into the veins, the pleural cavity, etc., in an attempt to increase the amount of water vapor in the breath, and he went on to the injection of camphor, the odor of which could be detected in the animal's breath, and a solution of phosphorus in oil, which came out of the animal's mouth and nostrils in a white cloud. One is tempted to regret that Magendie did not perform this last experiment in a dark room, with the possible result of producing a veritable hound of the Baskervilles nearly a century before Sherlock Holmes began his investigations on this subject.

It was in the same year as the reading of this paper that Magendie received his first and only promotion in the Faculty of Medicine, when he was advanced from aide to prosector in anatomy. Even this modest step forward did not occur casually, but was accompanied by reverberations. An anonymous account of the episode [3] states that the claims of a rival candidate were urged in the committee of selection "by a powerful member of the medical profession." The two persons who would naturally have been most concerned with the appointment were Chaussier, professor of anatomy, and the rising surgeon, Dupuytren, head of the anatomical laboratory. Chaussier, who had been granted the joint chair of anatomy and physiology in consequence of his work in the reorganizatoin of the Écoles de Santé in 1794, was actually a member of the committee of selec-

[3] Magendie was the subject of one issue of a series of pamphlets, edited by Déloges, giving short biographies of the most eminent Parisian physicians of the period, Célébrités médicales et chirurgicales contemporains: à chacun selon ses oeuvres, 1841.

tion. It is said that he supported the appointment and was able to tip the scales in Magendie's favor, since he had known him from his student days and had always held a high opinion of his worth. There is nothing more than the persistent tradition of an antagonism between Magendie and Dupuytren to support the belief that Dupuytren may have been the "member of the profession" actively opposing the promotion.

Curiously enough, Chausier's intervention on Magendie's behalf was not the prelude to a friendly relationship between them. An unfortunate conjunction of circumstances and Magendie's violent temper resulted almost immediately in a breach which was never fully repaired. It was one of Magendie's new duties as prosector to prepare rare pathological specimens for demonstration. On one occasion he had worked carefully on such a specimen for three days, dissecting out the parts to be demonstrated, and he had finally hung the cadaver to dry from the ceiling of the anatomical laboratory. To the embarrassment of both the prosector and the Faculty of Medicine it completely disappeared. Chaussier did an extraordinary thing. He called Magendie on the carpet and told him that if the cadaver were not at once found, he could only conclude that Magendie had stolen it. The young man was so infuriated by this ill-considered charge that he seized a heavy lead inkpot from the professor's desk and raised his arm to hurl the missile at his accuser's head. Then, realizing in a flash that a rash act might result in murder, he lowered his arm with what seemed to him to be a superhuman effort. The experience left him weak and trembling and it was some days before he recovered from the physical effects of his anger, of which the memory could never be effaced. Ten years later, when both Chaussier and Magendie were being considered for a seat in the Academy of Sciences, Magendie declined to withdraw in deference to Chaussier's age (he was seventy-five) and his undoubted attainments, and prosecuted his own candidature vigorously and successfully.

Magendie remained as prosector in the anatomical laboratory for two years. In 1813 he voluntarily resigned this post, having registered his medical diploma at the prefecture a few months earlier with a view to engaging in medical practice. He also announced a course of private lectures and demonstrations on what was for him the new subject of experimental physiology, renting for the purpose an amphitheatre in ancient buildings, originally belonging to the seminary of St. Nicolas of Chardonnet, where in Revolutionary times there had been housed a medical college carrying on its roll such names as those of Dupuytren, Béclard, Roux and even the great Bichat himself. It was at this point that Magendie definitely renounced surgery and anatomy for medicine and experimental physiology. Until this time it had been taken for granted by his contemporaries that surgery was his career. He had had excellent training in this branch of the medical sciences, beginning with his association with Boyer, and his constant occupation in dissection had been the best possible practice for the acquisition of manual skill. His decision to break with all this was described as a *volte-face* and it was felt that an explanation was in order. There was a general tendency to blame Dupuytren. Flourens [4] does not give names, but he says that a definitely offensive campaign was directed against Magendie at this period of his career and that "for his haughty and imperious nature it proved an intolerable ordeal," from which arose "an invincible repugnance to all acknowledged competition." It was to escape from this situation, according to Flourens, that Magendie "renounced surgery."

Dupuytren was not only head of the anatomical labora-

[4] Flourens, M., *Éloge de F. Magendie*, 1858, p. 5.

tory at the Faculty of Medicine and the most important of
the assistant surgeons at the Hôtel-Dieu, but had recently
(in 1812) been made professor of operative surgery.[5] He
was endowed with an implacable will and the determination to rise to the very top of his profession. He made many
enemies since he had no scruples about crushing anyone
who got in his way. His colleagues called him the "brigand
of the Hôtel-Dieu" and, it was said, had as low an opinion
of him as a man as they had a high one of his ability as a
surgeon.[6] In illustration of his callous egotism the story
was told that in 1810 he asked the hand of the daughter of
Boyer in marriage, but when it was time to sign the contract
he refused to appear, apparently because the *dot* of 50,000
francs was not enough; at all events, in the same year he
married another young woman whose *dot* was 100,000 francs.
He was only six years older than Magendie and it is claimed
that because he saw in the younger man a formidable rival,
he brought pressure upon Magendie to induce him to aban-
don his intention of becoming a surgeon.[7]

It may be true that Magendie was influenced by the tac-
tics imputed to his rival, but it was not consistent with his
nature to back down from a fight. On the contrary, com-
bativeness was very early established as one of his chief
characteristics. Dr. Genty[8] suggests that Magendie may
have felt that since the field of surgery was already occupied
by such rising men as Dupuytren and Richerand, he could
more readily make a name for himself in another branch
of the medical sciences; but this attitude is perhaps too

[5] Although a surgeon's skill necessarily dies with him, his methods may be
handed on. Dupuytren's name still makes its appearance in medical nomenclature, viz, Dupuytren's contracture, delirium, egg-shell symptom, fracture
hydrocele, operation (amputation at the shoulder joint), phlegmon, pow-
der, splint, listed in Gould's *The Practitioner's Medical Dictionary* (1916).

[6] Lutaud, A., *Bull. Soc. fr. d'hist. de la méd.*, 14:373, 1920.

[7] *London Med. Times and Gaz.*, 11:558, 1855.

[8] Genty, M., *Biogr. méd.*, 9:117, 1935.

calculating to be characteristic. It seems to have occurred to no one that Magendie may have renounced surgery because experimental physiology had captured his imagination. His initial interest in the subject had been proclaimed by his theoretical paper of 1809, and the striking success of his first experiments on the effects of poisons would naturally have sustained it. There is also to be considered the coincidence of the death of his father in 1813, which may have removed paternal pressure on an elder son to carry on his father's branch of the profession.

Quite apart from its significance for his own career, the reorientation of Magendie's interests in 1813 was important for the history of physiology. His lectures in experimental physiology met with a success as flattering as had the earlier courses in anatomy and operative surgery. Accompanied as they were by demonstrations on living animals, these lectures launched the science of experimental physiology as an end in itself, a discipline for its own sake, not as a mere adjunct to anatomy or medicine.[9]

In this same year, 1813, there was a sudden output of five papers of an entirely different calibre from the solitary one of 1811. The first of these,[10] read before the Academy of Sciences, January 25, was the direct sequel of Magendie's work with Delille in 1809, a continuation of experiments on vomiting, a subject which a more fastidious experimenter might have avoided. He was attempting to discover the role played by the stomach in regurgitation, a question of long debate, which for the preceding fifty years had been held to be settled by the opinion of the great authority, Haller (1708-1777), that the stomach itself was the organ of vomiting. The committee to judge Magendie's experiments was an illustrious one, its members being von Humboldt,

[9] Bernard, C., *Diabète*, 1877, p. 30. Bernard places this landmark about 1818.

[10] *Procès-verb. Acad. d. Sc.*, 5:152, 174, 1813.

Cuvier and Pinel with Percy (1754-1825) as chairman. Magendie injected tartar emetic into a vein of a dog and then had his visitors insert their fingers through an incision in the abdominal wall in order to feel the downward movement of the diaphragm and the complete relaxation of the stomach itself each time the dog retched. One member asked that the nerves of the diaphragm be cut, and it was found that now the animal gave every outward appearance of retching but was unable to bring up any vomitus. The crowning experiment was the substitution for the dog's stomach of a pig's bladder filled with colored fluid, the proper attachment to the oesophagus being made. When tartar emetic was injected into the jugular vein the dog vomited the colored water from the bladder and air descended the oesophagus to fill the emptied bladder. The stomach was thus shown to be a passive agent in the act of vomiting, i.e., its own walls were flaccid and its contents were expelled by the compressing action of other muscles; furthermore, the swallowing of air was shown to be an essential feature of the process. The committee was so delighted with this exhibition that their report reads like a paean of praise. They recommended that the memoir be given honorable mention, they begged the author to continue his valuable experiments, they even proposed that he apply for funds to defray his expenses in performing them, and they suggested finally that he try experiments on animals without diaphragms.

The second memoir had to do with the function of the epiglottis in the act of swallowing.[11] The accepted teaching of the time was that the epiglottis was necessary to cover the glottis to prevent food from entering the trachea. By removing this organ in dogs, rabbits and guinea pigs Magendie found that the epiglottis is not necessary for swal-

---

[11] *Procès-verb. Acad. d. Sc.*, 5:205, 1813.

lowing; the glottis will close firmly enough to prevent food from entering the trachea without the epiglottis to cover it.

The third paper of this year was a privately published pamphlet containing a description of Magendie's method of demonstrating retinal images to his classes. It consisted in removing the fat from the eye of a freshly killed albino rabbit and holding the eye to the light in such a way that the images of external objects could be seen through the thin sclera at the back of the eyeball.

The fourth paper was a memoir presented to the Academy of Sciences [12] reporting a continuation of the work on emetics. Its chief importance lay not at all in the experimental results, which Magendie thought demonstrated that pulmonary inflammation caused by the injection of tartar emetic was less severe if the vagi were cut, but in calling to the attention of physicians the necessity for the rational use of this drug. The dangers of its improper use were great. Sixty patients, many of whom had come under his own observation, had died in the Paris hospitals within a period of two years from its use as a purgative, either in an impure form or in wrong dosage. In earlier times it had been customary to throw into a pot of water or wine a handful of antimony-bearing earth and to use the decoction to purge whole armies or even whole cities. So many people had been killed by this purgative that laws had been passed against its use a century or so before, and physicians called it *remedium in extremis.* Properly administered, however, Magendie considered it to be a valuable aid in medicine.

The final memoir for this year,[13] read in October, continued the investigation of the mechanics of the digestive tract, and was concerned with the action of the oesophagus in vomiting and swallowing. Magendie attempted to show the falsity of the current belief that the oesophagus was a

[12] *Procès-verb. Acad. d. Sc.,* 5:244, 1813.
[13] *Procès-verb. Acad. d. Sc.,* 5:252, 1813; 447, 1814.

uniform muscular tube along which the food was propelled toward the stomach. The new facts which he brought forward were that while the upper half of this organ appeared to contract after the manner of voluntary muscle, the lower half exhibited peristaltic movements under control of the vagus nerve; and that this lower part of the oesophagus often remained contracted after the stomach was full; that vomiting could occur when the oesophagus was gone if tartar emetic were introduced directly into the stomach, provided that the vagi were left intact, although injection into a vein under these circumstances was ineffective. He was later to use the observation of two types of muscular movement in the oesophagus as a refutation of Bichat's analysis of "contractility" into three vital properties. The presence of "vermicular" (peristalitic) movements in the lower part of the oesophagus had been seen earlier, but Magendie seems to have been ignorant of this fact.

This was an early instance of a characteristic of his experimental procedure which was remarked upon by Dubois, who said that Magendie was "so completely indifferent to the discoveries of others that when he completed an experiment he was apt to say to the onlookers, 'This is the first time I have ever seen anything like this,' and be entirely unaware that some one else had already done the same thing." [14] Magendie himself once acknowledged that he was often chagrined to discover that someone had anticipated him in an experiment.[15] This did not mean, however, that he was ungenerous about giving credit where he thought it due. If he were shown that someone else had a prior claim to a discovery, he did not hesitate to admit that while he had thought the priority was his he had been mistaken. The trouble seems to have arisen from his confessed habit of consulting authors after and not before he had completed

[14] Dubois, F., Éloge de M. Magendie, 1858.
[15] J. de physiol. expér. et path., 7:84, 1827.

a particular piece of research. He was less inclined to look for leads in "the literature" than to follow up those which opened before him in the course of actual experimentation.

His accomplishments for the year 1813 went some way to justify Magendie in his rather public renunciation of anatomy for physiology. His contribution to our knowledge of the mechanics of vomiting is still mentioned in the most modern text-books.[16] He was correct in assuming the essential passivity of the stomach during vomiting and the swallowing of air as its invariable accompaniment. However, he failed to observe that while the fundic region certainly becomes flaccid, the pyloric end of the stomach contracts and shuts the stomach off from the duodenum. The stomach is therefore not the completely passive agent in vomiting that he thought it to be. His observations on the role of the vagus were absolutely sound. Some emetics act selectively on vagal endings in the gastric mucosa, others on sympathetic endings, still others on both. Tartar emetic, as he showed, belongs to the first group. It is also true that for some still unknown reason emetics act more readily if applied locally to the surface of the stomach than if introduced into the body in some other manner, e.g., hypodermically or directly into the blood stream.

In April of 1813 the doors of the Société philomathique were opened to Magendie. Membership in this society was valued next to that in the Academy of Sciences since its roster contained the names of all the most famous scientists of the Paris of that day. It met not to hear original papers by its members but to listen to abstracts and reports of the scientific work not only of France but of the rest of Europe and, occasionally, of far away America. It was, in short, what we should call a journal club and it was designed to

---

[16] Bard, P., *Macleod's Physiology in Modern Medicine*, 1938, p. 657. Best, C. H., and Taylor, N. B., *Physiological Basis of Medical Practice*, 1939, p. 797.

keep its members abreast of the times not only on topics of immediate interest to themselves but in all fields of scientific inquiry. Sometimes these résumés of papers originally read before other scientific organizations were printed in the *Bulletin* of the Société philomathique before they were published elsewhere. Magendie's first experience in scientific journalism, in which he later became greatly interested, was gained as editor of the section of the *Bulletin* devoted to medical and related sciences. He held this post for two years after his election to the society. Almost immediately, one of his characteristics, which was destined to become a byword, began to be evident, namely, his disconcerting habit of blurting out criticisms in a truculent manner without regard for the reticences ordinarily imposed by courtesy. At the bottom of his résumé of an article in English on the heart, originally appearing in the *Philosophical Transactions of the Royal Society of London,* he added: "This memoir, whose conclusions are no more intelligible in English than they are in French, contains a number of experiments which are opposed to those of Legallois. I am at the moment engaged in repeating them; I will publish the results I get whatever they turn out to be." [17]

Magendie later (in 1818) took advantage of the pages of the *Bulletin* to voice his denunciation of two scientists who had separately expressed disagreement with him on the role of the stomach in vomiting.[18] One of his critics was a former fellow student, M. Maingault, who had published a memoir contradicting Magendie's conclusions on the ground that they did not fit certain experimental findings. This paper had been presented before the Society of the School of Medicine and the professors Legallois and Béclard were charged with an examination of it. They repeated

[17] *Bull. de la Soc. philomat.,* 4:199, 1815.
[18] *Bull. de la Soc. philomat.,* —:107, 1818.

the experiments but confirmed Magendie. M. Maingault was so offended that he withdrew his memoir and rushed it into print before the examining committee could make its report. Magendie could therefore dismiss M. Maingault with the caustic comment that his efforts had been "impelled, one liked to believe, by an interest in science." The second critic was rather more imposing. He was M. Portal, a well-known member of the Academy of Sciences, and he had presented before that body in October, 1817, a memoir on vomiting, which had attacked, according to Magendie, who was himself present, "by assertions for which no proof was given and by mere reasoning, a doctrine based on numerous experiments recognized as definitive by the Academy of Science and by all those who have taken the trouble to repeat them." The actual experiments by which M. Portal had supported his contentions, Magendie had at once repeated before his class in experimental physiology and had demonstrated to the satisfaction of all present that the claim that the stomach was passive in the act of vomiting was not at all invalidated by them. With regard to some experiments of 1771 which M. Portal had cited, Magendie was content to remark that he did not know what the properties of *nux vomica* were in 1771, but certainly "nowadays it does not behave as M. Portal has claimed it did then."

In October, 1813, Napoleon lost the battle of Leipzig and for a time it seemed as if this event in the outside world were to have its repercussions on the personal career of a scientist. The defeat had brought about the demolition of the Grand Army and more soldiers were needed. In November the Emperor and the Senate decreed that 936,000 men must be called to arms. Conscription was ordered and Magendie was among those whose names were drawn. There was definite resistance to the draft in Paris and Magendie was twice able to evade the call to service. But the dragnet was being drawn tighter and although by the end of January, 1814, only 20,000 recruits had been mustered and Napoleon had been obliged to draw upon his private treasure to equip them, by the end of February the army list showed 650,000 names. Magendie was called for the third time and continued evasion seemed impossible. Fortunately the Academy of Science intervened and demanded exemption for the brilliant young physiologist. The Empire did not share the Republican views of Fourquier-Tinville, who in 1794 said at the trial in which Lavoisier was condemned to the guillotine, "The Republic has no need for scientists." By a special Imperial decree of January 20, 1814, Magendie was exempted from military service. The Minister of the Interior, M. de Montalivet, wrote to him on March 5: "You owe this favor to your success in science and I have no doubt that you will redouble your efforts to make yourself more worthy." It is not stated whose voice was first raised on Magendie's behalf, but one would like to believe that it may have been that of Laplace, who probably remembered only too well the unnecessary death of his friend and colleague, Lavoisier. The minutes of the meeting of the Academy of Sciences for March 21, 1814, record Magendie's thanks for the exemption from service in the army which had been obtained for him.

The backwash of Napoleon's wars did touch Magendie in another way. The year 1814 was also the year of the great typhus epidemic which reached France from Poland and Germany.[19] It must be remembered that although the activities of Magendie of which there are documentary records belong to the field of experimental physiology, since the registry of his medical diploma he had been engaged in the practice of medicine as well. The epidemic of typhus made a great impression upon him and in his subsequent lectures to medical students he made several references to the excellent opportunities which he had had of studying

[19] *Phén. phys.*, 1842, v. iii, p. 13.

the disease. The following account shows how his scientific curiosity was carried over into his medical practice:

"In 1814 a murderous epidemic, typhus, brought mourning and consternation into the very heart of the capital; in spite of the help of physicians (many of whom paid for their unselfish devotion with their lives) the scourge struck down many victims. All sorts of remedies were tried, most of them without success. I happened many times to open veins, less as a curative measure than as experimental research; in these exploratory bleedings I remarked that when the disease was to terminate happily, the blood coagulated, while in the opposite event, it remained fluid." [20]

The almost superhuman activity of the hard pressed Napoleon did not long delay the collapse of the whole fabric of his political edifice. The invasion of France by the allies, the occupation of Paris, the banishment to Elba in 1814; the landing of the Emperor in France in March, 1815, the Hundred Days, Waterloo in June and the exile to St. Helena followed swiftly on one another. France as a whole had been indifferent, if not hostile, to Napoleon's last desperate effort to reestablish his power. M. Cuvier, permanent secretary of the Academy of Sciences, as a prelude to his report on the scientific advances of 1815, gave expression to his country's weariness of war in words which again became poignant in 1940-41. He said:

"Another year of devastation and terror! Strife once more staining our country with blood; the very existence of this fair realm placed in jeopardy; the peace and prosperity of inoffensive citizens suddenly without protection or guarantee; vast armies flooding our provinces, invading our cities, snatching away from a conquered capital the treasures of art lately won as the fruit of other violences: such have been the consequences for innocent sufferers of a wicked war."

[20] Phén. phys., 1842, v. ii, p. 198.

He went on to voice a confidence in the scientist's isolation from the troubles of a war-ravaged world which we today may not altogether share:

"But science is our consolation and refuge; today every nation respects it: in the midst of the tumult of war the descendants of Archimedes among us have nothing to fear from an enlightened soldiery, to whom their names and their work are known and who are happy to become for the moment their disciples. Perhaps it is actually in the most terrible times that, taking refuge in the cloisters of meditation, shunning in the exaltation of their spirit the horrors that surround them, they sometimes attain the most fortunate conclusions, the most fruitful discoveries. We shall see that the list of accomplishments for this year yields nothing to those of our most peaceful years." [21]

However, M. Cuvier had nothing to report of Magendie's activities in 1815 except some additional experiments on the connection between nausea and the swallowing of air. In regard to these he mentioned the rather pathetic case of a young conscript whose singular ruse to avoid the draft had apparently been unmasked by smart detective work on the part of some of Magendie's medical students. The young man, with the object of feigning illness, had practiced swallowing air until he was able to inflate not only his stomach but his intestines and to cause himself excruciating pain. He was in consequence diagnosed as having a severe case of tympanitis, a state which would automatically exempt him from military service. When the artifice was discovered, he was declared fit for duty.[22] Magendie, who had so recently escaped conscription himself by more honorable means, was apparently not directly involved in the exposure

[21] Cuvier, G., *Mém. de l'Inst. Sc. math. et phys.*, 1813, 1814, 1815, p. cxcv.
[22] *Procès-verb. Acad. d. Sc.*, 5:596, 1815. Cf. Cuvier, G., *Mém. de l'Inst. Sc. math. et phys.*, 1813, 1814, 1815, p. ccxxxii.

of this deception. Contrary to what M. Cuvier said, he seems not to have found the last year of the war particularly conducive to productive research. He was engaged in the comparatively routine exercise of preparing a text-book.

5

THE PUBLICATION OF THE PRÉCIS AND EXPERIMENTS ON NUTRITION, CIRCULATION AND EMETICS
1816-1817

"On trouvera donc, avant tout, dans ce livre, des faits dont j'ai autant qu'il m'a été possible, constaté directement la réalité." [1]

MAGENDIE's text-book of physiology, the *Précis*, a copy of the first volume of which he was able to present to the Academy of Sciences early in January, 1816, was an important consequence of his private teaching. On the title page he is described as having obtained his medical degree from the Paris Faculty and as being a teacher of anatomy, physiology and symptomatology. A month after the formal presentation came the report of the inevitable committee, the members of which seemed particularly impressed by the preface. This, like the utterances of Mr. Gradgrind, was in praise of facts.

"Facts, and facts alone, are the foundation of science. . . . When one devotes oneself to experimental research it is in order to augment the sum of known facts, or to discover their mutual relations. . . . What are the vital or animal spirits of the ancients, Galen's faculties, the archaeus, the vital properties, but arbitrary guesses which have served for centuries to hide utter ignorance of the cause of life? Physiology is a science still in its cradle." [2]

[1] *Précis*, 1816, p. v.
[2] *Précis*, 1816, pp. ii-iii-iv.

It was Magendie's object to present facts of the reality of which he had convinced himself by observations on man in health and sickness and by experiments upon living animals. He confessed himself interested in possible applications of the principles of physics and chemistry to vital phenomena, and stated that the book was designed for the use of medical students who would benefit from a clear and simple statement of what was positive in physiology.

This declaration of faith in facts has left Magendie vulnerable here and there, as, for instance, when he provides us with the following problematical information regarding hair: "Since the hair is a bad conductor of electrical fluid, the head is put into a sort of isolation, whence it results that the brain is less influenced by electric fluid." [3] We can, however, without hesitation subscribe to the dictum: "The more voluminous the buttocks and the more they are charged with fat, the greater will be the solidity of the sitting posture." [4] If his own observations led him to question the validity of what others had long considered a well-established fact, he had no hesitancy in doing so. The most notorious example of this is the avowal of his scepticism regarding the existence of corpuscles in the blood of warm-blooded animals and the statement of his belief that what had often been described and pictured in scientific works as blood corpuscles were in reality nothing more than bubbles of air.[5] It is to be noted that in subsequent editions of the *Précis* these particular passages are omitted and pages of text inserted which describe these corpuscles in detail.

The *Précis* deals first with the elementary chemistry of the body and proceeds at once to a discussion of Bichat's doctrine of vital properties. Magendie repeated the gist of

[3] *Précis*, 1816, v. 1, p. 157.
[4] *Précis*, 1816, v. 1, p. 269.
[5] *Précis*, 1817, v. 2, p. 305.

his paper of 1809 in the first edition and thought it worth while to rewrite and expand the passage for the subsequent editions of 1825 and 1836. The language of the text-book, whether it expressed an increasing tendency towards empiricism or merely a pedagogical attitude, was even more emphatic than that of the original essay. A list of Bichat's five vital properties was still provided as part of the medical student's theoretical stock-in-trade, but only organic sensibility and insensible organic contractility were allowed any right to the name of vital property, and even these two Magendie was inclined to reject as "useless and dangerous suppositions" because they could not be directly observed by means of the senses. The student of medicine was particularly warned against the unfortunate application of the doctrine of vital properties to therapeutics. The theory that there was an opposition between vital and physical properties was stigmatized in the later editions as "one of the most childish absurdities to which the weakness of the human understanding has ever given birth." In the early essay Magendie had compared the principle of gravity and the vital principle as being alike unknowable except in their phenomenal manifestations. In the text-book he pointed out that the phenomenal manifestations of the principle of gravity had been given mathematical expression in the laws of gravity, whereas in physiology no progress whatever had been made towards the discovery of general laws governing the manifestations of the vital force. "Of all the illusions of modern physiologists, the most deplorable has been that of believing that by forging a new term, vital principle or vital force, they have done something analogous to the discovery of gravity." The glory of Newton did not consist in having discovered gravity, which was known before his time, but in having stated that the attraction between two bodies varies directly with their mass and

inversely with the square of the distance between them.[6]
Magendie was also at pains to correct Bichat in matters
of fact, e.g., regarding the elasticity of the walls of the
arteries,[7] but he refers his students more than once to
Bichat's Descriptive Anatomy.[8]

The general plan of the book is to give first a description
of the special sense organs and their functions, which is
followed by a section on the brain made up about equally
of anatomy and psychology. There is then a disproportion-
ately long discussion of the voice, with references to his
memoir on the epiglottis and other experiments. The first
volume is concluded with an account of posture and movement. The second volume, which did not appear until 1817,
is much more realistic in treatment than the first, for here
Magendie is dealing with aspects of physiology to which his
own contributions had been genuine and where he was able
to refer his students to experiments already classical, e.g.,
the work of Réamur, Spallanzani, John Hunter and Berzelius. The subjects covered were digestion, lymph, blood
and circulation, respiration, secretion, excretion, the genital
organs and pregnancy. The accounts of his own contributions were complete enough to make it possible for the
reader of physiological literature to be referred to the text-
book instead of to the original papers for Magendie's discoveries,[9] and subsequent editions were enlarged to include
references to his later experimental work. Some experiments
which had not been made the subject of special reports

[6] *Précis*, 1816, v. 1, 1st ed., pp. 14-18; 4th ed., pp. 32-38.
[7] *Précis*, 1817, v. 2, p. 320.
[8] *Précis*, 1816, v. 1, p. 160.
[9] Nearly all of Magendie's scientific papers were read before the Academy
of Sciences. Before 1835, the year when the *Comptes rendus* began to be
published, memoirs read before the Academy, if they eventually appeared
in print, did so in privately printed pamphlets or in any one of the
numerous and often short-lived journals of the day. After 1835 all
memoirs, together with much of the discussion, appeared in the *Comptes
rendus*.

were mentioned, e.g., there is a description of his method of
obtaining pancreatic juice by exteriorizing the duct and a
statement of the properties of the juice, which he found to
be salty to the taste, alkaline and coaguable by heat. Regarding the function of the fluid he said: "It is impossible
to say what purpose the liquid of the pancreas can serve." [10]
This was seven years before the famous paper of Tiedemann and Gmelin, which is one of the great landmarks in
the history of the physiology of the pancreas and which
completely overshadowed Magendie's efforts in this field.

Magendie referred to his collaboration with Chevreul,
Dupuytren and Delille, and he acknowledged with gratitude the constant assistance of his student, Edwards, in his
experiments and in the preparation of the book. He also
mentioned in a number of connections the work of Parisian
contemporaries whose experiments had interested him. In
fact, the *Précis* set a new fashion in text-books by calling
the attention of students of medicine to experiment as a
source of scientific knowledge. The most popular text-book
of physiology of the day was Richerand's (1779-1840)
"Nouveaux éléments de physiologie," first published in
1801, which by 1830 had passed through ten editions and
had increased its bulk from one to three volumes. In it
there was no attempt to give an account of contemporary
experimental work, although some hospital cases were reported by way of illustration. It was thoroughly orthodox
in its adherence to Bichat's doctrines and was an excellent
example of what Magendie in the preface to his *Précis*
called "systematic physiology." It may be worth while to
cite as an example of the adaptation of fact to theory Richerand's discussion of the presence of nitrogen in the animal
body. He asks what can be the source of the nitrogen present in the flesh of a man who has been a vegetarian. Respiration cannot account for it, since only oxygen is absorbed

[10] *Précis*, 1817, v. 2, pp. 366-368.

from the air. Is it not to be expected, he concludes, that this element of animal substance is a product of vital action, that instead of receiving it in our food we form it ourselves by a *hyper-chemical* act, that is to say, one which chemistry cannot imitate?

The *Précis* was well received. It went through four French editions, although the last one in 1836 was a mere reprint occasioned by the destruction of the third in a fire in the rue Pot-de-Fer. The second edition of 1825 is perhaps more often referred to than the first since it contained an account of Magendie's experiments on the nervous system, which were to give rise to one of the most violent controversies in the history of physiology. The *Précis* was eventually translated into both German and English, and an American edition appeared as late as 1845. One French edition was printed in Brussels and Magendie told of a curious mistake made by the publishers which he was inclined to regard as a case of fraud. While in Brussels on a visit he called upon his publisher and was shown a sample copy of the work. He was much surprised to find that for the diagrams of sections of the central nervous system in the first volume there had been substituted a diagram from the atlas of Jules Cloquet whose ideas on the subject were diametrically opposed to those of Magendie since he represented the spinal cord as entirely filling the vertebral canal. The publisher had apparently found it more economical to utilize some old plates already in the printing shop than to construct new ones from Magendie's drawings.[11]

The up-to-dateness of the *Précis*, at least so far as Magendie's own work was concerned, is indicated by the inclusion in the second volume of a very full account of some experiments on nutrition which Magendie had reported to the Academy of Sciences in the previous August. The memoir

[11] *Syst. Nerv.*, 1839, v. 1, p. 67.

on "Food substances without nitrogen" [12] has become a classic in physiological literature. It described an attempt to determine whether animals could live without nitrogenous food or, as we should say, without protein. When he fed a dog on a diet of sugar and distilled water, he found that the dog grew thin, its muscles became wasted and ·the animal died in about a month. What is much more significant to us, he noted the appearance of ulcerations of the cornea, which soon grew so deep that they resulted in complete perforation and allowed the fluid contents of the eyeball continually to escape. The emaciation and the corneal ulcers occurred in spite of the fact that the dog ate 120 grams of sugar a day and seemed to digest this food perfectly. Another dog on a diet of olive oil and water died in an emaciated state but showed no corneal ulcers. A third dog on a diet of butter and water developed an ulcer on one eye and also died greatly emaciated. Magendie's conclusion that animals cannot live without nitrogenous foods was correct, but it has only recently been pointed out that he also gave as perfect a description of xerophthalmia as one could wish, this being one of the recently recognized deficiency diseases, or an avitaminosis, specifically the result of lack of vitamin-A. This vitamin is not found in olive oil, but it is present in butter, so that we should have expected the reverse of what Magendie recorded with regard to the occurrence of ulcers in the second and third dogs. Perhaps the explanation of the appearance of one ulcer in the dog on the butter diet is that cows furnishing the butter were kept in a stable and ate no fresh grass, in which case their butter would have a low vitamin-A content.

This memoir has led physiologists to ask whether Magendie must not be regarded as having sown the seed for the vitamin hypothesis as well as having established the need

[12] *Bull. de la Soc. philomat.*, 4:137, 1816. *Précis*, 1817, v. 2, p. 388-395.

for protein in the diet.[13] It is interesting that the committee of the Academy of Sciences appointed to report on this memoir stated their opinion that it was desirable that the author should determine the proportions of nitrogen necessary to maintain life. The answer to this problem could not be forthcoming for nearly a century when more could be known about amino-acids, which of them could be synthesized by the animal body and which have to be supplied in food.

In later editions of the *Précis* Magendie reported further experiments on the effects of diets composed of other single substances which are common articles of food, but which prove inadequate to maintain life when taken alone. It has been pointed out that he was among the first to use rodents for nutritional investigations, a procedure which has been thoroughly exploited since his time.[14]

Also referred to in the *Précis* were some rather bizarre experiments, first reported in 1816,[15] which had been carried out with the help of the chemist, Chevreul (1786-1889). The intestinal gases of four executed prisoners were analyzed, the meal which they had eaten an hour before their execution having consisted of prison bread, gruyère cheese and diluted red wine. A particularly macabre touch was the emphasis on the youth of the prisoners, which made them excellent experimental material.

A much more important paper of this period was the memoir read before the Academy of Sciences in February, 1817, "On Arteries in circulation."[16] In the *Précis* Magendie has discussed his reasons for believing that the propulsion of the blood through the capillaries of the lungs is brought about solely by the force of the heart beat.[17] To experiment

[13] McCay, C. M., *Science*, 71:315, 1930.
[14] Bing, F. C., *Science*, 74:456, 1931.
[15] *Bull. de la Soc. philomat.*, 4:129, 1816. Cf. *Précis*, 1817, v. 2, p. 103.
[16] *Procès-verb. Acad. d. Sc.*, 6:175, 1817.
[17] *Précis*, 1817, v. 2, p. 308.

directly on capillaries was ruled out by his principle that
only what was immediately perceptible to the senses was
experimental evidence.[18] He therefore used the larger
arteries and reported his failure to produce the slightest
evidence of contraction in them, although he tried all the
means of stimulation at his command, viz, pricking with a
sharp instrument, pinching and application of the galvanic
current. He concluded that arteries do not have contractile
powers and that therefore the role they play in circulation
must be purely a passive one; that their chief characteristic
is their elasticity, and although this property may contribute
slightly to the pushing of the blood on through the circulatory system, once the arteries have been distended, nevertheless the actual propelling force comes from the beating
of the heart. This in a broad sense is still held, but arteries
can contract under the proper stimuli. Magendie's own
words show where he went wrong in concluding that the
arteries have no irritability, or, as we should say now, no
contractility. He states that he was looking for a "twitch,"
and that is not the type of contraction displayed by smooth
muscles of which the arteries are composed. He went to
the Jardin des Plantes and dissected the aorta of an elephant
in order to have as large an artery as possible for examination, but he was unable to find any trace of a "muscular
tunic" in it. He argued that if there were none to be found
in the vessels of so large a beast, surely there could be none
in smaller animals, and he claimed that "it was a fallacy to
base upon these imaginary fibres an action which cannot
come from them." In his elaboration of this contention he
pronounced peremptorily on reports of such fibers which
had been said to play "so important yet so chimerical a

[18] August Krogh received a Nobel prize (1920) for his observation of the
independent contractility of the capillaries. He extended the empire of
the senses by his use of greatly enlarged cinematographic projections of
photomicrographs.

role." The dogmatic manner of his statement would not endear Magendie to anyone holding the opposite and incidentally the correct view. He was evidently looking for striated muscle and so missed the presence of the unstriated variety, which was shown a quarter of a century later by Jacob Henle to be present in the endothelial coat of at least the lesser arteries.

Also in February, 1817, there was presented to the Academy of Science a report of a resumption of the experiments on emetics with a new collaborator, Pierre-Joseph Pelletier (1788-1842), a remarkably skilful chemist, who was five years younger than Magendie.[19] They had published a preliminary report in 1816 in one of the Paris medical journals under the title, "Chemical and Physiological Researches on Ipecacuanha," but it is to the memoir read before the Academy of Sciences that Magendie and others have subsequently referred for the date of the discovery of emetine. The majority of later references to this discovery cite Pelletier's name only, but it is evident from the reports, not only in the minutes of the Academy of Sciences but also in the detailed account in the *Bulletin* of the Société philomathique, that Magendie and Pelletier had equal shares in the discovery. Indeed, these contemporary records put Magendie's name first, although that arrangement may have been prompted merely by alphabetical priority. The experiments reported showed that different species of ipecacuanha plants owed their emetic properties to a substance which Magendie said was named *emetine* by Pelletier. This substance was more active than ground ipecacuanha root and was free from the latter's nauseous odor. The odor, they found, was entirely associated with a certain fatty material which possessed no emetic properties apart from its odor.

Associated with his seniors in these experiments was Joseph-Bienaimé Caventou (1795-1877), at this time a

[19] *Procès-verb. Acad. d. Sc.*, 6:166, 1817.

young man of only twenty-two, who was still working for his diploma in pharmacy under the famous chemist, Thénard (1777-1857). Caventou and Pelletier were very shortly to gain renown for their isolation of a number of chemical substances of great value to the medical profession, notably quinine sulphate, which they identified in 1820. On the present occasion the lack of emetic properties in the fatty constituent of ipecacuanha was established by using poor Cavantou as the research animal. He actually brought himself to swallow six grains of the vile-smelling fat without being obliged to vomit.[20] On another occasion he gave additional proof of a venturesome disposition by swallowing enough emetine to produce violent vomiting and then neutralizing the effect by swallowing a decoction of nutgalls (tannic acid).[21] Both Magendie and Pelletier tried the new emetic on themselves, two grains being sufficient to make them vomit, the same dose also proving effective for all their experimental animals. They even induced some of their students to follow their example. After vomiting, all the subjects slept soundly, and when they awoke were delighted to find that there were no traces of nausea. It is also recorded that Pelletier took some emetine to cure a gastric upset, and the desired effect was obtained. It was found that 6-12 grains were sufficient to cause the death of a dog after it had vomited violently, so that they were more than ever convinced that the six grains of obnoxiously smelling substance swallowed by Caventou without untoward results must be a substance entirely different from emetine. They considered that the value for medicine of their new preparation rested in its being more powerful in its effects than ipecacuanha root and in the possibility of its being administered to patients without the inconvenience of the vile odor heretofore associated with this emetic.

[20] *Formulaire*, 1821, p. 64.
[21] *Formulaire*, 1821, p. 75.

These important results were a direct sequel of Magendie's paper on emetics of 1813, but the investigation was still incomplete, for emetine had not yet been isolated in a form pure enough to make an analysis possible, although the authors of the memoir of 1817 were convinced that it was a specific substance and identical in the three species of ipecacuanha which they had examined. Pelletier and Dumas presently gave the analysis of what they thought was pure emetine,[22] but since that time it has been shown that their "pure" emetine consisted of at least three separate alkaloids, and the exact composition of emetine is still a matter of dispute.

[22] *Formulaire*, 1821, p. 75.

6

BEGINNINGS OF OFFICIAL RECOGNITION AND INTEREST IN MEDICAL PRACTICE
1818-1822

"Je m'applaudis, dans l'intérêt de cette femme, de lui avoir rendu la santé, mais dans l'intérêt de la science il est à regretter d'être privé des renseignements qu'aurait fournis l'examen anatomique des partis." [1]

FOR NEARLY a decade Magendie's scientific papers had been appearing. Student after student assisted him in his experiments, obtained a medical degree and, more often than not, disappeared from the world of physiological research into the world of medical practice. His reputation was growing and as early as 1816 he was sufficiently known abroad to have been made an associate of the Medical Societies of Stockholm and Copenhagen and a corresponding member of the Philosophical Society of London. In 1817 he received the same recognition from the Medical Societies of Wilna and of Philadelphia and from scientific societies in Hanover and Caen. Whether it was because he was an orderly person or merely one of those with a reverence for official documents, he seems to have carefully kept everything of that nature which he received in the course of his life. These papers were preserved in a leather brief case which bore his name in gold letters. Both case and contents were on

[1] *Phén. phys.*, 1842, v. 1, p. 284.

view, at least until 1940, in the Musée Gilbert of the Paris Faculty of Medicine. The American document is conspicuous because it is made of sheepskin and has still attached to it a faded blue ribbon. Most of Magendie's memberships in foreign societies, however, did not come until about ten years later.

At home he had suffered a disappointment when, early in 1816, a vacancy occurred in the Academy of Sciences through the death of Tenon (1724-1816), who had once been a surgeon at the Salpetrière. Magendie submitted his name but Duméril [2] (1774-1860), already professor of Anatomy and Physiology in the Paris Faculty of Medicine, was elected.

Although Magendie was beginning to be known as the only professional exponent of experimental physiology, he was still actively engaged in the practice of medicine, as some of his published observations and investigations bore witness. Under the heading of medical curiosities comes a report [3] of the strange accomplishment of a soldier who as a child had seen a Jew reverse his tongue and thrust it down his pharynx. The fascinated child had tried to do the trick himself but had failed because the tongue had been held down firmly by the membrane along its base. One day he made so violent an effort to swallow his tongue that the membrane was torn and there was a considerable hemorrhage. Far from being disconcerted, the boy was enchanted, since now he could thrust the tip of his tongue behind the palate and epiglottis clear down into his oesophagus. He retained this accomplishment after he reached manhood and displayed it for the benefit of Magendie, who seems at

[2] The greatest triumph of Duméril's early days had been his victory over the ambitious Dupuytren in 1798 in a competitive examination for the directorship of the anatomical laboratories. He was made professor of Anatomy and Physiology in 1801, and in 1823 became the first occupant of the first independent chair of Physiology in the Paris Faculty of Medicine.

[3] *Bull. de la Soc. philomat.*, 4:157, 1816.

this time to have regarded almost anything connected with swallowing as being worthy of a place on the record.

A more interesting case of the relation between his experimental activities and his medical practice is his memoir of 1817 [4] on the use of prussic acid in pulmonary phthisis. Gay-Lussac at this time was making his classic researches on hydrocyanic acid and Magendie described how this deadly chemical agent killed a dog so quickly that it was almost as if the animal were struck by lightning. The drug was already in clinical use in pulmonary diseases, but because it was lethal in very small quantities Magendie thought that adoption of the method of Gay-Lussac in its preparation would contribute to precision in the assessment of dosage. In M. Pelletier's laboratory he himself prepared some of this acid so that he might be sure of its purity and administered it, greatly diluted, to one of his patients who was troubled with a dry cough every morning and night. The treatment was a complete success. He tried the remedy on fifteen other patients, in all cases with success. Finally, he persuaded Dr. Lerminer at the Charité to use hydrocyanic acid on twenty patients in his wards, and together the two physicians were watching the results at the time the memoir was read. The paper was soon (1820) [5] translated into English for the benefit of American physicians. The small pamphlet was printed in New Haven, Connecticut, and bore the stamp of approval of the famous Benjamin Silliman, Professor of Chemistry, Pharmacy, Mineralogy and Geology at Yale College, who made himself indirectly responsible for the purity of the product supplied to the profession if obtained from Dr. Alfred S. Monson, "located at the corner of York and Elm Streets of that city."

[4] Procès-verb. Acad. d. Sc., 6:236, 1817.

[5] Physiological and chemical researches on the use of the prussic acid or hydrocyanic acid in the treatment of diseases of the breast, and particularly in phthisis pulmonalis by F. Magendie, M.D., etc. Translated from the French, with notes, etc., by James G. Percival, M.D., 1818.

Two other papers appeared in 1818 which were of particular interest to the practising physician. The first [6] of these was an attempt to classify the different kinds of concretions which are to be found in the human bladder and in the urine.[7] The contributing factors to the condition and means for its alleviation were indicated. Magendie was of the opinion that the essential cause was over-indulgence in nitrogenous foods. Meats and coffee were particularly to be avoided. He cited the case of a financier, his patient, who, when his affairs flourished and his diet consisted of rich foods, was troubled with gravel in his urine; when, however, the patient lost his fortune and became a ruined man, the vexatious gravel disappeared and he was cured because he could no longer afford rich foods.

The second paper is prefaced by a curious tirade against his own profession.[8] A young girl had come to him with an aneurism of the aorta. She had apparently consulted more than one *bona fide* physician, besides having had recourse to such outsiders as "gossips, charlatans, pharmacists, magnetizers, herbalists, etc," without having obtained relief from any of them. The immediate difficulty was insomnia, which was causing great distress. By means of small doses of morphine acetate, administered at night, the necessary sleep was obtained. The young woman protested that she could not take opium, but under the disguise of "strong and weak pills" Magendie was able to administer the morphine and obtain the desired results. He concluded from his experience in this and other cases that both the

[6] Recherches physiologiques et médicales sur les causes, les symptomes et la traitement de la gravelle, 1818.

[7] These were illustrated in a plate which the title page informs us was "colored with care," and we can agree that they are portrayed not only in their natural colors but in a symmetrical arrangement suggesting a chaplet of more precious stones.

[8] *Bull. de la Soc. philomat.*, —:54, 1818.

acetate and sulphate of morphine could be used as quieting agents.

There is also a set of papers of this period written from a purely physiological point of view. Opposition when Magendie was convinced that he was right only made him stubborn. He had never been able to dismiss from his mind the verdict of non-proven which the committee of the Academy of Sciences had brought in when at the very beginning of his scientific career he had offered what he considered to be adequate refutation of the idea that the lymphatic system is the sole means of absorption of substances finding their way into the blood stream. He now thought that he could clinch the matter by pointing to the peculiar lymphatic systems which he had seen in dissecting certain birds and reptiles. Specimens of the large green woodpecker, a swan, even a crocodile donated by Cuvier, came under his scalpel, and in none of these types was he able to find chyliferous vessels leading from the intestine to the subclavian vein.[9] To be sure, one academician, presumably a gourmet, said he was certain he had seen such vessels in a woodpecker in aspic, but Magendie branded this as a mere illusion, evidently a case of a "cold bird and a bottle." He did find a peculiar system of glands resembling salivary glands in the thorax, and vessels like lymphatics coming from the head and from the fore limb to join the subclavian vein, but this was by no means the extensive lymphatic system to be found in mammals. So far as can be discovered by gross dissection Magendie was right about the lymphatic system in birds,[10] and experts on avian anatomy refuse to pronounce an opinion as to the mode of absorption of fatty substances from the bird's intestine. Magendie was not content to deal merely with the anatomical aspect of the question, but attempted to explain the mechanism of ab-

[9] *Bull. de la Soc. philomat.*,—:119, 135, 145, 1819.
[10] Groebbels, F., *Der Vögel*, 1932, v. 1, p. 117.

sorption. Was it a purely physical phenomenon, or one peculiar to life, he asked. He had already ridiculed in his text-book [11] the prevailing vitalistic view that absorption was due to "the sensibility of absorbent mouths and the insensible organic contractility" of the chyliferous vessels, an explanation at once recognized as having its source in Bichat. His experiments now led him to conclude that all blood vessels, arteries or veins, living or dead, large or small, possessed the physical properties necessary to explain absorption. In modern terms, they are permeable.[12]

Since the days of his interneship Magendie, curiously enough, had had no regular hospital appointment. Apparently it now occurred to him that it would be an advantage not to have first to convince a friend in charge of a ward that a new remedial agent was worth trying, but to have hospital patients of his own to whom it could be administered. He therefore presented himself at the central bureau of the Paris hospitals, July 15, 1818, and was successful in the competition for a place as a physician regularly attached to a service. The confirming order was signed by a minister on August 7, but it was not until July 12, 1826, that Magendie was actually proposed as a substitute physician at the Salpétrière.

Concrete evidence of Magendie's awareness of the needs of the medical profession is to be found in his "Formulaire," first published in 1821. By that time, so many accounts of new drugs had appeared that it seemed to him a good idea to gather the material together and present it in such a fashion that it would be of practical use to physicians. The book which he made, although it contained some 300 pages, was actually small enough to slip into a coat pocket, and its full title gives an excellent idea of its contents: "Formulary for the preparation and use of many new remedies, such as

[11] *Précis*, 1817, v. 2, p. 162.
[12] *Procès-verb. Acad. d. Sc.*, 7:109, 1820.

nux vomica, morphine, prussic acid, strychnine, veratrine,
salts of quinine, emetine, iodine, etc." The *etcetera* was
elaborated in subsequent editions into "iodide of mercury,
cyanide of potassium, croton oil, salts of gold, salts of platinum, chlorides of calcium and sodium, alkaline bicarbon-
ates, digestive pastilles of Vichy, bark of the root of the
pomegranate tree, preparations of phosphorus, etc., etc."
Nearly all the drugs mentioned in the title of the first edition had been subjects of memoirs by Magendie himself.
The general plan of the book is to give first a brief statement of the discovery of the substance; second, a detailed
description of the method of its preparation in a pure state,
or as nearly pure as was possible at the time; third, its
action on various animals and on normal, healthy man in
different doses (these details were nearly always the result
of Magendie's own observations); and finally, its use in
the treatment of disease, the dosage and mode of administration (here were included opinions of physicians who had
successfully used the remedy even as far away as "New-
Yorc"). The book was printed in one of the tiniest streets
in the Latin Quarter, which still bears the curious name of
"Gît-le-coeur," and its modest price, one franc fifty cen-
times, disclosed in an advertisement in Magendie's own
Journal, of which more hereafter, seems in keeping with its
size and the surroundings in which it came into existence.
It evidently took on well, since in the next year two reprints
were necessary, without change of text, and by 1835 it had
been considerably enlarged and had arrived at its eighth
edition. There were several different translations into English and into German, Dutch, Italian and Scandinavian by
1830. By means of this little book Magendie was able to
spread abroad his doctrine of the value of a knowledge of
the action of chemical agents on living organisms and successfully to introduce into medicine the use of strychnine,

morphine, iodides and bromides.[13] It has become a classic in the history of pharmacology.

Magendie was still a free lance in the teaching of medicine. In November, 1818, the chair of Anatomy and Physiology became vacant in the Paris Faculty of Medicine. The four favored names among the large number of applicants considered for the post were Béclard, Roux, Cloquet and Magendie. All of these men were well known for their work as teachers and for their original research. Béclard received the appointment.

Magendie, however, in the next year, 1819, was successful in being put on the list of lecturers at the Athenée Royal. There he gave a series of evening lectures on anatomy and physiology, which began the last of November and ended in early summer. Among his fellow lecturers was Fourier, whose famous "series" in mathematics still bears his name. The price for these lectures was 120 francs a year, 90 francs for six months, ladies half price, with a corresponding reduction for *bona fide* students from the different Paris Faculties. Magendie augmented his income in this way for several years.

In 1820 Magendie became president of the Société Médicale d'Émulation de Paris, in whose *Bulletin,* it will be remembered, his first paper had appeared. The Société in the immediately preceding years had lost ground. It had ceased to publish its own proceedings in 1812 and united with the journal edited by Leroux, Corvisart and Boyer, which, from 1812 through 1817, Magendie used almost exclusively for the publication of his papers. With the passing of Leroux's journal, the Société made a fresh alliance with *Le nouvel journal de médecine, chirurgie et pharmacie,* of which Magendie shared the editorship along with Béclard, Orfila and four others, although he himself contributed to it only two original articles. When he accepted the presi-

[13] Koppanyi, T., *Sci. Monthly,* 41:316, 1935.

dency in succession to Breschet the Société was on the verge
of becoming defunct, but it was afterwards said that the
next three or four years were the most prosperous in its
whole history and that the credit for this rejuvenescence was
chiefly due to his vigorous administration.[14] The revival was
rather short-lived as decline had set in again by 1824.

Perhaps the most lasting result of Magendie's connection
at this time with the society whose name had first been
associated with that of Bichat, was the bringing out in 1822
of the first annotated edition of Bichat's "Physiological Researches on Life and Death." This treatise, first published in
1800, had by 1805 gone through three editions, and Magendie's edition, the fourth, was much augmented by his critical
foot-notes. His preface indicated the chief ground of his opposition to Bichat, who, he said, "continually contrasted
life and the reign of physical law, as if living beings were
not bodies before they were either vegetables or animals."
Magendie thought that Bichat's renown was well founded
on the great number of his exact observations, the ingenious
conduct of his experiments and his lucid style, but he regretted the "deceptive hypotheses" on the basis of which
Bichat had organized the presentation of his experimental
findings. It seemed to Magendie that the truths which the
book contained owed their publicity to the unfortunate
popularity of its errors. The notes on the text were made
bulky by the inclusion of descriptions of such of Magendie's
own experimental results as were corrective either of Bichat's
facts or of his deductions from them. The chief point of
attack was Bichat's distinction between organic and animal
life, which Magendie regarded as misleading because it
isolated phenomena which were in reality in close relation.
Bichat's rather absurd idea that symmetry characterized the
organs of animal and asymmetry those of organic life was

[14] Cherest, J., *Recueil d. Travaux de la Soc. méd. d'émulation de Paris*, 30:5,
1850.

disposed of with the comment that "the brain is as asymmetrical as the kidneys." Bichat's conception of organic sensibility as a minimum concentration of a property which at a greater concentration became animal sensibility was dismissed by Magendie, first, on the ground that organic sensibility was purely conjectural (the stomach is not 'sensible' of nourishment) and, secondly, for the rather unexpected reason that the idea of the presence of a vital property in varying degrees of concentration was a "quantitative idea borrowed from physics and inappropriately applied to a vital property." The curious suspension of Magendie's mind between the old vitalism and the new scientific determinism is apparent here. The greater part of his refutation of Bichat is made to rest upon his experimental findings, e.g., he attacked the distinction between animal and sensible organic contractility on the ground that his analysis of the movements of the oesophagus showed the presence in a single organ of both types of contractility, so-called; and he used his results on the elasticity of arteries to undermine Bichat's analysis of organic contractility into sensible and insensible, since Bichat had illustrated this analysis by referring to different parts of the circulatory system. It seems not improbable that the direction taken by a good deal of Magendie's early research was dictated by his interest in Bichat. His comment on the passage in which Bichat spoke at length of the instability of vital phenomena and the consequent inapplicability of mathematical methods to their expression was that Bichat was not a competent judge, being insufficiently acquainted with the methods of physics and chemistry. Magendie himself thought that physical methods had already been usefully applied to questions of respiration, limits of temperature, etc.

Magendie had come to have considerable experience with medical journals not only as a contributor but also as an editor. His connections with Leroux's *Journal* and *Le nouvel*

journal de médecine, chirurgie et pharmacie have already
been pointed out. He now decided that the time was ripe
for a journal which should be devoted exclusively to experimental physiology, and in January, 1821, he brought out
the first number of his *Journal de physiologie expérimentale,*
to which title he added, beginning with volume two, *et
pathologie.* As a matter of fact, from the very beginning,
clinical and experimental articles appeared side by side. It
was Magendie's own venture. He was the sole editor, the
sole owner, the sole arbiter of what it should contain. He
had deposited a sum sufficient to finance its publication for
several years, but the journal was so well received that with
the second number it paid for itself. This was all Magendie
wanted, for he explicitly stated that he had not founded
it as a financial speculation, and he undertook to devote
all that came in above expenses to its improvement. The
format which he chose was octavo, which was also used
for other journals of that day.

The first number was rather padded with his own work,
including, without changes, the original memoir on absorption of 1809, the more recent one on the same subject of
1820, the memoir on lymphatics in birds of 1819, a note on
narcotine and another on the structure of the human lung.
An account of his experiments on hydrophobia is particularly interesting in view of the stir which his supposed cure
was presently to make, not only in the medical world, but
also in the public press. He told of collaborating with the
surgeon Dupuytren in injecting into the veins of a young
man afflicted with this dread disease a gummy extract of
opium, without, however, obtaining any beneficial results;
and with Breschet, head of the anatomical laboratories of
the Faculty of Medicine, in injecting some of the saliva
of another hydrophobia patient into a dog, in which case
the dog within a month became mad. Pelletier and Caventou
contributed an article on a new analysis of quinine; Breschet

wrote on hydrocephalus; and Andral, *fils*, who was working
with Magendie, wrote on veratrine and on the production
of peristaltic movements in the seminal vesicles of the
guinea pig by means of the galvanic current. In fact, this
first number is an excellent report on Magendie's interests
and associates at the moment. Subsequent issues were much
less personal.

The volume of Magendie's *Journal* most prized by col-
lectors is the second (for 1822), which contains not only
the description of the experiments which gave rise to the
Bell-Magendie controversy, but also Kergaradec's memoir
on auscultation of the foetus by means of Laennec's newly
introduced stethoscope. The eighth volume is of particular
interest since it contains Poiseuille's memoir describing the
haemodynamometer. The journal was intended primarily
for the physician and the articles dealing with pure physiology were often accompanied by citation of hospital cases
illustrating the principles brought out by animal experimentation. Magendie was generous in giving space to articles by his pupils and associates, nearly all of whom made
some reference in their text to his work. He also published
translations or abstracts of papers by Bell of England,
Rollando of Italy, Tiedemann and Gmelin of Germany. The
general principles of his editorial policy are implied in a
foot-note to an article of his own on circulation in the first
number of the second volume:

"Nothing is more harmful to the progress of medicine than
the absurd isolation which the majority of physicians wish to
maintain with respect to the natural sciences; and on what
basis do they affirm in so trenchant a manner that there can
be no application of physics, chemistry and mechanics to animal economy, if they do not know these sciences? For the sake
of their own prestige they should begin by making themselves
physicists, chemists, etc., and then they would change their
opinion. If doctors persist in this singular attitude, before fifty

years are over our profession will be one of the lowest in society; it would be rightly regarded as merely ignoble empiricism; happily, I do not believe that this will be the case. . . . Imagining without always observing, inventing phenomena instead of seeking to discover them by experiment, men of great promise have wasted their talent and their efforts in hair-splitting; science has gained nothing; on the contrary, the experimental method followed by Harvey being quite abandoned, a discovery made by such a man is obscured and lost in the welter of polemics to which it gives rise. . . . That I may not be accused of disobeying my own counsels, in this number I submit for the criticism of my confrères certain work on circulation. I will receive with thanks facts and arguments showing where I am wrong. Nothing is more agreeable than to replace error with truth. I ask all who wish to send me an account of their work to do so at least a month before the publication of an issue, in order that I may have time to repeat the principal experiments myself before sending the journal to press."

To facilitate these communications Magendie published in each number of the first two volumes of his *Journal* the address of his bachelor quarters at 30 rue de Seine, a stone's throw directly behind the Institut where the Academy of Sciences met every Monday afternoon. After the first two years the reports of Magendie's own work were mostly reprints from the proceedings of the Academy of Sciences, and he restricted his activities in connection with the *Journal* more nearly to those usual for an editor. The numbers continued to appear regularly at quarterly intervals for ten and a half years; the last was that for April, 1831.

In 1821 Magendie had received "very honorable mention" for his memoir on absorption, which had been submitted in competition for the Academy of Science's prize in experimental physiology. It is perhaps worth mentioning that there seems to be some slight discrepancy between the facts and M. Flourens' interpretation of them with regard to the original establishment of this prize. According to M. Flourens, it was Magendie's unremitting experimentation which had made the need felt for such a prize. M. de Laplace is reported to have said to his wealthy old friend, M. de Montyon, Minister of the Interior:

" 'It is most regrettable that scientific bodies should not have at their disposal the means of keeping up the zeal of workers who are obtaining valuable results; the young Magendie, for example, who invariably bases his physiological investigations upon experiment, deserves to be encouraged.'

" 'But are not words from you the most potent encouragement?' parried M. Montyon, inspired perhaps by guile, perhaps by politeness.

" 'They do not suffice,' replied Laplace. 'For those who aspire to climb to a place in our Academies rungs of the ladder are necessary, and these rungs should be competitions with prizes.'

" 'You shall have all the credit,' interposed the modest benefactor; 'spend what you think is necessary. I ask only the honor of having satisfied one of your wishes.' "

M. Flourens concludes his account of this polished interchange with the remark, "Soon the prize in experimental physiology was established and Magendie was honored (couronné)."

The story to be gleaned from the minutes of the Academy of Sciences does not convey quite the same impression. The first reference to the prize is in 1818 when Laplace was appointed chairman of a committee to deal with a sum of money given by the anonymous founder of the Statistics Prize for an award of the same value, 7000 francs, in Experimental Physiology. The king gave his approval of the new prize in an ordinance of July 22, 1818, and in August a committee composed of Hallé, Pinel, Berthollet, Percy and Cuvier was appointed to take charge of its administration. On November 15 of the following year Magendie entered the competition with two volumes of his text-book and a collection of memoirs. Then the baron de Montyon died and on March 19, 1821, it was ordered that the three prizes which he had established for the Academy of Sciences should henceforth bear his name. On the same day, the winners of the prize in Experimental Physiology were announced. The money was to be shared equally between Dutrochet and Magendie's pupil, Dr. Edwards. As alternates were named the German physiologists, Tiedemann and Gmelin, and then came Magendie with a "very honorable mention." This does not seem to be any too adequate a "crown" for one whose work was supposed to have inspired the institution of the prize.

As a matter of fact, Magendie was on the verge of arrival at the top of M. de Laplace's ladder without the assistance of "rungs." Although there were smaller societies like the Société philomathique and the Société Médicale d'Émulation where the scientific aspects of medicine were discussed and although some of the more eminent physicians had found seats in the Academy of Sciences, the physicians of Paris resolved at about this time to revive the ancient Royal Academy of Medicine and Surgery. The ordinance for the creation of the Royal Academy of Medicine was signed by Louis XVIII at the Tuileries, December 20, 1820. In the first list of members were the names of many men who had played, or were to play, some part in Magendie's life: on the medical side, Duméril, Professor of the Faculty of Medicine, Récamier at the Hôtel-Dieu; in surgery, Dupuytren of the Faculty of Medicine, now a favorite of Louis XVIII and a baron; in pharmacy, Pelletier, assistant professor at the School of Pharmacy; as associates, the baron Cuvier, Gay-Lussac and Thénard (to be baron later); and as a nonresident member, Laennec of Quimper. On February 6, 1821, the lists were considerably extended and His Majesty was pleased to confirm among other nominations that of

François Magendie, whose only title was doctor of medicine. It is often stated that Magendie was a member of the Academy of Medicine from its foundation, but it is to be noted that he was in the second, not the first, list of members to be approved by the king.

Although he was still under forty and rather young for the Academy of Sciences, a second attempt was now made to find a place for him in it. When the third number of his *Journal* was being brought out, the nominating committee of the Academy was split over the choice of nominees for the place of the late M. Bichard; two of the committee held out for a zoologist, one refused to take sides, while Pinel and Duméril insisted that an anatomist be chosen and that Magendie could be so classified. The zoologist was successful in the balloting. In November, the death of Corvisart brought about two vacancies, one a seat in the Academy of Sciences and the other the chair of Medicine at the Collège de France. Hallé was given the latter and Magendie was again proposed for a seat in the Academy of Sciences. Chaussier, his former teacher, with whom he had had a violent scene in his early days as prosector of anatomy, was his rival. It was felt in some quarters that the younger man should retire gracefully to allow the older scientist to take precedence. It was whispered that as Chaussier was already seventy-five Magendie might not have too long to wait for another vacancy of the same chair. Magendie refused to be influenced by these considerations. He pressed his claims vigorously and this time he was successful.

At the last moment, according to Flourens' account, which is perhaps not unspiced with malice, Magendie felt unwilling to learn the results of the balloting at first hand. He shut himself up in his room and sent two of his students to learn the verdict while he waited in a fever of anxiety. The first student returned so pale and excited that he could only sink into an armchair, incapable of uttering a word.

Then the second burst into the room. He was red in the face, gasped and threw himself at full length on the floor, also without a word. Magendie was convinced that the worst had happened, but putting aside his own feelings, set himself to revive his stricken pupils. Soon one of them was able to announce the good news, and Magendie shouted joyfully, "All my trouble has been repaid, my goal is reached!" On December 10, 1821, at the early age of thirty-eight, he had become a member of the Academy of Sciences.

He was immediately put on the committee for the administration of the Montyon prize in Experimental Physiology, on which he continued to act for the rest of his life, and he soon became the arbiter of opinion on practically all memoirs of a physiological nature. These tasks he was most conscientious in fulfilling and some of his reports are masterpieces of clear exposition.

In the Academy he felt himself to be among friends, yet he could not change his nature and he did not change his habits. We learn from Flourens that he gave vent to "fits of anger, the rudeness and unexpectedness of which disconcerted the members and upset all Academic tradition. He never intimated discreetly that an opinion was erroneous, that a fact might not be exact; he said so outright. . . . When physicians came to solicit his vote on some measure on the ground that he was a fellow physician, he quickly showed them where they stood; and if the claims on his support proved to be really good, he might yield, but he would growl, 'You have my voice, but not my hand!' " To this tendency to gratuitous rudeness Magendie added the exhibition of an unbounded egoism and an unfortunate lack of self control. Flourens in calling attention to these characteristics attempted also to account for them. He said:

"Our Academician had a dangerous tendency of a very serious nature; having consecrated himself without reserve to physiology he considered this field to be his own individual domain.

Not a single point about this science could be broached without his taking offence, not only if he had worked on the subject in question, but even if he merely held it in reserve in his own mind while searching for some new aspect of it which experiment might give him. Under these conditions a worker who stepped over the line became an enemy. A childish rage then seized M. Magendie, he was no longer in possession of himself; that part of his nature which had been fostered by the unrestrained exercise of democracy came out, so that a decent person, a man of spirit, felt that in such injustice there was something inferior to himself."

As is often the case, such outbursts were not sustained. Magendie would back down if his opponent kept his temper long enough to show him where he was wrong,[15] and there are many witnesses to plead that in private and social life he could be charming and gracious. To some his brusqueness in official life seemed a mere pose; others explained it by saying that he had been spoiled by too early and too flattering recognition, although it may be remarked that this recognition had not as yet found issue in any very lucrative rewards. In any case, his reputation for rudeness and ill-temper was now firmly established and repercussions of it were constantly occurring throughout his life.

Hallé's tenure of the chair of Medicine at the Collège de France was extremely brief, for he died in February, 1822. The recommendation to the king of a candidate to hold this chair was a prerogative of the Academy of Sciences. In July the merits of five candidates, including Laennec and Magendie, were discussed and after two ballots Magendie's name was presented to the king for confirmation. The chair was given to Laennec. The latter was very different from Magendie both in temperament and in political affiliation. Magendie was a stormy petrel and an extreme

[15] Bernard, C., *Substances toxiques*, 1857, p. 28; *Pathologie expérimentale*, 1880, p. 483; *Physiologie opératoire*, 1879, p. 43.

liberal. Laennec was in Royalist favor, having lately been appointed physician to the duchesse de Berry, and he was a quiet and retiring Breton. It has been stated quite frankly that he had the most admirable qualities "except those of a true professor, . . . those which are necessary to command an audience." [16] Laennec's fame rests not on his powers as an expositor, but on his introduction into medicine of auscultation through the use of that instrument which has since his time come to be the invariable badge of the practising physician.

[16] Cousin, V., *De l'enseignement et de l'exercice de la médecine et de la pharmacie*, 1850, p. 172.

7

THE BELL-MAGENDIE CONTROVERSY
1822

"J'annonçai donc, comme un fait nouveau et que je venais découvrir, que les racines antérieures présidaient au mouvement et les postérieures à la sensibilité." [1]

THE year 1822 saw Magendie at the height of his powers with his scientific reputation fully established. It is to the experimental work accomplished in this year that he owes his distinguished place in the history of physiology. Unfortunately, a controversy which immediately arose over his claims to priority has never been settled. The events are clear and their sequence well-established, but a just evaluation of their significance is still a matter of acrimonious debate.

Charles Bell (1774-1842) in 1821 was junior partner in the famous Hunterian School of Anatomy at Great Windmill Street, London. For years he had given lectures on the anatomy of the nervous system and had tried to introduce some order into this, the most intricate of all the systems of the human body. His assistant, and incidentally his brother-in-law, John Shaw (1792-1827), whom he had trained from the age of fifteen, was co-lecturer with him. Few experiments on living animals were carried out at the Great Windmill Street school, and these few were performed by Shaw, since Bell not only had an aversion to vivisection but thought little knowledge could be gained from animal

[1] *Syst. Nerv.*, 1841, v. 2, p. 64.

93

experimentation. In a letter to his brother, George, in Edinburgh, Charles Bell wrote on July 1, 1822:

"I should be writing a third paper on the nerves, but I cannot proceed without making some experiments which are so
unpleasant to make that I defer them. You may think me silly
but I cannot perfectly convince myself that I am authorized in
nature or religion to do these cruelties—" [2]

It is unfortunate for Bell that he did not end his sentence
at this point, as some of those who quote this passage do,
for in the next few words he naïvely betrays his view of the
motives behind the pursuit of scientific investigation—"to
do these cruelties—for what?—for anything else than a little
egotism or self aggrandisement."

Bell's "self aggrandisement" did not take the form of
publishing his work so that others could know of it. For at
least ten years before 1821 no paper or printed report had
come from him. The members of his family had repeatedly
tried to persuade him to publish his views, but he could
not bring himself to do so. Eventually, on July 12, 1821, he
read before the Royal Society of London a paper entitled,
"On the nerves; giving an account of some experiments on
their structure and functions, which lead to a new arrangement of the system." [3] In this paper he described a sub-
division of the system of classifying nerves which he had
introduced at the Great Windmill Street school, viz, that all
nerves which have anything to do with the act of breathing
or speaking should be designated as "respiratory nerves."
Taking the fifth and seventh cranial nerves as examples, he
asked the pertinent question, "Do these nerves have the same
function?" To answer it, he had John Shaw cut the fifth
nerve on one side of the head of an ass. During this operation the animal gave evidence of suffering acute pain, but

[2] Bell, C., *Letters*, 1870, p. 275.
[3] Bell, C., *Philos. Trans.*, 111:398, 1821.

no change in the movements of its nostrils was observed, although movements of the lips were lost. Upon cutting the seventh nerve there was no evidence of pain, but respiratory movements of the face were lost, sensitivity in this case being still present. The seventh nerve he therefore classified as a respiratory nerve, i.e., one having to do with the act of breathing or speaking and incidentally serving for the expresssion of the face as well. Bell added: "The same destruction of structure and function will be observed in nerves which take an extensive course throughout the body," which may perhaps be interpreted to mean that in other than respiratory nerves he had observed loss of movement as the consequence of cutting of the nerve.

John Shaw was most enthusiastic over his brother-in-law's method of teaching the anatomy of the nervous system and published its essentials in foot-notes of the laboratory manual which he wrote for the use of their students in anatomy. Shaw had acquired some facility in speaking French when, after the battle of Waterloo, he accompanied Bell on a trip to Brussels with the object of studying gun-shot wounds, and he thought that he might give French physiologists, of whom Magendie was the best known and most influential, some knowledge of Bell's system of classifying nerves. Therefore, early in September, 1821,[4] Shaw went to Paris, met Magendie and talked over with him the essentials of Bell's system and the differences in function of the fifth and seventh nerves.

As one might have anticipated, Magendie asked for a demonstration. Shaw attempted to give one between the hours of four and five o'clock in the morning at the Veterinary School at Alfort on the outskirts of Paris. M. Dupuy, the professor of veterinary science, a particular friend of Magendie, was to assist Shaw, and there was also present

[4] A letter of Charles to George Bell, dated August 30, 1821, says, "John Shaw is off to Paris."

the famous phrenologist, Spurzheim (1776-1832). The latter had met Shaw in 1814 in London where he had been a guest of Bell and had given an exposition of his system of phrenology at the Great Windmill Street school, much to the amusement of Bell, who thought it arrant nonsense.[5] Spurzheim was, however, no charlatan when it came to a knowledge of the nervous system,[6] and Shaw was therefore demonstrating before experts. In London when doing the operation for Bell he had used an ass, but here at Alfort he was given a horse. He cut the skin on the side of the animal's face, saw a large nerve and announced that upon the cutting of this nerve there would be immediate paralysis of the nostril. He cut the nerve, but the nostril moved as briskly as ever. In embarrassment he said that he must have cut the wrong nerve. The spectators were most kind and gave him every encouragement. He searched the wound, found another nerve, cut it, and this time the nostril was paralyzed. This part of the demonstration having now been successful, it was evident that he had established that paralysis resulted from cutting a branch of the seventh nerve. He now said that if he cut the fifth nerve there would be paralysis of the lip which would interfere with mastication. He cut the nerve; Magendie looked carefully, but was unable to satisfy himself that there was any derangement of this function, and the demonstration was over.

Shaw presented Magendie with the new edition of his laboratory manual, which was just off the press, and also gave him a verbal account of the paper which Bell had read a month previously at the Royal Society. Magendie was deeply impressed and in the next number of his *Journal* (October, 1821) gave a résumé of the paper as he

[5] Bell, C., *Letters,* 1870, p. 217.
[6] In 1821 Spurzheim had successfully defended a thesis on the brain and obtained a doctorate in medicine of Paris, and in 1822 he brought out a revised edition of his six-volume work on the nervous system.

had understood it from Shaw's French, which Shaw himself confessed was somewhat inadequate. Magendie repeated the experiments performed by Shaw at the veterinary school and found that his results confirmed Shaw's report of Bell's experiments on the fifth and seventh nerves, "except the effect of section of the suborbital (fifth) nerve on mastication, the influence of which was not evident to me." He made it clear that all his information regarding Bell's work had come from Shaw and that he hoped soon to receive a copy of Bell's paper.

There is one statement in Magendie's account which has an important bearing on the interpretation of the events which followed, namely, "I am told that Bell limited himself in his Royal Society memoir to the nerves of the face"; but he went on to say that according to Shaw's manual Bell recognized two great divisions of the brain corresponding to the anterior and posterior columns [7] of the spinal cord, and compared the manner in which certain of the cranial nerves leave the brain to that in which the spinal nerves leave the cord. These observations had been made on the lower animals. The main idea was the classification of nerves into (i) thirty-two "regular" nerves, i.e., those having two roots, *viz*, the thirty-one spinal nerves and the fifth cranial (which are "common to all animals from worm to man" and are "charged with sensibility and general motility"); and (ii) "irregular" nerves, i.e., those having a single root, such as the third, fourth, sixth, seventh and tenth, the seventh being at the same time a "respiratory" nerve. Magendie concluded his account with a very gracious comment on the value of Bell's work.

Magendie did *not* refer to a foot-note in Shaw's manual which nevertheless seems to have a definite bearing upon

---

[7] Throughout this discussion the older terms "anterior" and "posterior" will be retained to avoid confusion. In modern usage *ventral* replaces *anterior,* and *dorsal* replaces *posterior*.

the subsequent course of events.[8] "Some curious experiments have been made in Great Windmill Street on the comparative degree of sensibility of the two origins of these nerves. Though in these experiments there was sufficient observed to induce us to believe that there is much difference between the two sets of fibrils,—yet, from the difficulty of making them, the facts are not yet so distinct as to permit us to mention them."

This evidently had reference to the "one or two" experiments on the spinal nerves of living animals done by Shaw with Bell, the notes of which were claimed to have been taken down by his pupil, Mr. Caesar Hawkins, on March 21, 1821. In these notes it is stated that touching the ventral roots gave rise to convulsions, but no effect could be obtained on so treating the posterior root, its ganglion or the posterior part of the cord. Satisfied that the results obtained on the living animal were uniform, they turned to stunned animals to confirm their results, so as to avoid the infliction of unnecessary pain. It is strange that there is no reference here to Bell's having tried similar experiments eleven years before; the notes dated 1821 seem to indicate that they are entirely new observations.[9]

When the paper read before the Royal Society by Bell was printed, a copy was sent to Magendie and in the next number of his *Journal* (the first issue of 1822) he acknowledged having received it, and now quoted in translation those portions of the text which contained the experimental data on the fifth and seventh nerves. Magendie repeated Bell's experiments and found that whereas Bell stated explicitly that there was no evidence of pain on cutting the seventh nerve, in Magendie's experiments the animal cried out and gave every evidence of feeling pain. He said that he

[8] Shaw, J., *Manual*, 1821, p. 277.
[9] Shaw, J., *London Med. & Phys. Journ.*, 48:343, 1822. Cf. Shaw, A., *Narrative*, 1839.

Magendie, lithograph by Maurin.

did not doubt the accuracy of Bell's statement, for he himself had found animals whose nerves could be pinched and even twisted without evidence of the animal's perceiving it, and he thought that Bell's ass must have been this type of insensitive animal.

The next article in this number of Magendie's *Journal* is a translation of one written by Shaw after his return from Paris, in which he tried to account for his failure to produce paralysis of the lip in the horse at the Alfort demonstration. He claimed that it was due to a difference in distribution of nerves in the ass and in the horse. The next issue of the *Journal* included still another article by Shaw on facial paralysis. No one could have been more courteous to a foreign scientist than Magendie was on these occasions.

From all this it seems an inescapable conclusion that the attention of everyone concerned had up to this time been riveted on the two cranial nerves, and the divergence of opinion occurred in that Bell had found the fifth related to sensitivity, although cutting it produced paralysis of the lip, whereas Magendie could see no paralysis; and again Bell had found the seventh to be concerned with respiratory movements together with expression of the face with no evidence of pain on the part of the animal when the nerve was cut, whereas Magendie had found distinct evidences of pain on cutting the nerve.[10]

Magendie twice wrote to Bell an appreciation of his work on these nerves of the face and suggested that it might be presented for the Montyon Prize in Experimental Physiology. Bell wrote to his brother:

"My discoveries have made more impression in France than here, and I have received a second message from Magendie saying that if I would send them any short account I should

[10] The facts of the case are that each of these two nerves is both motor and sensory, but the fifth is predominantly sensory, the seventh predominantly motor.

have the prize medal. This is a ridiculous thing for an old fellow, but I mean it to recoil on them here." [11]

This was the situation when Magendie in June, 1822, published his classical account of "Experiments on the functions of the roots of the spinal nerves" in his *Journal*. This paper is now quoted in full, since it is one of the famous papers in the history of physiology, a model of exposition, clear, concise and convincing:

"For a long time I have wanted to try an experiment in which I should cut in an animal the posterior roots of the nerves which take their rise from the spinal cord. I have attempted it many times without success because of the difficulty of opening the vertebral canal without injuring the cord, and, consequently, without killing or, at least, seriously injuring the animal. Last month there was brought into my laboratory a litter of eight pups, six weeks old; these animals seemed to me very suitable for a fresh attempt to open the vertebral canal. In short, I was able with the help of a very sharp scalpel, and, so to speak, at a single stroke, to lay bare the posterior half of the spinal cord enclosed in its sheaths. To have this organ almost bare, it remained only for me to cut the dura mater which encloses it: this I easily did; I had then before my eyes the posterior roots of the lumbar and sacral pairs and on raising them successively with the blades of the small scissors, I was able to cut them on one side, the cord remaining intact. I did not know what would be the result of this procedure; I sewed up the wound with a suture in the skin, and observed the animal; I at first thought the limb corresponding to the cut nerves to be entirely paralysed; it was insensible to pricking and to the strongest pressures; it also seemed to be immobile; but soon, to my great surprise, I saw it move in a very obvious manner, although sensibility was still quite extinct in it. A second, a third experiment gave me exactly the same results; I began to regard it as probable that the posterior roots of the spinal nerves might

[11] Bell, C., *Letters*, 1870, p. 275.

very well have different functions from the anterior roots, and that they were more particularly destined for sensibility.

"It naturally occurred to my mind to cut the anterior roots, while leaving the posterior roots intact; but such an enterprise was easier to contemplate than to execute; how could I lay bare the anterior part of the cord without involving the posterior roots? I admit that the thing at first seemed to me impossible; nevertheless, I did not cease to reflect upon it for two days, and finally I decided to try to pass in front of the posterior roots a sort of cataract knife, the blade of which, being very thin, would permit the possibility of cutting the roots by pressing them with the edge of the instrument, on the posterior face of the bodies of the vertebrae; but I was obliged to give up this manoeuvre, because of the large veins which the canal contains on this side, which I opened at each movement forward. In making these attempts I perceived that by pulling on the vertebral dura mater, one could catch sight of the anterior roots united in bundles, at the moment at which they were about to pierce this membrane. I needed no more, and in a few moments, I had cut every pair that I wanted to divide. As in the preceding experiments, I made the section only on one side in order to have a means of comparison. One can imagine with what curiosity I followed the effects of this section: they were not painful, the limb was completely motionless and flaccid, whilst it preserved an unequivocal sensibility. Finally in order that nothing might be left undone, I cut the anterior and posterior roots at the same time; there was absolute loss of feeling and movement.

"I repeated and varied these experiments on various kinds of animals: the results which I have just announced were confirmed in the most complete way, both for the anterior and the posterior limbs. I continued these researches and I will give a more detailed account of them in the next number; I am content to be able to state positively today that the anterior and posterior roots of the nerves which arise from the spinal cord have different functions, that the posterior roots seem to be particularly destined for sensibility, while the anterior roots seem to be especially connected with movement." [12]

In the meantime, Bell had read before the Royal Society on May 2, 1822, the second part of his paper on "respiratory" nerves, entitled, "On the nerves which associate the muscles of the chest, in the actions of breathing and expression. Being a continuation of the paper on the structure and functions of nerves." [13] This completed his account of his idea that instead of there being one respiratory nerve, the vagus, as was the current opinion, a great many others, but chiefly the seventh, should be included under this head. This certainly had nothing to do with the functions of the anterior and posterior roots of the spinal nerves, but it is evidence of what aspect of the nervous system was uppermost in Bell's mind at this time. Magendie published an abstract of this article in the next (October, 1822) issue of his *Journal,* and followed it with an account of further experiments of his own on the spinal nerve roots.

He had found that if the posterior roots to a limb were cut, injection of *nux vomica* produced the usual convulsions of the whole body; if, however, the anterior roots were cut, the limb remained motionless, although the rest of the body was convulsed. But this is only half of the story when one is experimenting on the functions of nerves; extirpation and observation of changes from normal behaviour should be checked by direct stimulation. Magendie's methods of stimulation were "pinching, pulling and pricking" and application of the galvanic current. He observed unmistakable evidences of pain on stimulating the posterior roots, scarcely any on stimulating the anterior ones; similarly, stimulation of the anterior roots produced strong convulsive movements, while stimulation of the posterior roots produced feeble

[12] *J. de physiol. expér. et path.,* 2:276-279, 1822.
[13] Bell, C., *Philos. Trans.,* 112:284, 1822.

movements. He concluded, "The facts, then, are confirmatory of those which I have announced; only they seem to establish that feeling is not exclusively in the posterior roots any more than movement in the anterior ones."

He included at the end of this article a narrative of the events which had taken place between the publication of this and the preceding issue of his *Journal:*

"When I wrote the note contained in the last number, I believed that I was the first person who had thought of cutting the roots of the spinal nerves; but I was soon undeceived by a brief communication from Mr. Schaw (*sic*), which this young and industrious physician had the kindness to send me as soon as he had received this number of my *Journal.* It is stated in this note that Mr. Charles Bell had done this section thirteen years ago, and that he had recognized that section of the posterior roots did not prevent the continuation of movements. Mr. Schaw adds that Mr. Charles Bell consigned this result to a little pamphlet printed solely for his friends, but not for general distribution. I at once asked Mr. Schaw if he would be so kind as to send me, if possible, Mr. Charles Bell's pamphlet, so that I might render him the complete justice that was his due. A few days later I received it from Mr. Schaw. The title of the pamphlet is: 'Idea of a new anatomy of the brain, submitted for the observation of his friends, by Charles Bell, F.A.S.E.' The pamphlet is very curious in that one finds in it the germ of the author's recent discoveries on the nervous system. On page 22 there is to be found the passage indicated by Schaw. I transcribe it *in toto*:

"'Next, considering that the spinal nerves have a double root, and being of the opinion that the properties of nerves are derived from their connections with the parts of the brain, I thought that I had an excellent opportunity of putting my opinion to the test of experiment, if different endowments were in the same cord, and held by the same sheath. On laying bare the roots of the spinal nerves, I found that I could cut across the fasciculus of nerves, which took its origin

from the posterior portion of the spinal marrow, without convulsing the muscles of the back; but on touching the anterior
fasciculus with the point of the knife, the muscles of the back
were immediately convulsed.'

"One sees by this citation of a work which I could not know
of, since it had not been made available to the public, that
Mr. Bell, led by his ingenious ideas on the nervous system, had
been very near to discovering the functions of the spinal roots;
nevertheless, the fact that the anterior roots are destined for
movement, while the posterior roots belong more particularly
to feeling appears to have escaped him: it is, therefore, to having established this fact in a positive manner that I must limit
my claims." [14]

Here we have Magendie's position clearly stated, the
amount of credit which he felt to be due to Bell, and the
facts upon which he based the validity of his claim to the
discovery.

As the whole subsequent controversy centers about this
privately printed pamphlet, no copy of which was generally
available for scientists even in England, let alone France,
it must be examined carefully. At the present time there
are only three copies [15] known to be in existence, one at
the British Museum (on a blank page of which is written
in ink, "With Mr. Bell's respectful compliments, 34 Soho
Square"), one in the possession of the Royal Society of
London and one in the Surgeon General's Library at Washington. The pamphlet bears no date whatever. Both Bell
and Shaw always stated that it was published in 1809.
Examination of the records of the office where the printing
was done show that the pamphlets were delivered to Bell
in 1811,[16] and this is the date now accepted. The following
extracts are taken from the copy at the British Museum.

Bell begins by stating that the prevailing doctrine of the

[14] J. de physiol. expér. et path., 2:366-371, 1822.
[15] Only two are mentioned by J. Fulton (Selected Readings, 1930, p. 252).
[16] Flint, A., Jr., J. de l'anat. et physiol., 5:520, 1868.

anatomical schools is that the brain is a common sensorium; that impressions, differing in kind by virtue of the organization of the extremities of the nerves, are carried along the nerves to the sensorium; that the mind, by the same nerves which receive sensation, sends out the mandate of the will to the moving parts of the body (p. 4). Now Bell held that he had grounds for the belief "that the cerebrum and the cerebellum are different in function as in form; that the parts of the cerebrum have different functions; . . . that the nerves of sense, the nerves of motion, and the vital nerves, are distinct through their whole course, though they seem sometimes united in one bundle; [17] and that they depend for their attributes on the organs of the brain to which they are severally attached." He thought that the idea that each nerve had its own function would "do away with the difficulty of conceiving how sensation and volition should be the operation of the same nerve at the same moment" (p. 6). The illustration which he used of distinct functions for different nerves was that of the different papillae on the tongue, some of which are for taste and others for touch. If one of the former is touched with a sharp steel point, "I do not know that a point touched the tongue, but I am sensible of a metallic taste" (p. 9). This suggests that Bell had the idea of what is now known as Johannes Müller's law of specific energies, that, for example, a sensory nerve will give rise to one particular type of sensation and no other, no matter what kind of stimulus is applied.

As an anatomist Bell was much impressed by the differ-

[17] Bichat had this idea: "I was amused one day to follow attentively all the filaments of the sciatic nerve in a rather long space; now those which higher up composed the outside bundles were found lower down mostly in the central bundles. This observation proves that the nerve bundles are not destined as such for feeling and for movement, and that if the same nerves do not serve this double purpose, the difference is in the filaments and not in the bundles." *Anat. gén.*, 1801, v. i, p. 128.

ences between the cerebrum and the cerebellum and he concluded (p. 19) that "there cannot be such sympathy or corresponding movement in the cerebrum and cerebellum as there is betwixt the lateral portions of the cerebrum; that the anterior and posterior grand divisions of the brain perform distinct offices . . . Further we can trace down the crura of the cerebrum into the anterior fasciculus of the spinal marrow and the crura of the cerebellum into the posterior fasciculus. I thought that here I might have an opportunity of touching the cerebellum, as it were, through the posterior portion of the spinal marrow, and the cerebrum by the anterior portion (p. 21). To this end I made experiments which, though they were not conclusive, encouraged me in the view I had taken."

Then Bell continued:

"I found that injury done to the anterior portion of the spinal marrow convulsed the animal more certainly than injury done to the posterior portion; but I found it difficult to make the experiment without injuring both portions.

"Next considering that the spinal nerves have a double root, and being of the opinion that the properties of the nerves are derived from their connections with the parts of the brain, I thought that I had an opportunity of putting my opinion to the test of experiment, and of proving at the same time that nerves [18] of different endowments were in the same cord, and held together by the same sheath.

"On laying bare the roots of the spinal nerves, I found that I could cut across the posterior fasciculus of nerves, which took its origin from the posterior portion of the spinal marrow without convulsing the muscles of the back; but that on touching the anterior fasciculus with the point of the knife, the muscles of the back were immediately convulsed.[19]

[18] Note the slight discrepancy of phrasing between Magendie's quotation of this passage and the first edition of the pamphlet.

[19] It will be noted that this is almost exactly the experiment which John Shaw is said to have performed on March 21, 1821, the interpretation of which was still in doubt in September of that year.

"Such were my reasons for concluding that the cerebrum and cerebellum were parts distinct in function, and that every nerve possessing a double function obtained that by having a double root. I now saw the meaning of the double connection of the nerves with the spinal marrow; and also of the cause of that seeming intricacy in the connections of nerves throughout their course, which were not double at their origins.

"The spinal nerves being double, and having their roots in the spinal marrow, of which a portion comes from the cerebrum and a portion from the cerebellum, they convey the attributes of both grand divisions of the brain to every part; and therefore the distribution of such nerves is simple, one nerve supplying its destined part. But the nerves which come directly from the brain, come from parts of the brain which vary in operation; and in order to bestow different qualities on the parts to which the nerves are distributed, two or more nerves must be united in their course or at their final destination. Hence it is that the first nerve must have branches of the fifth united with it."

It has been pointed out by Waller in his interchange of letters with Sir Arthur Keith in the London *Lancet* in 1911 [20] that in order to credit Bell with the discovery that the anterior roots of the spinal nerves are for motion and the posterior for sensation, one must also believe that he distinguished the cerebrum as exclusively motor and the cerebellum as exclusively sensory. This is just what Bell did not do. He says (p. 27), "The cerebrum I consider as the grand organ by which the mind is united with the body. Into it all the nerves from the external organs of the senses enter; and from it all the nerves which are agents of the will pass out." Nothing could be clearer; to Bell the cerebrum, whose nerves he considered to come out through the anterior roots of the spinal nerves, is both sensory and motor. This view is expressed in the pamphlet not once only, but a second time (p. 29): "The convex bodies which are seated in the

[20] Waller, A. D., *The Lancet*, 180:614, 1911.

lower part of the cerebrum, and into which the nerves of sense enter, have extensive connection with the hemispheres on their upper part. From the medullary matter of the hemispheres, again, there pass down, converging to the crura, Striae, which is the medullary matter taking upon it the character of a nerve; for from the Crura Cerebri, or its prolongation in the anterior Fasciculi of the spinal marrow, go off the nerves of motion." So much for the cerebrum. Of the cerebellum he says (p. 26): "The nerves proceeding from the Crus Cerebelli go everywhere (in seeming union with those from the Crus cerebri); they unite the body together and control the actions of the bodily frame; and especially govern the operation of the viscera necessary to the continuance of life": and again (p. 36), "The secret operations of the bodily frame, and the connections which unite the parts of the body into a system, are through the cerebellum and nerves proceeding from it." This is not so clear; but what he is attempting to describe is evidently the functions of the involuntary, or, to use the more modern terminology, the autonomic nervous system, which he classifies as "vital nerves." He characterizes their action thus (p. 15): "The secret operations of the vital organs suffer the control of the brain, though we are unconscious of the thousand delicate operations which are every instant going on in the body." The key word is "secret," as is shown by his use of it not once but three times when he speaks of "vital nerves."

The essence of Bell's conception is this: the cerebrum is the common center for both sensation and motion; the pathway for transmission of both sensation and motion lies in the anterior columns of the spinal cord and comes out through the anterior roots of the spinal nerves; the cerebellum is the center for the secret action of the "vital nerves," and the pathway for these unconscious and involuntary acts is along the posterior columns of the spinal cord and out through the posterior roots of the spinal nerves.[21] Therefore he thought that the posterior and anterior roots must have different functions, and proof of this assumption was offered by his famous experiment: when he stimulated the posterior roots there was no visible effect, any activity thus aroused was "secret"; but when he stimulated the anterior roots there was muscular movement. He further interpreted this observation to mean that the anterior roots were more "sensible," or, in modern terms, more "sensitive" than the posterior roots, i.e., they were more easily stimulated. It was this aspect of the experiment to which Shaw referred in the passage of his laboratory manual quoted above.[22] In the famous sentence of the 1811 pamphlet beginning, "On laying bare the roots of the spinal nerves . . . ," both parts were equally important. The first part was not a mere confession of failure to produce evidence of pain or to excite motion by stimulation of the posterior root, but it was a positive observation on the degree of excitability of these particular nerve roots.

Search as diligently as you can, there is no statement to

[21] The fact that Bell ascribed both sensory and motor functions to the anterior spinal nerve roots is universally ignored by his supporters. It was, however, recognized by so influential a physiologist as Johannes Müller, and in the English translation of his famous *Elements of Physiology* (1844) we find the following passage: "He (Bell) seems, it is true, to have supposed at first that the anterior roots contained nervous fibres for sensation as well as those for motion, while the posterior roots governed 'the operations of the viscera'" (p. 304).

[22] Bell had this idea as early as 1810, as is shown in the letter to his brother which is often quoted as being the first expression of a distinction in the functions of the dorsal and ventral spinal roots: "Experiment I. I opened the spine and pricked and injured the posterior filaments of the nerves— no motion of the muscles followed. I then touched the anterior division— immediately the parts were convulsed. It is almost superfluous to say that the part of the spinal cord having sensibility comes from the cerebrum, the posterior and insensible part of the marrow belongs to the cerebellum. Taking these facts as they stand, is it not curious that there should be established a distinction in the parts of a nerve and that a nerve should be insensible." (Bell, C., *Letters*, 1870, p. 170.)

be found in the 1811 pamphlet, or even the implication, that the dorsal roots of the spinal nerves are for sensation, the ventral roots for motion, because that was not Bell's idea at all. Just as he thought at this earlier time that the ventral roots conveyed both sensation and motion, so in 1821 he thought that the fifth cranial nerve, although mainly sensory, was motor as well, since upon cutting it "the power of elevating and projecting the lip, as in gathering food, was lost"; likewise, the seventh cranial nerve, in his opinion, not only supplied the muscles of the face, its main function, but "its branches penetrate to the skin," which implied that this nerve was also both sensory and motor.[23]

Whatever the nature of the distinction which Bell thought that he had established in the functions of the two spinal nerve roots in 1811, it is clear that it did not assume for him then the importance which the same—or an altered— distinction took on after 1822. He buried the record of his crucial experiment in an obscurely worded, privately printed pamphlet "submitted for the observation of his friends," of which only one hundred copies were printed; [24] and within a decade he had even forgotten the exact year in which the printing was done. Furthermore, when he brought out in 1816 the fourth edition of the three volumes of the

[23] Eighteen years later after the whole matter had been threshed out again and again in the light of Magendie's paper, Alexander Shaw (1804-1890), who succeeded his elder brother John as Bell's assistant after John's death in 1827, wrote, "In 1821 Bell thought that the anterior column of the spinal marrow was a prolongation from the cerebrum, while the posterior was continuous with the cerebellum; and that the former presided over muscular motion, while the latter was the seat of sensation." In making this categorical statement Shaw was, of course, influenced by the events occurring between 1821 and the time at which he wrote his "Narrative of the discoveries of Sir Charles Bell in the nervous system," 1839. The statement cannot be taken as evidence of Bell's actual belief in 1821. For Bell's vacillation in his conception of the functions of the cerebrum and cerebellum as shown by his own statements, v. Olmsted, J. M. D., *Bull. Med. Hist.*, 14:341, 1943.

[24] Vulpian, *Leçons*, 1866, p. 109.

"Anatomy and Physiology of the Human Body," written in collaboration with his brother John, his description there of the spinal nerves does not contain the slightest hint that he recognized any difference in the functions of the two spinal nerve roots. In describing each spinal nerve he says simply, "This nerve arising by double origin from the spinal marrow, like the other nerves of the spine, passes . . . etc." In other words, he treats each spinal nerve as if it were a unit and traces it to a muscle. There is no direct reference to function.

Had Magendie added nothing to his first paper and had he been content with the results of his experiments as they were summarized in the minutes of the Academy of Sciences for July 22, 1822,[25] he would have presented a better case in opposition to Bell's theories and inconclusive statements of experimental results than he did after he had pushed his inquiries further by his experiments on stimulation, as opposed to cutting, of the two roots. It was the apparent hedging of the conclusion announced in his second paper, viz, that "sensitivity is not exclusively in the posterior roots, any more than movement in the anterior," that gave his contemporary critics, not only in England, but in France and Germany as well, their foothold. His third paper,[26] which was an attempt to localize the seat of sensitivity and motility in the cord, reiterated this qualified conclusion with the comment that "the indices of sensitivity in the anterior roots are scarcely visible." It may be observed that even in his first communication Magendie never stated that each root of the spinal nerves was concerned exclusively with either motion or sensitivity; he said, "The posterior roots seem to be particularly destined for sensitivity, while the

[25] *Procès-verb. Acad. d. Sc.*, 7:348, 1820-23. "M. Magendie communicates the discovery which he has just made, that if one cuts the posterior roots of the spinal nerves, one intercepts only the sensation belonging to these nerves, and if one cuts their anterior roots, one intercepts only the movement belonging to them."

[26] *J. de physiol. expér. et path.*, 3:153, 1823.

anterior roots seem especially connected with movement."
His observations in all cases were correct for the experiments as he conducted them. Reflex action, which was later
elucidated by Marshall Hall, explains the movements which
Magendie found on stimulating the posterior roots, and the
source of the sensitivity of the ventral roots was shown by
Claude Bernard to be due to the peculiar course of certain
posterior root fibers.[27] The position which Magendie maintained for fifteen years after his first experiments was this:
if the posterior roots are cut, sensitivity is gone, but motion
is conserved; if, however, the posterior roots are stimulated,
the effect is mainly sensory, though there are movements;
if the anterior roots are stimulated, the effect is almost
entirely motor, and the evidences of pain are "presque
nuls," as he allowed Desmoulins to express it in the latter's
treatise on the nervous system of vertebrates, which he
wrote in collaboration with Magendie.[28] It was therefore
manifestly unfair for Flourens[29] and Longet[30] to have
taxed Magendie with inconsistency and "retrogression."

Magendie's hesitancy with regard to purity of function
of each of the two spinal roots was generally ignored, so
that within ten years physiologists were to agree that the
difference in function of the roots of the spinal nerves had
been established, and that this discovery was second only
to that greatest of all landmarks in the history of physiology, Harvey's discovery of the circulation of the blood.
In England Shaw immediately took up cudgels on behalf
of Bell;[31] Alexander Walker claimed the discovery for himself; Herbert Mayo, now described as "an unfriendly pupil
to Bell," who had taken on as his assistant Caesar Hawkins,

[27] Bernard, C., *Pathologie expérimentale*, 1880, p. 521.
[28] Desmoulins, A., *Anatomie des systèmes nerveux des animaux à vertèbres*, 1825, p. 777.
[29] Flourens, M., *Éloge de F. Magendie*, 1858, p. 45.
[30] Longet, F.-A., *Anatomie et physiologie*, 1842, v. 1, p. 28.
[31] Shaw, J., *London Med. and Phys. Journ.*, 48:343, 1822.

the transcriber of notes for Shaw's experiments on the spinal nerves, was more generous, for he said that although he had the idea (the Shaws intimated that he had got it from Caesar Hawkins), "when I was engaged in experiments to determine the fact, M. Magendie's were published, which established the justness of my conjecture."[32] Mayo's paper containing this statement was translated into French and published in Magendie's *Journal*. In France Magendie stoutly affirmed that the discovery was his, although he was perfectly willing to concede that without his knowledge Bell before him had seen that stimulation of the ventral roots caused a convulsive movement in muscles.

In one of his letters Bell speaks of indirect news of Magendie's experiments having reached him from France. This letter is dated April 5, without mention of the year, but it is correctly placed with the letters of 1823. Bell said:

"There was a letter in the *Morning Herald* [33] giving an account of a conversation in a stage coach in the south of France,

[32] Mayo, H., *Anatomical and Physiological Commentaries*, July, 1823.

[33] The following paragraph, which appeared in the London *Morning Herald* for March 27, 1823, in an article headed "Private Correspondence. Toulon, March 14, 1823," is the one to which Bell refers: "The Medical Professor spoke on no subject but his own science. I essayed to draw him out. He informed me the Medical School at Paris, that was closed so arbitrarily, was again about to be re-instituted; but a great portion of the students had determined never to return. The merits of the different medical authors, French and English, were freely canvassed, and contrasting those of both countries, I was obliged to acknowledge that we had no set-off against the journal of experimental physiology by Magendie. His experiments on animals for the last five years have given us more information on the structure and uses of the vital organs than all the writings of other physiologists. About three weeks ago he made a very extraordinary discovery, and one likely to lead to most important results. He divided the principal nerves of an animal at different times, to become acquainted with their several uses. To his great astonishment, he found invariably in dividing a pair of nerves proceeding from the spinal marrow, that he deprived the animal of motion and instinct. On cutting the one to the right the animal was deprived of instinct, and dividing the left, of motion, without destroying life. This very curious fact has not yet had time to be known in England."

which the Tourist sent home, believing the news could not
have reached England, of astonishing experiments on the nerves
performed in Paris by Magendie—*mine, viz.* We wrote the editor." [34]

We now come to the most distressing part of the whole
story. Bell decided, now that Magendie's experiments and
his clear-cut statement of the implications had drawn attention to the matter, that he would do well, even at this late
stage, to publish his own views. He therefore brought out
a book in 1824 entitled, "An exposition of the natural system
of the nerves of the human body, with a republication of the
papers delivered to the Royal Society on the subject of
nerves.[35] These Royal Society papers were, however, so
altered in their wording as to make their statements conform
more nearly to the concept of the nervous system which
followed from Magendie's 1822 paper than their original
expressions would allow, and Bell made no mention of any
changes, stating that these were "the papers which I presented to the Royal Society."

The following are examples of the changes which were
introduced in the "republications." With regard to the fifth
nerve in 1821, "It is the nerve of . . . the muscles of the face
and jaws;" subsequently, ". . . the muscles of the jaw." In
1821, "It alone of all the nerves of the head receives roots
from both the medullary process of the cerebrum and the

[34] Bell, C., *Letters,* 1870, p. 279.
[35] It is to be noted that Bell did not include a reprint of the original
pamphlet, "Idea of a new anatomy of the brain," in this book. Instead,
he prefaced his "republication of papers delivered to the Royal Society"
by an essay of about the same length as the 1811 pamphlet, which is in
essence a paraphrase of the original pamphlet. The contrast between the
two lies in the inclusion in 1824 of concrete statements about the functions of the dorsal and ventral roots, such as (p. 21): "It has been
acknowledged that the anterior roots of the spinal nerves bestow the
power of muscular motion; and the posterior roots sensibility." Such
statements are not to be found in the original "Idea of a new anatomy
of the brain."

cerebellum;" subsequently, ". . . roots from both the column of sensibility and that of motion." In 1821, "Its branches . . . are especially profuse to the muscles which move the lips upon the teeth;" subsequently, ". . . are especially profuse to the lips." In regard to the seventh nerve in 1821, "Its branches penetrate to the skin;" subsequently this is entirely omitted. In 1821, "The loss of motion of the lips was so obvious that it was thought a useless cruelty to cut the other branches of the fifth;" subsequently, "The loss of sensibility of the lips was so obvious, etc." In 1821, ". . . the seventh is the respiratory nerve of the face;" subsequently, ". . . is the nerve of motion to the muscles of the forehead, eyebrow, etc."

Such changes can only have been made in the light of knowledge gained subsequently to the writing of the original paper. Perhaps the Shaws—for when John died in 1827, his younger brother, Alexander, took his place, and both were wholeheartedly devoted to Bell—were responsible for their brother-in-law pushing his claims so unduly. In the 1830 edition there was included a note, for which Bell said he was "indebted to a pupil," i.e., Alexander Shaw, setting forth Bell's claims against those of Magendie. These claims were elaborated by the author of the note and published as a book in 1839 under the title, "Narrative of the Discoveries of Sir Charles Bell in the Nervous System." Even if the Shaws are partly to be blamed, Bell must take some share in the responsibility, for in the preface of his first edition of "An Exposition of the natural system of the nerves," which was immediately translated into French and published in that language in 1825, he said that there was an attempt in France to deprive him of the honor of having been the first to establish the difference in function of the posterior and anterior roots of the spinal nerves. Again, in his lecture before the London College of Surgeons in 1828, he publicly announced his claims and went so far as to refer to Magendie in these derogatory terms:

"He may even, in short, have employed his fingers, those 'pickers and stealers,' as Shakespeare calls them, without control of his head—without intention or ideas of any kind—with a perfect purity which belongs to entire ignorance." [36]

The clue to Bell's failure to find the dorsal roots sensitive is found in his "Exposition of the natural system of the nerves." [37] He says that in a living rabbit he cut the posterior roots—

". . . I was deterred from repeating the experiment by the protracted cruelty of the dissection. I therefore struck a rabbit behind the ear, so as to deprive it of sensibility by the concussion, and then exposed the spinal marrow. On irritating the posterior roots of the nerve I could perceive no motion consequent, on any part of the muscular frame; but on irritating the anterior roots of the nerve, at each touch of the forceps there was a corresponding motion of the muscles to which the nerve was distributed. These experiments satisfied me that the different roots and different columns from whence these roots arose were devoted to distinct offices, and that the notions drawn from the anatomy were correct." [38]

If Bell's rabbit had not been stunned, he would have secured positive evidence of sensation, i.e., pain, and his conclusions would not have been limited to "notions drawn from anatomy."

Bell made no secret of his hostility to animal experimentation. He said:

"I feel a hesitation when I reason upon any other ground than on the facts of anatomy. Experiments are more apt to be misinterpreted." [39]

[36] Bell, C., *London Med. Gaz.*, 1:618, 1828.

[37] Bell, C., *Natural System*, 1824, pp. 29-30.

[38] This again shows that Bell had merely the idea that different nerve roots have different functions. He was not attempting to ascribe any one particular function to each as "sensibility" or "motility."

[39] Bell, C., *Philos. Trans.*, 116:163, 1826.

Again,

'Experiments have never been the means of discovery; and a survey of what has been attempted of late years in physiology, will prove that the opening of living animals has done more to perpetuate error, than to confirm the just views taken from the study of anatomy and natural motions. . . . When the popularity of these doctrines (those of Gall, Spurzheim and Magendie) is considered, it may easily be conceived how difficult it has been, during their importations to keep my Pupils to the example of their own great Countrymen. Surely it is time that the schools of this kingdom should be distinguished from those of France. Let physiologists of that country borrow from us, and follow up our opinions by experiments [40] but let us continue to build that structure which has been commenced in the labours of the Munros and the Hunters. The whole history of medical literature proves, that no solid or permanent advantage is to be gained, either to medical or general science by physiological experiments unconnected with anatomy." [41]

Magendie's replies to these criticisms were more the plaint of an injured spirit than the furious and biting denunciation which opposition from his colleagues in the Academy of Sciences could upon occasion draw from him. He wrote in his *Journal* in 1830:

Bell's investigative mind, although it is rather speculative, his great skill in the art of dissection, his rare talent for drawing, will always secure him a distinguished place among the anatomists of our era. Why must this scientist spoil his work and injure himself by not rendering to his rivals the justice due them? Why must he cling to that barbarous patriotism which rejects everything that does not come from his own country? Why does he persist in his pretensions to discoveries which he has not made?" [42]

[40] His footnote (p. 307) reads: "See the experiments of M. Magendie on the distinctions in the roots of the spinal nerves."
[41] Bell, C., *Philos. Trans.*, 113:299, 1823.
[42] *J. de physiol. expér. et path.*, 10:1, 1830.

Again,

"One should not say that to perform physiological experiments one must necessarily have a heart of stone and a leaning toward cruelty. I would pardon a man of the world for such language. Such prejudice is easy to understand, but that it should be held by an operative surgeon like Charles Bell is not easy to conceive, all the more as not one of the facts which compose the physiology of the day have been proved, or could be proved, except by experiment. Has not the important discovery of Charles Bell on the functions of the seventh and fifth nerves been made and proved through experiment? M. Bell might have heaped reasoning upon reasoning before he could ever have established a like result, although his natural sagacity would have made him suspect it." [43]

At first, in spite of Shaw's defence of Bell in the *London Medical and Physical Journal*, some British journals gave the credit to Magendie. From Bell's own university city came in 1824 a well-reasoned account of the contemporary advances in the knowledge of the functions of the nervous system which contained the statement, "Mr. Bell does not seem to have drawn any positive or general inference from his experiment on 'convulsing' the muscles." [44] Soon, however, the propaganda of the Shaws had its effect; and besides, by 1830 Bell's influence in London had become overwhelming. He was instrumental in bringing about the foundation of University College and was a leading spirit in the Middlesex Hospital. Anyone venturing to criticize Bell did so at his peril. Dr. Pattison, the first occupant of the chair of anatomy at University College said at the first distribution of prizes, "Bell's mistaken idea that the fifth nerve bestowed motion and sensation on the parts on which it was ramified had been corrected by M. Magendie and Mr. Mayo." He was cried down by the students, dismissed from

[43] *J. de physiol. expér. et path.*, 10:190, 1830.
[44] *Edinburgh Med. and Surg. J.*, 21:141, 1824.

his post on the charge of incompetence and half the professors in the university resigned in protest.[45]

In 1834 Alexander Walker maintained his claims to the disputed honor in a book with the descriptive title, "The nervous system, anatomical and physiological: in which the various parts of the brain are for the first time assigned, and to which is prefixed some account of the author's earliest discoveries, of which the more recent doctrine of Bell, Magendie, etc., is shown to be at once a plagiarism, an inversion and a blunder associated with useless experiments, which they have neither understood nor explained." However, the claims of Walker may be dismissed at once, since, although his date, 1809, is prior to Bell's,[46] he thought the functions were exactly the reverse of what they really are. Dr. Elliotson of St. Thomas' became and remained a staunch supporter of Magendie, but nearly all British authorities and German ones as well soon gave Bell full credit for the discovery. In France, because of the influence of Flourens and to a less degree that of Longet, the sentiment was entirely against Magendie and remained so. By 1840, however, the changes which Bell had incorporated in the text of his Royal Society papers began to create comment. The *British and Foreign Medical Review* for that year hoped that "Sir Charles Bell" (he had been knighted) "may see the propriety of not giving such a handle to his opponents as is afforded by what certainly has the appearance of underhanded dealing."

Eleven years after Magendie's death, Vulpian [47] pointed out the injustice done Magendie and emphasized the falsification in Bell's texts. An American physiologist, Austin Flint, Jr., at almost the same time made a valiant defence

[45] Waller, A. D., *Lancet*, 180:1719, 1911.
[46] Walker, A., *Arch. Univer. Sci.*, 3:172, 1809.
[47] Vulpian, *Leçons*, 1866, p. 105.

of Magendie.[48] He drew up in parallel columns Bell's original statements and the changes which were later introduced. His paper was written in English just before Claude Bernard wrote his defence of Magendie,[49] but not until the next year (1868) was it translated into French for Robin's journal.[50]

In 1911 Sir Arthur Keith, upon falling heir to Bell's old post at the Middlesex Hospital, in his inaugural lecture awarded the honor of having discovered the functions of the spinal roots to his predecessor, Bell. This was too much for A. D. Waller, professor of physiology at University College, London, whose father had been one of Magendie's pupils. Letter followed letter to the editor of the *Lancet* over a period of two years. Every aspect of the controversy was aired twice over, and others besides the original disputants participated in the discussion. The correspondence ended without either side having yielded an inch. Waller finally summed up his position in a statement which he published in *Science Progress.* He was convinced that Bell's claims were entirely unjustified, but he was prepared to

[48] Flint, A., Jr., *J. de l'anat. et de la physiol.*, 5:520, 1868.

[49] Bernard, C., *Rapport*, 1867, p. 154.

[50] Flint had gained the friendship of Bernard several years earlier when he was studying in Paris. Bernard had presented him at that time with the operating table which Magendie had had made in 1831 for his new laboratory at the Collège de France and which is now to be seen in the Army Medical Museum in Washington, D. C. The table bears the following inscription: "This operating table was made for François Magendie in 1831, and was used by Magendie in the Physiological Laboratory of the College of France from 1831 to 1854, and by Claude Bernard from 1854 to 1861. In 1861 it was given by Claude Bernard to Austin Flint, Jr. Upon this table Magendie frequently demonstrated the Properties of the Roots of the Spinal Nerves, discovered by him in 1822, and Bernard discovered the Functions of the Spinal Accessory Nerves in 1844, the Glycogenic Function of the Liver in 1843, the Digestion of Fats by the Pancreas in 1843, the Influence of the Sympathetic Nerves upon Animal Heat in 1851. Feb. 10, 1878."

make allowances for frailties attendant upon thwarted ambition. He said:

"A man who has thought around and about something is apt to deceive himself when another man puts his finger on the spot and pulls out the plum; he may be forgiven for exclaiming, 'But that's my plum; I found it long ago and showed it to that fellow who says he found it." [51]

So recently as 1937 the present writer, upon protesting against the use of the 1834 falsified version of Bell's 1821 paper as a medical "classic," [52] was answered that the changes from the original were of no consequence and that "there was glory enough for all." [53] Some anatomists still claim the discovery for Bell on the ground that they consider that the law of the direction of conduction [54] in the spinal nerve roots was *implied* in the privately printed pamphlet of 1811. It has been pointed out above that this pamphlet does not distinguish the functions of the cerebrum and cerebellum as motor and sensory respectively, and that any distinction between the functions of the roots of the spinal nerves in that paper depends on a prior distinction between the functions of these two parts of the brain. That Charles Bell was totally unaware of such an implication is established, in the writer's opinion, by the fact that he tried to introduce it, after Magendie's paper was published in 1822, not in the pamphlet, it is true, but by his emendations in the "republications" of his Royal Society papers. Moreover, even if the distinction between sensory and motor functions had been implied in the 1811 pamphlet (a hypothesis which the writer does not admit), implication does

[51] Waller, A. D., *Sci. Progr.*, 6:81, 1911.
[52] Olmsted, J. M. D., *Science, N.S.*, 86:520, 1937.
[53] Kelley, E. C., *Science, N.S.*, 87:167, 1938.
[54] I.e., nervous impulses giving rise to sensation travel inward from the periphery to the central nervous system and those for motion move in the reverse direction.

not constitute proof in the eyes of a modern physiologist any more than it would have to Magendie, nor is Bell's attitude toward experiment (that of the rigid anatomist of his day) tolerable to him. The physiologist is therefore inclined to give all the credit for this discovery to Magendie. He is, however, willing to grant that the immediate stimulus for Magendie's experiments on the spinal nerve roots was Shaw's demonstration at Alfort on the two cranial nerves, and that the feasibility of such experiments was suggested by what Magendie had read in Shaw's "Manual." The anatomist, on the other hand, should admit that the only distinction between the functions of the two spinal nerve roots actually demonstrated by Bell according to his pamphlet [55] was a difference in the degree of their excitability, and nothing more. The designation, "Bell-Magendie rule," which in medical literature is used to indicate the direction of conduction in the spinal nerve roots, remains to represent a compromise between the points of view of the older type of anatomist who arrived at function by way of inference and the physiologically-minded investigator who insists upon experimental verification.

[55] Note that Shaw's *Manual*, 1821 (p. 277), describes the Great Windmill Street experiments also as being "on the comparative degree of sensibility of the two origins of these nerves."

8

EXPERIMENTS ON THE CENTRAL NERV-
OUS SYSTEM, WORK ON HYDROPHO-
BIA AND THE FIRST ENGLISH
VISIT
1823-1824

"Ceci me rapelle une circonstance de mon premier voyage en Angleterre que je suis bien aise de vous citer." [1]

MAGENDIE now transferred his attention exclusively to the nervous system as a subject of research. This was not merely an aftermath of the encounter with Charles Bell, for the nervous system was proving to be a popular topic for investigation in the early 1820's. The phrenological theories of Gall and Spurzheim had made even the man in the street aware of his brain, and at the same time their work on the tracts of the spinal cord was receiving the serious consideration which it deserved from such a scientist as Cuvier, who was the arbiter of all things anatomical. Of the younger men working in the same field Flourens was the most prominent. His series of papers on "Sensibility and Irritability," in one of which he described his experiments, now justly famous, on pigeons deprived of their cerebellum, was gaining for him, if not fame, at least notoriety in the eyes

[1] *Syst. nerv.*, 1839, v. 1, p. 198.

of French scientists. On the same day, July 22, 1822, that
Magendie reported before the Academy of Sciences his neat
experiments on the dorsal and ventral roots of the spinal
nerves, Cuvier's report on Flourens' work was also given.
In the following year Duméril and Magendie were on the
committee for the Montyon prize in Experimental Physiology and they divided the award between Flourens, in
recognition of his work on the brain, and a pupil of
Magendie, Michael Fedora, a Sicilian, who had written on
one of his master's former subjects, absorption.

Physiologists of that day were perhaps no more or no less
generous than those of our own time, but an experimenter
of the 1820's seemed to find it difficult to obtain credit for
originality. Rolando in Italy had published a paper on the
brain in 1809, and when Flourens' paper appeared there
were cries that nothing new had been done, that Flourens
had merely plagiarized Rolando. The Italian's work was so
little known in France that Magendie had the experimental
part of the original article translated into French and the
translation published in his *Journal*. At the same time he
defended Flourens against the charge of plagiarism, but
perhaps was not as tactful as he might have been. He said
that although there was a striking resemblance between
the work of the two men, their conclusions were quite different; Rolando saw in the cerebellum the source and origin
of all movements; Flourens saw this organ merely as the
regulator or balancer of bodily movements, for he claimed
that movements were possible, even energetic ones, with the
cerebellum gone, although such movements were not well
coordinated. Then Magendie continued, apparently forgetting at one point that he was not addressing Flourens
directly:

"I myself know that one can discover things long since known;
but, far from feeling chagrin, one should be gratified, for this
at least proves that nature has not denied you the capacity for

observation, and one with propriety replies to accusations of plagiarism if one does work that is really new." [2]

Magendie now did "the young French physiologist" what he probably considered the honor of turning his own attention in the same direction. There was another aspect of Flourens' papers on sensibility and irritability which was interesting to him. He had had Cuvier's report on Flourens' work reprinted in the last number of his *Journal* for 1822. The report called attention to Flourens' attempt to fix the seat of sensation and the source of movement in the brain, his experimental procedure having been to cut nerves and stimulate the central and peripheral cut ends. Magendie wished to attack the same problem in the light of his experiments on the spinal nerve roots and he published his results in his *Journal* in April, 1823.[3] He found that if he touched the dorsal part of the cord there were distinct evidences of pain, but if he touched the ventral part there were scarcely any, and in the case of the central part none at all. The question arose how sensitivity travelled from the cord to the brain. He referred to the opinion of certain anatomists (there is no mention of Charles Bell in this note) that sensation was referable chiefly to the cerebellum and movement to the cerebrum, but he was convinced that anatomy without physiology could not settle this question. His own experiments on total removal or profound lesions of the cerebellum left him convinced that there was in these cases no loss of sensitivity. There was, however, in animals with the cerebellum injured or removed an inability to execute forward movements, and he cited the instance of a duck which swam only backwards for the week it survived.[4] Again, if he removed the cerebral hemispheres he

[2] *J. de physiol. expér. et path.*, 3:95, 1823.
[3] *J. de physiol. expér. et path.*, 3:153, 1823.
[4] Magendie commented on this duck's behaviour in the 1824 edition of his *Précis*. When Mulligan of Edinburgh came to publish his translation of

found no interference with movement. On the contrary, animals so treated ran about continuously.[5] He explained the results of Rolando's experiments, in which the removal of the cerebral hemispheres in mammals and birds had led to a state of stupor, as the consequence of hemorrhage and blood clots. He concluded that the thalamus, cerebral peduncles and corpora quadrigemina, located beneath the cerebral hemispheres, were concerned with movement. Further sectioning of the brain led him to discover the state of exaggerated tonus, which we now call decerebrate rigidity, made famous by Sherrington's classical work on the subject. Magendie said:

"If the section is made immediately before these two eminences (the optic tubercles) everything stops; the animal falls on its side, with its head thrown back, feet stretched out stiff and directed forwards. I have seen young rabbits remain several hours in this position. To put an end to it, one must cut behind the optic tubercles. Immediately the fore feet lose their stiffness, and frequently are bent like the hind feet, and the head falls forward."

This is exactly the way in which the demonstration of decerebrate rigidity is performed today, the landmarks of the cuts having become somewhat more precise, and it is the inclusion of this observation which gives Magendie's "Note" of April, 1823, its real importance. Strangely enough, Charles Bell later called attention to this state of exaggerated tonus in man suffering from certain types of brain tumor. Bell was an excellent draughtsman and one of his most

this edition in 1826, he translated "canard" as "water dog" (p. 190). Sir Charles Sherrington has perpetuated this *canard* (i.e., the "water dog") in Schafer's *Text Book of Physiology*, 1900, v. 2, p. 897.

[5] This observation was later attributed to Goltz (*Arch. f. d. Ges. Physiol.*, 51:570, 1892). Magnus in recent years has described more precisely the results of cutting the brain stem at different levels. The condition of extreme activity which Magendie noted means that the cut was so placed that part of the thalamus was left functional.

perfect sketches portrays this man, head thrown back, back arched, arms folded, legs and feet rigidly extended.[6]

The close parallelism in the lines of thought being pursued by Flourens and Magendie continued to be evident. It was obvious that each investigator was beginning to find annoying the trespassing of the other on the territory he had marked out for himself. In November, 1823, after Flourens had reported to the Academy of Sciences the action of certain drugs on different parts of the brain, Magendie, in commenting on the paper, cited the work which his pupil, Fedora, was pursuing along this very line. In his *Journal* he published observations which he himself had made of the curious result of application of drugs such as tartar emetic directly to the surface of different parts of the brain, e.g., the corpora striata and quadrigemina. Both he and the auditors of his course had been startled to see the animals used in demonstration leap forward and run vigorously when the corpora striata were touched.[7]

At the end of the following March, Magendie reported to the Academy some experiments on olfaction after cutting the first nerve. Flourens retaliated by depositing a "paquet cacheté" (a procedure adopted when an investigator felt that there might be some dispute as to priority of discovery), the contents being observations on the olfactory tubercles and the branches of the fifth nerve. Magendie had observed that when he cut the first cranial nerve in puppies they could still detect such vapors as tobacco smoke and ammonia. This led him to conclude that olfaction cannot be mediated solely by the first (olfactory) nerve but that the fifth is also concerned. As a further test he wrapped pieces of Gruyère cheese, wood and cork in separate paper parcels, and when these packets were thrown to a dog

[6] Bell, Sir C., *The Anatomy and Philosophy of Expression as Connected with the Fine Arts*, 5th ed., 1865, p. 160.

[7] *J. de physiol. expér. et path.*, 3:376, 1823. Cf. *Lancet*, 1:439, 1823.

with its olfactory nerves cut the dog, he claimed, more often seized the packet containing the cheese than either of the other two.[8] This experiment cannot pass unchallenged. One would like to see the exact statistical record of such trials and be assured that there was no unconscious indication of the cheese packet by the experimenter. As it stands, the results of the second experiment are incredible. What one means by the term "olfaction" is, after all, a matter of definition. We now consider as olfactory only those sensations which are aroused by impulses coming into the brain over the first cranial nerve; those coming in over the fifth in response to such stimuli as ammonia and tobacco smoke are referred to as "common sensitivity," which is characteristic of the mucous membranes of the nose, mouth, etc. One of Magendie's experiments was to cut the first nerve in a toad which lived in the laboratory for a long time and always turned away or wiped its snout with its foot when ammonia, acetic acid and the like were presented to its nostrils; but, as was pointed out later, this could hardly be olfaction, since other toads with their olfactory nerves cut showed similar movements of avoidance if the irritating fluids were presented to their rear ends.

Three weeks after the presentation of the memoir on olfaction, Magendie carried the war into the enemy's territory with a paper on the cerebellum. He found that cutting the large commissure to the cerebellum in the region of the pons behind the fifth nerve caused an animal to roll over and over towards the injured side.[9] This rolling might last for days at the rate of one revolution per second. On one occasion he performed this operation on a rabbit, and thinking that the animal would soon cease rotating, he placed it

[8] *J. de physiol. expér. et path.*, 4:169, 1824. Cf. Bernard, *C. syst. nerv.*, v. 2, p. 226.
[9] *Procès-verb. Acad. de Sc.*, 8:57, 1824; *J. de physiol. expér. et path.*, 4:399, 1824.

gently in a box of straw with food and water nearby. On his return to the laboratory next morning he was surprised to find the rabbit neatly wrapped up in the straw like a bottle of precious wine and still rolling over and over.[10] He had discovered circus movements, a type of forced movement which was one of the foundation stones of Jacques Loeb's "The Mechanistic Conception of Life."

The last paper of this group was a sequel to the one on olfaction and described the reciprocal experiment of cutting the fifth cranial nerve.[11] Magendie noted so many results of this operation that he erroneously ascribed all sensations in the anterior part of the head, even sight, to this nerve. He had no adequate tests for the different modalities of the senses, and if, for example, he had noted, as he might have done after cutting the fifth nerve, that the wink reflex was abolished, he would have ascribed this phenomenon to loss of vision. Sight, of course, remains normal, but pain is absent from the cornea, with the result that there is no impulse to wink when the cornea is touched. This protective mechanism being gone and the nutrition of the eyeball being affected as well through loss of nervous control of the blood vessels, the eye becomes easily infected and corneal ulcers develop. Magendie did observe these "trophic" disturbances and assumed that they were the direct, instead of an indirect, effect of cutting the fifth nerve. This was the origin of the idea of special "trophic nerves" whose sole function it is to preside over the nutritional state of an organ. Such nerves have never been identified, although the question of their existence is still debated. Claude Bernard claimed that they were nothing more than vasomotor nerves.[12] Recently it has been shown that corneal lesions such as those observed by Magendie are due to a

---

[10] Syst. nerv., 1839, v. 1, p. 260.
[11] J. de physiol. expér. et path., 4:176, 302, 1824.
[12] Bernard, C., La chaleur animale, 1876, p. 218.

lack of acetylcholine normally released by the endings of the fifth nerve, since artificial instillation of this substance into the eye effects a cure of the symptoms.

Before the end of this year, 1824, the Montyon Prize committee awarded three gold medals, one of which went to Flourens. The next year, Magendie, who was always on the Montyon committee, balked at giving Flourens another prize, this time in money, a matter of 895 francs. The other members of the committee were greatly impressed by the memoirs which Flourens had submitted, and they would have divided the prize between him and M. Chossat, had they not been swayed by the consideration that although the actual data submitted by Flourens were new, his work after all was a continuation of the same problem for which he had already received two prizes. It may have been a mere coincidence, but it was probably not one to help Flourens over his disappointment, that one of his papers submitted for the prize was on audition and different causes of deafness and Magendie took occasion, at the very meeting at which the adverse report refusing Flourens the prize was presented, to describe the spectacular case of a deaf-mute who was cured of his infirmity at the age of nine years.[13] The rivalry between the two men, beginning at this time, was recurrent for the rest of Magendie's lifetime, and it may have been partly in pique that Flourens always gave first credit to Bell in regard to the discovery of the functions of the roots of the spinal nerves.[14]

The most spectacular of Magendie's papers of this period was not concerned with the nervous system but arose out of his clinical experience. Although it can scarcely be regarded as having contributed to his permanent reputation it undoubtedly brought him a remarkable temporary notoriety. In October, 1823, the resident physician of the Hôtel-

[13] *Procès-verb. Acad. d. Sc.*, 8:231, 1825.
[14] Flourens, M., *Du système nerveux*, 2nd ed., 1842, p. 13.

Dieu, M. Caillard, called him in to view the case of a man
in the last stages of hydrophobia. The patient uttered
constant shrieks, had a horror of water, attempted to bite
the attendants and had to be restrained in a strait jacket.
Magendie was met at the hospital door by a group of medical students who urged him to hurry as there was not a
moment to lose. The patient had been copiously bled, but
still had violent paroxysms. Magendie had a short time before innoculated a healthy dog with saliva from a mad
patient and had found that the dog developed hydrophobia
within a month. He now wished to try this experiment
again, but so violent were the seizures of the patient that
he could not collect sufficient saliva for the injection. He
remembered his former experiments on mad dogs, where
injection of warm water into their veins had quieted them.
As a desperate measure he resolved to try it on this patient
who was practically *in extremis*. It required five or six of
the strongest students to hold the man down. At last Magendie succeeded in getting the needle into the arm vein
and he introduced two pints of warm water directly into
the circulatory system. The pulse rate fell from 150 to 80,
the patient became calm and could even drink water. M.
Caillard now removed the strait jacket which had up to
this time been necessary. In a quiet manner the sick man
asked permission to go down into the court to urinate. It
was thought that he was still delirious, but at length, half-
supported by medical students, he walked towards the door.
A vessel was provided and the patient passed a pint of such
odorous fluid that it was necessary to remove it at once.
He asked for his relatives and when they came he talked
rationally with them. He was now the center of interest
of the whole hospital staff, doctors, surgeons, nuns and medical students, but, unfortunately, two days later he suffered
a severe hemorrhage of the intestines. This was soon con-
trolled and the patient felt well enough to take some chicken

broth. Then he began to have acute pains in his joints. When he was first brought to the hospital it had at once been decided to bleed him in the customary manner, but he was so violent that two lancets were broken off in his foot and, according to Magendie, it was these broken points which caused the inflammation responsible for the severe pain. The patient's mind now became affected, he was convinced that someone was trying to smother him and he died on the ninth day after the injection of water into his veins. At the autopsy Magendie was most struck by what he termed the "putrefaction" of the blood. He was unaware of the "laking" of the blood by water, i.e., the breaking down of the corpuscles and consequent escape of the cell contents; and, of course, he could not realize that untold numbers of bacteria had probably been introduced with the warm water. At any rate, he concluded that he had cured the hydrophobia and that death was due to a "local disease" wholly unconnected with it,[15] and it is probable enough that the immediate cause of death was septicemia, rather than hydrophobia.

As soon as Magendie had published the account of this treatment for hydrophobia in his *Journal* the newspapers seized upon this new and spectacular "cure." The London *Times* devoted considerable space in its "valuable pages" (the phrase is the *Lancet's*) to a full translation of the article and from this reliable source other English papers took their copy. Two London medical journals, the *Lancet* and the *Medico-chirurgical Review,* became involved in an undignified squabble because the former had withheld publication until the text of Magendie's article could be translated, while the latter had rushed into print with an account derived from a secondary French source, at the same time laying claim to "wonderful celerity" in obtaining news for its readers. The *Lancet* hastened to explode this pre-

[15] *J. de physiol. expér. et path.,* 3:382, 1823. Cf. *Lancet,* 1:441, 1823.

tension by describing its competitor's authority as "a miserable second-hand sketch," but succeeded only, on its own confession, in arousing in the bosom of the rival editor "the most rancorous feelings of envy, malice and uncharitableness." The only reputation which emerged unscathed was that of Magendie, who was generally acclaimed.

In November, 1825, Magendie was asked to serve as an expert witness at the trial of a former medical student, Castaing, who was personally known to Magendie's friend Breschet, professor of anatomy and physiology in the Faculty of Medicine. Castaing was accused of murder by poisoning his victim with morphine administered in warm wine with a dash of lemon to disguise the taste. The case attracted great attention both in France and England since it was almost the first to reveal to the public the possibilities of the new medicinal agents in the hands of ill-intentioned persons. A reviewer of an English version of Magendie's "Formulaire" remarked soon after this that the little book would be valuable both to the murderer and the suicide.[16] The reviewer was struck by the small amounts of certain of the drugs described which could cause death and the rapidity of their action. He prophesied that strychnine would be a favorite for murderers and prussic acid for suicides. Magendie was not the chief expert witness at the trial of Castaing, for the other two, Laennec and Chaussier, were even better known in the medical world than he. He acted as a member of the committee to review the results of the autopsy on the victim and this committee maintained that they could find nothing which would warrant the conclusion that death had been the result of morphine poisoning although they did note that there was constriction of the pupils. Chaussier under examination testified that narcotics should cause the victim to die with pupils widely dilated. When asked if morphine would produce this effect,

[16] *Medico-chirur. Rev.*, 1:47, 1824.

he said that it would, because morphine was a narcotic. The examiner was sufficiently well-informed to point out that this was not in agreement with the statements of Orfila (who had quoted Magendie's experiments in his text-book). Chaussier replied, "That may be, but I speak from my own experience." [17] Magendie was not asked to testify on this particular point, but if he was present when Chaussier was giving evidence, one wonders by what means this impulsive champion of scientific truth was kept silent.

At the conclusion of his summer courses in 1824 Magendie decided to visit London. There is no record of his having gone to the Hunterian School at Great Windmill Street to return the visit of John Shaw, but he did visit St. Thomas's Hospital and met some of the surgeons there, with one of whom, Dr. J. Elliotson, he went through the wards, observing his treatment of cases. He even converted this English-man to his point of view with regard to the Bell-Magendie controversy, for by the middle of the century Elliotson almost alone in England was firmly on Magendie's side.[18]

Magendie's most notable host in London was William Hyde Wollaston (1766-1828), whose scientific acumen made a great impression upon him. Some years after the English scientist's death, Magendie described him as one whose "hearing was so acute that you would have believed him blind, and his sight so piercing that you would have believed him deaf." [19] Wollaston was indeed a remarkable man, for he was one of the very few who, after the eighteenth century, excelled in nearly all branches of science.

[17] *Moniteur universel*, p. 1338, Nov. 15, 1823.

[18] Dr. Elliotson had a definite leaning towards the championing of minority causes, for he was later forced to retire from the presidency of the Royal Medical and Chirurgical Society because of his publication of a pamphlet describing the results he had obtained while operating on patients in the "mesmeric state." V. Elliotson, J., Numerous cases of surgical operations without pain in the mesmeric state. Cf., The Harveian Oration, delivered June 27, 1846.

[19] *Mém. Acad. de Sci.*, 14:157, 1838.

He had discovered the chemical elements palladium and rhodium, and had contributed fifty-six papers on such subjects as astronomy, botany, optics and mineralogy, each of which is regarded as having marked a distinct advance in the branch of science dealt with.[20] A fellow of the Royal Society for many years, he had been its secretary and vice-president, but not its president because of his unwillingness to clash with Sir Humphrey Davy's (1778-1828) ambitions in that direction. He had been in France in 1814 and had made a lasting friendship with Laplace, who, after several attempts, had succeeded only in 1823 in having him made foreign associate of the Academy of Sciences. It was therefore probably Laplace who was the source of Magendie's introduction to him.

Wollaston had on several occasions suffered temporary blindness in the left half of his visual field and just before Magendie's visit he had read two papers before the Royal Society on the subject of vision. The first, on the semi-decussation of the optic nerves, was the direct outcome of his own disability; the second was a most interesting discussion of perspective, ably illustrated with drawings by his friend, the artist, Thomas Lawrence.

Wollaston had heard Bell's papers at the Royal Society; had, in fact, even reported on them, and he was eager to become acquainted with Magendie's experiments on the nervous system at first hand. He had long since given up his medical practice, but maintained at the rear of his house at 14, Buckingham Street, Fitzroy Square, a private laboratory, the secrets of which he jealously guarded. It was here that Magendie repeated some of his experiments for his host's benefit. His own account is as follows:

"I am reminded of an occurrence on my first visit to England which I am happy to cite. I was in Wollaston's laboratory, occupied in repeating before this illustrious observer some of

[20] Gunther, R. T., *Early Science in Cambridge*, 1937.

my experiments on the nervous system. He was above all desirous of seeing for himself the effects of cutting the fifth cranial nerve, whether it really resulted in loss of sensation on that side. I wished to cut the nerve inside the skull, according to my usual procedure. However, by an accident which it is not always easy to avoid in so delicate an operation, I opened the cavernous sinus or the carotid artery, and caused an abundant hemorrhage around the brain. The animal was seized with convulsive tremors, and collapsed as if dead. Wollaston thought it was dead, and begged me to repeat the experiment on another animal. 'I would rather call this one back to life,' I said to him, 'and what is more, make him run as far as you please.' He thought that I was joking. While he awaited with imperturbable gravity the outcome of my somewhat defiant challenge, this is what I did. I removed the vault of the skull and the cerebral hemispheres, as you saw me do at our last meeting: immediately the animal stood up on its paws. Then when I cut the brain at a certain point, which you will learn later presides over forward movement, the animal shot off like an arrow, and we had great difficulty in catching it. Wollaston, whose mind was critical and precise and accustomed to reflection, was greatly struck with the definiteness and novelty of these results." [21]

Magendie was also invited to give more public demonstrations in London. Before a large audience of physicians he attempted to cut the fifth nerve in the rabbit, but because of hemorrhage he was obliged to try several times before he was successful. He showed in a dog that cutting the dorsal roots deprived the animal of sensation, while severing the ventral roots deprived it of motion; and he finally removed parts of the brain in successive slices to show the forced forward movements. Wollaston, who was present, was particularly interested in the experiments on the fifth nerve and its relation to sight, and he suggested that a lighted candle be held before the eye of the animal

[21] Syst. nerv., 1839, v. 1, p. 198.

with this nerve cut. The spectators were divided in their opinion as to whether there was any effect on sight: incidentally, they were using as criterion for the sensitivity of the eye movement of the iris, and not all were agreed as to whether pupillary response was an exact index of vision. Dr. Elliotson participated in one of the experiments and Herbert Mayo was curious enough to perform an autopsy on the rabbits with the fifth nerve cut. John Shaw was also present and reported that the large audience was delighted and eager to shake hands with Magendie because of the novel facts which he had presented. However, Shaw complained bitterly in the press later that all the credit for Magendie's experiments should have belonged to England. He felt himself "bound to say" that the principal experiments by which Magendie had attracted so much attention in London were actually suggested by himself (*viz*, Shaw), although he disclaimed Magendie's conclusions.[22]

The date of Magendie's return to France is indicated by his participation in a discussion on the origin and causes of yellow fever in the Academy of Sciences on June 28. Before his departure he became involved in a controversy that was being carried on at the time between the *Lancet* and its rival, the *Medico-chirurgical Review*. The surgeons at St. Thomas's Hospital objected to the presence of reporters, even from medical journals, at their operations, and the students in the operating theatre were warned that if any one of them should divulge facts for publication, he would instantly be expelled. The *Lancet* opened an attack on the "hole and corner surgery" at St. Thomas's, and the other medical paper as promptly came to the defence of the surgeons undesirous of publicity, maintaining that one "who destroys a patient from want of dexterity . . . suffers mortification enough in the operating room without the cruel and demoniacal torture of seeing his failure blazoned forth

[22] Shaw, J., *London Med. and Phys. J.*, 52:95, 1824.

to the public." The editor of the *Lancet* saw fit to ask the opinion of the visiting Frenchman in this debate and Magendie gave his verdict in his own *Journal* in the issue appearing just after his return. He took the side of the *Lancet* and said that if the surgeons instead of concealing their unfortunate cases had "candidly published their results, they would have rendered as great a service as they did in publishing their successful ones." It is clear that his concern was for the progress of surgery and not for the practice of surgeons. The *Lancet's* editorial, written after Magendie's departure for Paris, was most complimentary and expressed the hope for another visit in the near future, but the *Medico-chirurgical Review* took the opportunity to attack him for his vivisections. This was the beginning of the expression of public opinion against this method of physiological investigation.

It has been stated [23] that it was actually proposed in the House of Commons to evoke the Alien Bill and deport Magendie while he was in London because of cruelties attendant on his public demonstrations. Although there was much discussion of this bill going on at the time, there is no indication in the verbatim House reports for the year 1824 that there was ever any proposal that it be applied to Magendie. The mistake has probably arisen from giving a backward reference to certain events which took place in 1825, almost a year after his departure from England.

By an interesting coincidence it was while Magendie was actually in London that the preliminary steps in the organization of the "Society for the Prevention of Cruelty to Animals" were being taken. On June 16, at Old Slaughter's Coffee House in St. Martin's Lane, Mr. Richard Martin, member of parliament for Galway and dubbed by his personal friend, George IV, "Humanity Martin," in shocked

[23] Flourens, M., *Éloge de M. Magendie*, 1858, p. 14; Hoefer, *Nouv. biogr. gén.*, 32:690, 1863; Genty, M., *Les biogr. méd.*, 9:128, 1935.

tones told the story of the cruelty of a man who had "a hunter which had borne him at the head of the pack for eight or ten years" and who then sold the poor brute, after it had broken a leg, as a pit pony for four pounds.[24] If M. Magendie had dropped into the Coffee House and heard Mr. Martin's speech, it is not certain whether he would have known enough about the gentlemanly sport of hunting, in spite of his youthful dissipation of a legacy on horses and a groom, to point out, as other people did not fail to do, that the miracle was that a horse which had borne his master *at the head of the pack* had not been sold as a pit pony long before the end of eight years.

Mr. Martin's participation in the founding of this Society, which was to become so powerful in England, was the sequel to activities which two years earlier (in 1822) had resulted in the passage of a bill through both Houses of Parliament to protect horses and cattle against ill-treatment, the first piece of modern legislation of this kind. He had to contend against both indifference and ridicule while he was trying to get this and later laws passed and he earned for himself before the end a definite reputation for eccentricity. Members of the House asked rude questions as to whether asses were to be protected as well as horses, and when Mr. Martin rose to call for a division "to secure new privileges and immunities for beeves on this side of the channel," the members went home to supper without voting. The House of Lords in behalf of the sporting element threw out his first bill before it was finally reintroduced and passed. A correspondent of the *Times* [25] called attention to the insensitivity of the member for Galway to the sufferings from famine at that time of his constituents and even of his tenants. It was suggested that he would be better employed at home setting the poor to "building fences" on his

[24] *Times,* June 17, 1824.
[25] *Times,* July 3, 1824.

"splendid estate" than in London bringing "petulous cat-
tle-drovers and tempestuous carters" into the courts. The
Times on its own responsibility poked a little fun by calling
for Mr. Martin in behalf of some geese which were reported
to have been plucked alive. When he carried humanitarian-
ism to the length of supporting the cause of Queen Caroline, he lost the favor even of George IV.

In February, 1825, Mr. Martin was speaking in the House
in behalf of his bill "to prevent bear-baiting and other cruel
practices," and having disposed of bear-baiting he went on
to say, as he was reported in Hansard:

"There was a Frenchman by the name of Magendie, whom
he considered a disgrace to society. In the course of last year,
this man, at one of the anatomical theatres, exhibited a series
of experiments so atrocious as almost to shock belief. He would
not trust himself to express a further opinion upon this fellow's conduct, but he would merely say that he looked upon
those who witnessed it without interfering to prevent it almost
in the light of criminals. This M. Magendie got a lady's greyhound, for which he paid ten guineas. He first of all nailed its
front and then its hind paws to the table, with the bluntest
spikes he could find, giving as a reason for so doing, that the
poor beast in its agonies might tear away from the spikes if
they were at all sharp and cutting. He then doubled up its
long ears, and nailed them down to the table with similar spikes
(Cries of "Hear!" and "Shame!"). He then made a gash down
the middle of its face, and proceeded to dissect the nerves on
one side of it. First of all, he cut those nerves which belong to
the sight, and whilst performing that operation said to the spectators, 'Observe when I pass my scalpel over these nerves, the
dog will shut its eyes.' It did so. He then proceeded to operate
on those of taste and hearing. After he had finished those operations, he put some bitter food on the tongue of the dog, and
hallooed into his ear. The dog repudiated the food, and was
insensible to the sound. This surgical butcher, or butchering
surgeon—for he deserved both names—then turned round to the

spectators and said, 'I have now finished my operations on one side of the dog's head; as it costs so much money to get an animal of this description, I shall reserve the other side until tomorrow. If the servant takes care of him for the night, according to the directions I have given him, I am of opinion that I shall be able to continue my operations upon him tomorrow, with quite as much satisfaction to us all as I have done today; but if not, though he may have lost the vivacity he has shown today, I shall have the opportunity of cutting him up alive, and showing you the peristaltic motion of the heart and viscera.' (Great disgust at the statement of this cruel experiment was manifested by the House.) He was aware of the necessity of making some experiments on living animals; but then they should be performed in such a manner as to cause as little suffering as possible. That was the opinion of the most eminent professors. He held in his hand the written declarations of Mr. Abernethy, of Sir Everard Home, of the professors of medicine at Cambridge and Oxford, and of several other respectable gentlemen, to that effect. They all, he believed, united in condemnation of such excessive and protracted cruelty as had been practised by this Frenchman. He had heard that this fellow was again coming to this country to repeat his experiment. He therefore had mentioned it to the House, in the hope that it would gain publicity, and excite against the perpetrator of such unnecessary cruelty the odium he merited. He trusted that when it was known, the fellow would not find persons to attend his lectures, and would thus be compelled to wing his way back to his own country, to find in it a theatre for such abominable atrocities." [26]

When Mr. Martin's bill came up for debate two weeks later, both a private member and the Home Secretary, Sir Robert Peel, stated that the story of "cruelty to a greyhound by a French surgeon" had received a "full refutation." Furthermore, Sir James Mackintosh, who had begun his career as a graduate in medicine at Edinburgh and who was himself a charter member of the "Society for the Preven-

[26] Martin, R., *Hansard's Parliamentary Debates*, N.S., 12:657, 1825.

tion of Cruelty to Animals," spoke against physiological experimentation being made the ground of legislative enactments. He thought that both medical education and scientific research might be seriously impeded. He added that he had "the honor to be acquainted" with Dr. Magendie, to whom he had been introduced while he was living in Paris by their mutual friend, Baron Humboldt; Dr. Magendie had in fact acted as his personal physician when he had been ill in France and he was "bound in justice to say, and he should be base and ungrateful if he did not state the fact, that he had never been treated amongst medical men, with greater care and tenderness than he had received from Dr. Magendie. He felt no doubt, therefore, that if that gentleman had inflicted pain on any animal, it must have been when in the ardent pursuit of science, and with the hope, if not the conviction, that his experiments would be generally beneficial." [27]

Mr. Martin made a reply in which he refused to accept the refutation of his charges (there was some question as to whether the experimental animal had been a greyhound or a spaniel), and he said that he had that day gone to St. Bartholomew's Hospital and repeated his statement before witnesses, the regular English procedure for inviting a suit for libel. He added that "he knew for a fact that Dr. Magendie, while performing one of those barbarous operations on a dog in England, placed his mouth close to the ear of the suffering animal, and said, patting it with his hand, 'Soyez tranquille': then, turning to the spectators, he added, 'Il serait plus tranquille s'il entendait français.' "

The anti-bear-baiting bill was thrown out (23 ayes to 33 noes), principally on the ground that "it debarred the lower classes of society from their amusements," but it had included the first attempt at legislation against so-called "vivisection." Magendie became firmly fixed in the English

[27] Mackintosh, Sir J., *Hansard's Parliamentary Debates*, N.S., 12:1002, 1825.

and American mind as the prototype of all vivisectors. As late as 1879 he was described as "a monster of vivisection," and it was stated that "the wretch Magendie was undoubtedly the most abandoned criminal that ever lived." [28]

It must have been about fifteen years after this that an incident described by Claude Bernard took place. While Bernard and Magendie were at work together on an experiment, an American Quaker in characteristic dress, broad-brimmed hat, knee breeches and high-buttoned coat, walked into the laboratory and asked for Magendie. When they had been introduced, the Quaker said, "I have heard thee spoken of, and I see that I have not been deceived; for I had been told that thee does experiments on living animals. I have come to see thee in order to ask thee what right thee has to act thus, and to tell thee that thee must cease this kind of experiment, because thee has no right to cause these animals to die or to suffer, and because thee gives a bad example, and thee accustoms others to cruelty." Magendie tried to explain his point of view, pointing out that Harvey could never have been led to the discovery of the circulation of the blood, if he had not done experiments on the deer in King Charles's park. The physiologist and the Quaker parted without any change in the convictions of either, but it is clear that Magendie tried to avoid offending or antagonizing his critic. This was consistently his attitude. He refused to give way to prejudice against animal experimentation, but he never flaunted vivisection before those opposed to it. In his courses he was always careful to explain that knowledge of life processes demanded experiments on living animals, and that the physiologist, influenced only by his scientific curiosity, should no more be charged with cruelty than the surgeon who is dominated by the idea of saving his patient.[29]

[28] Dalton, J. C., *Internat. Rev.*, 8:120, 1880.
[29] Bernard, C., *Substances toxiques*, 1857, p. 14.

During the summer of Magendie's visit to London the English papers contained a number of distressing descriptions of cases of hydrophobia. A tailor bitten by a cat and several men and boys bitten by dogs died in convulsions. The treatment approved by the best lay minds, as represented by the *Times,* was application of the cautery and a week at the seaside. However, on September 20, 1824, a case was reported in which Magendie's treatment was applied for the first time in England. A young man, bitten on the wrist by a mad dog, was taken to Guy's Hospital with all the symptoms of hydrophobia. In pursuance of Magendie's recommendations the man was bled, 20 ounces being drawn. The patient became unmanageable, threw himself about and could not be held. Much time was lost in trying to get a needle into the vein. Another vein was tried but the patient's pulse stopped. As it was thought that mere water would now be of no avail, a few spoonfuls of spirits were added to the warm water and about 20 ounces of the mixture injected. The heart grew stronger, but then failed completely. A good many other unsuccessful trials of Magendie's treatment for hydrophobia were made in England and on the continent before the public completely lost faith. As the patients in all these cases were probably past the incubation stage when the "remedy" was applied, no great harm, if certainly no good, came of the impression which the extraordinary case at the Hôtel-Dieu in 1823 had made upon the mind of Magendie with its perhaps too great susceptibility to empirical evidence. He continued to work on "rage" in animals for the rest of his life, but no real advance was made in the treatment of hydrophobia before Pasteur.

Magendie's clinical use of injection of substances directly into the blood stream had been derived from his experiences with animals, which are in general more resistant to infection than man, a consideration of course unrecognized in his time. An unwarranted extension of the deterministic principle made him too prone to argue directly from the lower animals to man without due allowance for species differences. His reputation in America was great enough to lead to a rather drastic application of direct injection into veins on the part of Dr. E. Hale of Boston, an account of which found its way into the *Times* from "the Family Oracle of Health." [30] This young physician injected half an ounce of castor oil into his left arm vein. He was not too skilful in his operation and lost some 8 ounces of blood. He first noted an oily taste in his mouth, then came nausea and belchings, stiffness of the muscles of the jaw, and dizziness. Later there were severe disturbances in his bowels as if he had taken a violent purgative. The bandage on his arm slipped and he lost more blood. His arm began to swell and he became really ill. He survived, thanks, no doubt, to a pioneer constitution, although a month later he was still not perfectly restored to health. He was subsequently encouraged in adventure by the award of the Boylston Medical Prize.

[30] *Times*, Oct. 9, 1824.

9

MEDICAL PRACTICE, REPERCUSSION OF POLITICAL AFFILIATIONS, WORK ON CEREBROSPINAL FLUID

1825-1828

"Comment! on a pu avancer que l'étude expérimentale est contredite par l'observation clinique; . . . que s'il y a du désaccord entre les résultats annoncés par les expérimentateurs, c'est que l'expérience ne prouve rien! Messieurs, j'ai senti la rougeur me monter au front en lisant de semblables débats." [1]

MAGENDIE'S reception by the English physicians seems even to have increased his self assurance. A small instance of his determination to assert himself in what he considered to be his own especial sphere was his refusal, soon after his return (November, 1824), to sign a report, which both Cuvier and Duméril had already signed, on a memoir about lymphatic vessels in birds, a topic on which he himself had written. His experiments on human patients became not only bold but rash. Upon cutting into the eyeball of a female patient in order to remove a cataract, he actually touched the retina with his needle to see if it was sensitive. The patient experienced no distress; in fact, she was unaware that she was the subject of such an experiment and expressed joy at the flashes of light which, whenever the retina was touched, appeared in an eye previously without

[1] *Syst. nerv.*, 1839, v. 1, p. 204.

146

sight.[2] Magendie's conclusion, that the retina was insensitive, was not so startling as it seems, since he had no intention of denying that stimulation of the retina could give rise
to the sensation of light. Here he used the term sensitivity
to mean the function of a nerve in conveying those sensations common to the surface of the body (now distinguished
as touch, heat, cold and pain) which are easily recognized
from the muscular contortions on the part of the subject
when the appropriate nerve is stimulated, particularly if the
nerve contains pain fibres, as most sensory nerves do. He
drew no conclusion from the patient's perception of flashes
of light on *touching* of the retina, although this was a perfect example of "specific nerve energy." This was probably
because what he was looking for was evidence of pain. He
had already tested the retinas of all sorts of mammals,
amphibians and fish in connection with his experiments on
the fifth nerve and he had found that these animals exhibited no evidences of pain.[3] He was thus prepared for a
similar result in the human patient. His experiments did
much to combat the idea then prevalent that every sensory
nerve, even those of the special senses, served indis-
criminately for each of the common sensations, and his accurate description of all the phenomena resulting from his
experiment on his human subject was a valuable contribution to the conception of specific nerve energies, which, as
we have seen, lay at the back of Charles Bell's mind as
early as 1811, although it was for the first time stated clearly
only in 1826 by Johannes Müller (1801-1858).

Another bold experiment was the direct application of
the galvanic current to the nerves in the eye socket of man
by means of platinum needles inserted into them. Magendie reported that pricking the orbital branches of the

[2] *J. de physiol. expér. et path.*, 5:37, 1825. Cf. Bernard, C., *Pathologie
expérimentale*, 1880, p. 196.
[3] *J. de physiol. expér. et path.*, 4:180, 310, 1824.

fifth nerve was not dangerous, that it produced a sensation similar to that which occurred when the orbital nerve was injured, and that galvanism might be useful in cases of incomplete amaurosis.[4] He did not carry this method of treatment very far, but here, as in many other branches of medical science, he was the early pioneer. It has been claimed that the most beneficial result of his attempt to use galvanism as a therapeutic measure was the interest which he aroused in the mind of Duchenne, who was really the creator of the science of electrotherapy.[5]

At the very end of 1824 Magendie made an observation on a patient at the Charité, which was the beginning of a long series of researches. At an autopsy he discovered that the spinal canal was completely filled with liquid. So turgid were the nervous tissues that "the roots which belong to the nerves of feeling and to the nerves of movement" (*sic*) were forced apart.[6] Magendie contended that the fluid was secreted by the arachnoid membrane and that its presence was a natural phenomenon, not the pathological condition it was considered to be by others at this time. It was soon pointed out that Cotugno, as far back as 1769, had described the existence of "water" in the space between the dura mater and the nervous substance of the spinal cord and within the ventricles of the brain as well. Two years later, in connection with his second memoir on cerebrospinal fluid, Magendie published Cotugno's original Latin memoir in his *Journal,* accompanying it with a footnote which gives an illuminating sidelight on his procedure in experimental research:

"During the period of my early physiological researches, it often happened to me to make a discovery, and when, according to a custom which I still follow, I consulted the authors

---

[4] *Procès-verb. Acad. d. Sci.,* 8:395, 1826.
[5] Robinson, V., *Pathfinders in Medicine,* 1929.
[6] *J. de physiol. expér. et path.,* 5:27, 1825.

after I had finished the work, I found the whole discovery in
Haller. I was greatly provoked, I cursed more than once this
wretched book where everything was to be found; but I drew
this conclusion which will console many young doctors who
have similar bad luck, even if I found things which others had
discovered before me, I could, if I continued working, find
facts still undiscovered. I regard it as merely my duty to render
to each what is due him, and in order that the public may
judge for itself, I cite the references entire. That is the course
which I followed recently in connection with Mr. Charles Bell,
in regard to the functions of the anterior and posterior roots
of the spinal nerves. I am not a little surprised to see him even
at this present time keep up his pretensions to a discovery to
which he has no sort of right. I am going to do the same in the
case of Cotugno, so that everyone may judge what part I played
in the discovery of the normal existence of cerebrospinal fluid." [7]

A good many facets of Magendie's character are revealed in
this short passage. The predominating impression is one of
his innate honesty, but there is also an egoism which seems
almost to compete as a motive with an undeniable enthusiasm for scientific advance. There is, furthermore, an element of contradiction between the utter self-confidence of
his belief that within him resided the capacity to carry
physiology forward and the impulse to self-justification
which suggests that unlucky circumstances had made in-
roads on his native assurance.

Magendie had found time previous to 1825 to collaborate
with Desmoulins on a two-volume work on the anatomy of
the nervous system of vertebrates.[8] His very considerable
contributions since 1822 to a knowledge of the physiology
of the nervous system had already been assembled for convenient reference in the new edition of his *Précis* for 1824,
but in editing the part of Desmoulins' book devoted to this

[7] *J. de physiol. expér. et path.*, 7:84, 1827.
[8] Desmoulins, A., *Anatomie des systèmes nerveux des animaux à vertèbres*, 1825.

aspect of the subject, he included descriptions of his own experiments, notably the observation of circus movements displayed in mammals after wounding of a peduncle of the cerebellum.

Magendie did not repeat his summer visit to London, but he received a most gracious invitation in July, 1825, from Dr. J. Ellerby, a London surgeon and a friend of Dr. Overend, a former pupil of Magendie, to stay at his house, although he and Magendie had never met. Magendie went instead to the Pyrenees. When he returned in September, he reported to the Academy that he thought there were fewer cases of goitre than formerly, and this he attributed to a betterment of economic conditions, with a consequent improvement in diet and housing. He was right in thinking that diet and the incidence of goitre were related, but his guess that good housing was also concerned was not so apt. He also said that he had tried in vain to find a cretin in regions where formerly there had been many, and he ascribed this disappearance of cretinism to the same causes as the diminution in the incidence of goitre.[9] This observation is of especial interest, for although goitre was described in 1825 by Parry and ten years later by Graves, whose name has been given to the condition of hyperthyroidism, it was not until 1873 that Gull traced the origin of cretinism to lack of function of the thyroid.

Carefully preserved among Magendie's papers in the Musée Gilbert is a letter from New York, dated January 14, 1826.[10] Felix Pascalis, the writer, was a prominent American physician of French origin, president of a medical society and past editor of the *Medical Repository*, one of the earlier medical journals to be published in the United States. He wrote that he was desirous of establishing a class in physiology which would be acceptable to the newly

[9] *Procès-verb. Acad. d. Sci.*, 8:281, 1825.
[10] Olmsted, J. M. D., *Ann. Med. Hist.*, 3rd ser., 2:371, 1940.

founded College of Physicians and Surgeons of Columbia University. Since he wished information regarding the possibility of purchasing anatomical charts in Paris, it is to be presumed that he intended to carry on the old tradition under which he had been brought up at Montpellier rather than to attempt instruction in experimental physiology with demonstrations on living material as was advocated by Magendie. There is no record of Pascalis having carried out his intention. His letter does, however, inform us that, in translation at least, Magendie's *Précis* had reached the United States.

Since 1818 Magendie had been eligible to a post at one of the Paris hospitals, and although he had as yet no regular appointment, he made ward rounds at the Hôtel-Dieu with a small following of medical students. One of these students, who was in attendance in September of 1825, was A. Trousseau (1801-1867), who eventually became one of France's most renowned clinicians and author of a famous text on therapeutics and materia medica. His correspondence with his friend Bretonneau gives us a glimpse of Magendie's clinical instruction. He wrote:

"Magendie makes his visit to a ward in the Hôtel-Dieu. Before my eyes he manoeuvres with morphine, hydrocyanic acid and all the new drugs. If he gets any results which are worth the trouble, I'll let you know. Here are my reasons for following Magendie on his rounds: first, I talk physiology with him; secondly, I see the administration of new drugs; and thirdly, I can take my time in learning how to use Father Laennec's cylinder, because there are only five or six of us who follow this clinic." [11]

It was not until July, 1826, that Magendie received a formal hospital appointment and was made substitute at the Salpetrière to replace Dr. Ferrus, friend of his early youth.

[11] Triaire, P., *Bretonneau et ses correspondants*, 1892, v. 1, p. 524.

An earlier letter written on Magendie's behalf in 1818 by M. Chabrol, counsellor of state, had been unsuccessful in getting him a place. Among his sponsors for the second attempt were Comte Berthelot and Comte de Laplace, both of whom had influence with the government of the Restoration. Magendie was put on a ward for women suffering from incurable diseases. He was most sympathetic with these wretched creatures, listened with patience to the recital of their ailments and gave them what consolation he could. He told of one girl with a large tumor involving her whole left side. To give her relief from pain he performed the drastic operation of ligaturing the carotid artery. Hemiplegia and loss of mental faculties followed, although these symptoms abated; the tumor diminished, only to start its growth once more, because, he said, "she will not stick to my regime, but I haven't the heart to employ severe measures. Why should I rob this unfortunate creature of the only happy moments which are still permitted her?" [12] In addition to his efforts to relieve physical sufferings he was generous in gifts of small sums of money to his more necessitous patients. When he left the Salpetrière after four years, his patients gave him a "couronne" (the French formal arrangement of flowers) in witness of their satisfaction with his efforts on their behalf. The question which has been raised as to whether so relentless an experimental physiologist could have had as a physician a good "bedside manner" is perhaps in part answered by this demonstration at the Salpetrière and in part by the fact that the Academy of Sciences, when its members fell ill, was in the habit of appointing Magendie to visit the illustrious patients and convey expressions of its solicitude. He attended Poinsot in the summer, and Pinel in the autumn, of 1826 under these circumstances.

Magendie preferred hospital to private patients, often

[12] J. de physiol. expér. et path., 7:180, 1827.

sending to other physicians those who came to consult him. On one occasion this had a romantic result, for when he sent the daughter of the Marquis de Montferrier to consult Louis, the consultation ripened into romance and the physician married his patient. Nevertheless, without his seeking it, Magendie came to have a very distinguished personal practice. He seems to have been, if anything, less inclined to humor the exalted than the humble among those who came under his care. Flourens provides a picture of him as a physician at about the age of forty:

"Sceptical, without any favorite nostrums, even facetious, he listened to his patients' complaints and in turn made them listen to hard truths, scoldings or sheer caprices on his part. Even those who came to him abjectly believing in the utter infallibility of medical art left him with the conviction that they had nothing to be cured save their own credulity. To young doctors he was fond of saying: 'You haven't tried doing nothing yet . . . More often than not we cannot discover the cause of a disease. Our only function is to assist nature, which always tries to restore the normal state, by refusing to hinder her; we can hope only sometimes to be skilful enough to aid her.'"

Magendie apparently would not have resented the implied charge of heretical empiricism, since he expressed himself in similar terms in his published lectures. He said:

"A patient is attacked by typhoid fever: well, he will be subjected to a different treatment depending on whether he has been sent to this or that hospital. . . . One physician boasts of his purgatives, another prefers bleeding, a third pats himself on the back for his use of tonics, others finally, and I am of this number, let the disease run its course almost without interference, without even trying to put a brake on its progress."[13]

To convey the same impression there is also the story of a youthful patient for whom Magendie's prescription was

[13] *Phén. phys.*, 1842, v. 2, p. 5.

not medicine but permission to do what he wanted. The boy's symptoms were alarming, and although Magendie was usually sparing of his time for professional visits, in this case he gave unstintingly of it. After three days of watching, his face lost its anxious look, and taking the patient by the ear, he said: "You little rascal, you haven't let me have a moment's peace!" With a playful cuff, he added, "Arise and walk!" The happy father wanted to know what had been the matter with his son. "I don't know," replied Magendie, "nor could the whole Faculty of Medicine tell you if they were honest; there is only one thing certain, and that is that he is well now."

This unconventionality of manner was bound to lead to criticism, if not to misunderstanding, and, as we might expect, Dubois, the permanent secretary of the Academy of Medicine, took a very unfavorable view of Magendie as a physician. He charged that Magendie's interest in physiology had made him a mere sceptic, that instead of practising medicine at the bedside, he did so only in the amphitheatre; and finally, that he so neglected his services at the hospital that he appeared at rare intervals, allowing his internes in the meantime to carry out whatever treatment they in their ignorance thought best for the patients. Dubois was particularly severe about Magendie's lack of respect for the current medicaments, and it seems to have been true that in spite of his great interest in the therapeutic action of new drugs, he seldom prescribed them, preferring to let nature take her own course. As for the more old-fashioned and comparatively harmless nostrums, his advice to his pupils, which particularly horrified Dubois, was: "If it amuses you to administer that sort of treatment, by all means do so." Magendie had evidently so outraged the official defender of the orthodox medical faith that he had placed himself quite beyond the pale and was no more worthy to be called a physician.

His scepticism may be granted; it was the scepticism which germinated into scientific medicine. On the other hand, letters, preserved by Magendie and still extant, from grateful patients and their relatives, together with such unsolicited public testimony as that of Sir James Mackintosh, bear witness to his possession of that sympathetic attitude towards a patient which maintains the confidence, which, as Paracelsus said, is often a no less effective curative agent than the current nostrum. When we look back on the medical treatment in vogue in 1825, which nearly always began with the bleeding of the patient, scepticism with regard to it is rather refreshing. The modern physican looks with horror at the official statistics of death among hospital patients in 1828, one in six at the Hôtel-Dieu, one in five at the Charité.[14] Dubois' charge of neglect of duty may easily have resulted from the interpretation which he would naturally give to an episode like the following, which had a good deal of publicity at the time of its occurrence. The story has been preserved by Claude Bernard, who, writing at the beginning of the third quarter of the nineteenth century, said:

"Twenty years ago a doctor who did not bleed, and bleed drastically, in cases of pneumonia would have been considered an ignoramus or a dangerous innovator. The initiative in this fortunate revolution in the treatment of pneumonia was taken by a French physician-physiologist, Magendie. In 1841, when I was interne at the Hôtel-Dieu, on Magendie's service,[15] he had for a long time been opposed to bleeding in pneumonia cases, believing that bleeding, far from having a beneficial influence on the outcome of the disease, only made convalescence more difficult. The idea, quite out of agreement with the practice in every other medical service, seemed so bold and even rash, that often, when Magendie did not know it, the internes believed

14 The exact figures are 1 in 6.82 and 1 in 5.33. Hawkins, B., *London Med. Gaz.*, 1:713, 1828.
15 On leaving the Salpetrière in 1830, Magendie went to the Hôtel-Dieu, where he served for fifteen years.

themselves in conscience bound to disregard the prescription of the master and to bleed those pneumonia patients who entered the hospital suffering from great difficulty in breathing.

"At this time, Grisolle presented at a competition of the Academy of Sciences his 'Practical Treatise on Pneumonia' in which he established by the aid of statistics and observations that bleeding was the best treatment of pneumonia. Magendie, who was one of the judges of the competition, protested: 'I do not bleed pneumonia patients at the Hôtel-Dieu, they get well none the less; in fact, they recover more quickly.' Breschet, his colleague, who was also a member of this committee, could not refrain from smiling: 'You don't bleed your patients; that is true enough,' he said to Magendie, 'but your internes bleed them behind your back.'

"The next morning Magendie complained bitterly to me of this transgression against his orders; and I can assure you that from that time on not a single patient was bled, and still they recovered." [16]

Magendie's attitude on this question would weigh altogether in his favor from the point of view of a modern physician, but in his own day it was rank heresy against the accepted canons of medicine. The arcana of the doctrine could be fantastic. Magendie recorded an occasion on which he had been called into consultation in a case where the efficacy of simultaneous bleeding from the right arm and left foot was hotly discussed. The situation, he said, was comparable to some of the best scenes on the comic stage, and he prophesied that the time would come when people would refuse to believe that in the most civilized city in the world, in the first half of the nineteenth century, conscientious physicians could have entertained such absurd ideas.[17]

The faith of the laity in this medical dogma is expressed in an article on the death of Byron in the London *Times*

[16] Bernard, C., *Diabète*, 1877, p. 224.
[17] *Phén. phys.*, 1842, v. 3, p. 33.

just after Magendie had returned from his English visit. It was there stated:

"Lord Byron died in consequence of refusing to be bled when he had an inflammation in the chest. When it was proposed to him to be bled, he answered that he would not, for more people died, he believed, by the lancet than by the lance. He was fond of ending what he had to say with something pointed or striking.[18] It produced effect. Next day he became delirious and remained in that state eight days, when he died: but the medical men who were with him did not dare to disobey his orders. One thinks they might have ventured without much risk; if he had continued in delirium and died notwithstanding their bleeding him, he could not well have known of their disobedience; and if he had recovered, eccentric as he was, he could hardly be very angry at his life being preserved." [19]

Heretical views with regard to the practice of medicine, unconventional manners and liberal political sympathies, which were a legacy from a republican upbringing, were not the most useful qualifications for a career under the Restoration (1815-1830), a régime which was attempting to revive social customs and religious and political attitudes which had obtained before the revolution. The eighteenth century physician had been a polished person, suave and gracious in manner; a classical education equipped him to interlard his speech with intimidating Latin tags and his immaculate lace cuffs and jabot indicated his social pretensions. The physicians who were high in favor under the Restoration reintroduced this tradition in the first quarter of the nineteenth century.[20] Magendie was disdainful of tradition. He was interested in medicine as a science, not as an art, and he was totally indifferent to conventionality of manners. As far as personal appearance went, surviving

[18] Can the *Times* be punning on so solemn an occasion?
[19] *Times*, July 5, 1824.
[20] Triaire, P., *Récamier et ses contemporains*, 1899.

portraits suggest that he was not without a touch of vanity.[21] He was actually hostile to the monarchy of the Restoration and in sympathy with the liberals who were to bring about its downfall in the revolution of July, 1830. The administration of the University was in alliance with the government and Magendie had been at odds with its pro-Catholic policy for about ten years. It was to be expected that his general reputation would have repercussions on his official advancement.

When Laennec died in December, 1826, three candidates presented themselves for the chair of Medicine at the Collège de France. Pariset, physician at the Bicêtre, was typical of the old order. His deportment was above reproach. He was interested in public health and had been sent by the government on missions to Egypt and other countries to investigate the question of contagious diseases. He took part in the framing of the laws of quarantine, to the principles of which, incidentally, Magendie was alto-

[21] Magendie had his portrait painted at least twice. Neither the portrait of him as a handsome youth, which in 1938 was to be seen in the Collège de France, nor the one in the Paris Academy of Medicine, where he appears to be about thirty years old, is signed or dated, although the former is attributed to Guérin, who rose to fame during the Empire. In 1838 the sculptor, David d'Angers, was commissioned to make two plaques portraying Magendie in profile. One, about six inches in diameter, was cast in bronze, the other, fully life-size, was in marble. The mold of the former was still in the Louvre in 1938, and castings of it are not uncommonly seen. The latter, in 1938, was in the possession of Dr. Hauriot of Paris, to whose father it was presented by Magendie's niece, together with the writing case which was placed in the Musée Gilbert. Dr. Hauriot kindly allowed the author to have this portrait photographed for reproduction. The well-known lithographer Jules Boilly depicted Magendie as a young man, but gave him the rather bloated appearance typical of this artist's faces. Maurin succeeded in making a more dignified lithograph of Magendie in later middle life, and it is this portrait which is generally used. The portrait reproduced between pages 98 and 99 is from a small faded photograph found in Claude Bernard's album where he kept the photographs of his particular friends. It was presented to the author by Claude Bernard's nephew, M. J. Devay.

gether opposed. Récamier was more solid. He already held a post on the Faculty of Medicine and for twenty years had been physician-in-chief at the Hôtel-Dieu. Although he was a loyal supporter of Royalty, he refused to accept a baronetcy from Louis XVIII. Moreover, he was deeply attached to the Roman Catholic religion. Magendie, unlike both his rivals, was a pronounced liberal in politics and indifferent to religion. He had been unsuccessful in obtaining a post on the Faculty on an earlier occasion, and had only a few months before been made merely a substitute physician at the Salpetrière. His insistence on physiological experimentation had aroused adverse criticism and even hostile attacks, for orthodox members of the medical profession were still sceptical of the validity of conclusions drawn from experiments on living animals. It is possible that Trousseau in one of his letters to Bretonneau may have been voicing Magendie's general unpopularity in hospital circles at this time when he described his Journal as "poverty of poverties" [22] and added, "It is the kind of *Journal* which one would expect from a man who works alone, and who separates himself voluntarily from collaborators whose talent would dim his own star." [23] Nevertheless, for the very innovations in experimental physiology which aroused the suspicions of the medical profession, Magendie had the backing of the Academy of Sciences. By the overwhelming vote of 55 to 5 this Academy again sent Magendie's name to the king.

The Minister of Ecclesiastical Affairs and Public Instruction, the abbé Frayssinous, bishop of Hermopolis *in partibus in fidelium* (1765-1841), was most influential with the king. The abbé had been the leading spirit in the attempt to restore the prestige of the Roman church to its pre-revolu-

[22] At this time Magendie's *Journal* contained almost no original articles, but only abstracts or reprints.

[23] Triaire, P., *Bretonneau et ses correspondents,* 1892, v. 2, p. 49.

tionary state and to bring all education under the domination of the Church. As Grand Master of the University he was particularly obnoxious to the medical students who as a class were a hotbed of liberalism and a source of embarrassment to the government. Three years before they had expressed their indignation in such riotous disturbances during the reading of the eulogy of Hallé by the vice-rector of the University that the entire Faculty of Medicine had been suspended. The abbé was definitely annoyed when the Academy of Sciences insisted on recommending for the chair of Medicine once more the liberal whom the king had refused to appoint so short a time before. He sent for Magendie, who, accompanied by a friend, went to see the Minister. The interview was stormy. Magendie's tendency to carry physical explanations as far as they would go in the study of vital phenomena was well known, and he refused to compromise in any way. Any instruction which he would give must be in accordance with his own views without any softening of them to please the Church. As he left the abbé, he is reported to have said to his friend: "Well, he wasn't too much for me."

It was natural that the abbé should report to the king that Magendie was neither sufficiently devout, nor yet royalist enough, to be honored with the important chair at the Collège de France, and that in spite of Récamier having received only 5 votes out of 60 in the Academy, he preferred him to Magendie for the post. Récamier was given the chair. This action incensed Magendie's supporters in the Academy and among members of the medical profession, since the presentation of his name had been made in the proper way, and the king by placing Récamier in the chair on the mere advice of a Minister without regard to the recommendation of the Academy of Sciences had broken all the rules of procedure. The press entered the controversy with extraordinary vehemence, since it gave the liberal journals a point of attack on the government. The old custom of printing and broadcasting anonymous and abusive pamphlets was resorted to, and one addressed to the king's proctor attacked Récamier because he knew no Greek. It will be remembered that Magendie's knowledge of Greek was acquired as an afterthought and was perhaps not too profound. When Récamier gave his first lectures there were catcalls and scenes of wild disorder. This is said to have "saddened" rather than annoyed the lecturer. At any rate, Récamier retained the chair at the Collège de France until the Restoration government fell.

Meanwhile, Magendie continued to conduct his private classes in experimental physiology. We have an excellent idea of the nature and content of these lectures from the review of one series published in the *London Medical Gazette*. This was the winter course of fifteen lectures which he gave beginning November 15, 1828. The subjects which he treated were naturally those on which he had published memoirs, but there does not seem to have been much logic in the order of their presentation, *viz*, elasticity of the blood vessels, digestion, lymph, blood and circulation, respiration, absorption, cerebrospinal fluid, spinal nerve functions, use of potassium iodide in ulcerations, functions of the different parts of the brain, reproduction. Operations were performed before the class with the aid of an assistant, a medical student, and what they were like may be judged from a description which accompanied the lecture on the central nervous system. The first operation consisted in removing the cerebral hemispheres of a rabbit; then, in turn, the corpora striata, left and right thalamus and pons were removed; the cerebellum was divided longitudinally and then each side removed; finally, the medulla was cut and respiration ceased. At each stage the animal was freed in order to show the position assumed or the movements executed, such as rolling over or turning around in circles,

which are characteristic after the loss of appropriate parts
of the brain. It was no small feat in those days before the
use of anesthetics was introduced to perform with precision
the operations which permitted these effects to be successfully demonstrated.

The various odd committees and investigatory commis-
sions to which Magendie was appointed by the Academy of
Sciences, and upon which he seemed not only willing but
even eager to act, bear witness to reserves of energy and a
roving curiosity about all sorts of medical innovations and
anomalies. In November, 1826, he was appointed to supervise the treatment and education of certain young deaf
mutes on funds derived from the Montyon legacy. In April,
1827, he was asked to investigate the plausibility of slitting
the underside of the patient's tongue in cases of hydrophobia, a remedy which was reported to have been most
effective in Greece. In June of the same year, he was commissioned to look into the strange case of a woman in
Marseilles who had a mammary gland on her thigh from
which she nourished the young. The climax was reached
when in December, 1830, he was directed to inspect Miss
Eliza Mason's establishment for gymnastics for young ladies.
There is no record of his conclusions with regard to the principles upon which this institution was conducted, or of his
impressions of Miss Mason and her young ladies.

The year 1827 seems not to have been a happy one for
Magendie. It was embittered at the beginning by his failure
to secure the chair of medicine at the Collège de France
in spite of the support given him by the Academy of Sciences. He published no new scientific work of his own
during this year, although his *Journal* appeared as usual,
filled out with abstracts and reprints. Early in the year, one
of his oldest friends and an ardent supporter, the Marquis
de Laplace, fell ill, and Magendie attended him. On February 5 Magendie was able to report that his patient showed

signs of "a sensible amelioration of his condition." Two weeks later he was able to report "progressive and satisfactory amelioration," but Laplace then took a turn for the worse, and died on the morning of March 5. When the Academy met that afternoon, it immediately adjourned on the report of the sad news. Fourier in his eulogy of Laplace paid a warm tribute to Magendie's attendance on the Marquis. He said that Magendie "merited every confidence on account of his superior talents, and he watched by his patient's bed with the solicitude which friendship alone can inspire." [24]

During 1827 Magendie's previous work on cerebrospinal fluid was violently attacked. A Dr. Lefort accused him of trickery in manipulating his data, and even of having made false statements concerning the behaviour of so-called "immobile" horses.[25] Magendie had contended that an immobile horse was irresistibly impelled to move forward and could never move backward, and that this peculiarity was due to excessive pressure of cerebrospinal fluid on certain parts of the brain, especially the corpora striata. Dr. Lefort said that a horse which Magendie claimed to have cured had not been cured at all, but had had to be killed because it still exhibited the symptoms of this condition. Magendie replied with characteristic warmth that Dr. Lefort's letter consisted of lies and calumnies, lies because his statements were false, calumnies because Magendie's honor and scientific probity had been attacked. The horse in question had been cured; it had been harnessed to Magendie's cabriolet and had been driven about the streets of Paris. It had been sold while in excellent condition in the open market to a manufacturer of St. Denis, much to the disgust of the person who had originally discarded the horse as useless. Magendie claimed that it was the disgruntled former owner who had cooked up the

[24] Fourier, M., *Mém. Acad. d. Sci.*, 10:81, 1831.
[25] Lefort, *Arch. gén. de méd.*, 15:140, 1827.

story to have vengeance on him, and he added that, if he had not grudged the waste of time, he would have taken the case into court.

His findings regarding cerebrospinal fluid were turned to account in connection with the edition of Bichat's "Treatise on Membranes" which he brought out in 1827 at the invitation of the publisher. He thought that it was a good moment to correct Bichat's account of the arachnoid membrane because of its relationship with the cerebrospinal fluid. Two isolated foot-notes are of particular interest. In one Magendie called attention to Bichat's distrust of the microscope, a distrust which strikes a modern reader as being curious in the case of an investigator who has been regarded as one of the founders of modern histology. Bichat had said that the microscope was "a kind of agent from which physiology and anatomy never appear to me to derive much help." Magendie retorted:

"If a prudent and careful person studies the mechanism of the microscope and applies the instrument to the study of organs, he will obtain the most satisfactory results. It is easy, but not very wise, to condemn something one knows little or nothing about; it is a subterfuge of lazy vanity."

Some amends for these strictures and for the numerous intimations of errors and inexactitudes were made when Magendie spoke of the great candor which not only caused Bichat to include in his observations particulars at variance with his theory, but which also led him to make generous acknowledgment of his debt to Pinel. Magendie said:

"It is a pleasure to see a young man, full of vigor and talent, rendering frank homage to a modest scientist who has preceded him in his investigations and opened new paths for them; different enough from those who, to make a little noise in the world, do not shrink from poisoning the old age of the ven-

erable man whose kindness has brought them out of the ob-
scurity to which their inborn mediocrity condemned them."

By 1827 Magendie had had considerable experience of the
rivalry that may arise between scientists whose fields of
investigation overlap, although the references which he
makes here to venerability and mediocrity do not seem particularly applicable to the case of his own differences with
Bell and Flourens.[26]

Flourens was still at work on the brain. He proceeded
with more plan than Magendie, who turned from one thing
to another as the spirit moved him, or, more precisely, as
his own recent experiments and those of other people suggested new ones to his restless mind. Flourens had tried to
come to some conclusion as to the function of each of the
main divisions of the central nervous system, viz, that of
the cerebrum was thinking, that of the cerebellum equilib-
rium and coordination, that of the medulla respiration, that
of the spinal cord relation and motion.[27] In 1828, on the
occasion of the public session of the Academy of Sciences,
held in June of each year, Magendie read an essay "Concerning the Brain." [28] In spite of its title, it had no bearing
on Flourens' investigations of function, but was concerned
almost altogether with cerebrospinal fluid. The paper is of
importance because in it Magendie established the path of
communication of this fluid through an opening between
the fourth ventricle of the brain and the subarachnoid space
on the underside of the cerebellum at the tip of the calamus
scriptorius of the medulla. To show the exact relationship
of the channels along which the fluid passed he made fine

[26] The perennial character of scientific rivalry in France has been excellently
   rendered by Georges Duhamel in *Cécile Pasquier* (tr. by B. de Holthoir,
   1940), one of the novels of the Pasquier series.
[27] Flourens, M., *Mém. Acad. de Sc.*, 9:478, 1830.
[28] "Mémoire physiologique sur le cerveau," published as a separate pamphlet
   and reprinted, *J. de physiol. expér. et path.*, 8:211, 1828.

wax models of the cavities of the brain and presented them to the Academy. Although the modern tendency in anatomical nomenclature is to avoid naming a structure after its discoverer and to use a Latin name to designate position or appearance, this opening is still known as "Magendie's foramen" (apertura medialis ventriculi quarti).

Had the paper not gone beyond the announcement of this discovery, all would have been well; but Magendie laid himself open to criticism when he expressed approval of the practice of the ancients in using architectural terms for the different parts of the cerebrospinal system, e.g., the aqueduct of Sylvius, and himself compared the course followed by the cerebrospinal fluid to a tunnel under the Thames, going so far as to say that he had discovered the probable use of the pineal gland, which he looked upon as a "plug destined to open and shut the aqueduct." Furthermore, he had noted at autopsies that idiots had a great deal of fluid in the cavities of their brains and normal persons comparatively little. In particular, he reported the case of an old female singer at the Salpetrière who had degenerated into idiocy and whose brain yielded large quantities of fluid. The temptation to assume the relation of cause and effect was too much for him, and he even warned those who took pride in their high foreheads to humble themselves and beware lest this characteristic should indicate too great a proportion of liquid in their brain cavities. To show how the presence or absence of cerebrospinal fluid can affect the temperament, he cited his experiments on an old fox which was ordinarily extremely vicious. As soon as a large quantity of cerebrospinal fluid had been withdrawn, it lay down and remained gentle until the next day when the fluid had collected again, and it once more became vicious and tried to bite and to escape.

This paper gave Magendie's critics an excellent opportunity to point out his weaknesses. As usual, where accurate observation was concerned he was right, for Magendie's foramen exists and the cerebrospinal fluid does circulate, although not in the direction which he described; but he was guilty here, as in other cases, of great rashness in deduction, and was led into manifest absurdity in his attempt to ascribe to the pineal gland a more practical function than that which Descartes had assigned to it in making it the seat of the soul. His conclusions with regard to a connection between idiocy and quantity of cerebrospinal fluid were also made from insufficient data. The paper did not meet in France with the scathing comment to which it was subjected abroad. In England [29] and in America [30] his prestige was greatly damaged by the criticisms made at this time, and the publication of this memoir marks the point at which his reputation as a physiologist in those countries definitely began to wane.

The *Lancet* headed its review, "Magendie as a Physiologist!" It went on to say that although it did not wish to deny that Magendie had some merit as a physiologist, that merit had been greatly exaggerated. Forgetting the stand which it had taken when his name had been brought before the House of Commons four years before, it now decided that the charges of cruelty brought against him had been well founded. In regard to the paper on the brain it made use of such expressions as "superficiality," "premature conclusions," "extravagant speculation," "want of anatomical knowledge," "carelessness" and "ill-founded self-confidence." It even overreached itself by making the claim that "Magendie's foramen" was already well-known as "Bichat's fissure."

The American reviewer was even harsher. He said:

"Magendie advanced in his experimental career with a rapidity and success which gradually detached him from the

[29] *London Med. Gaz.,* 2:552, 1828; *Lancet,* 9:71, 1828.
[30] Godman, J. D., *Am. J. Med. Sci.,* 3:157, 1828.

temperate course of induction, and finally led to the extravagant views which we find him indulging in. His first decided indication of the vain idolatry of his own fancy was the experiments he made in London on the fifth pair of nerves; there, in opposition to analogy, experience and demonstration, he inferred from entirely inadequate data that the fifth pair was the exclusive organ of sensation, and that the olfactory, optic, etc., were entirely misnamed and misunderstood. Since that period we have regarded him as lost to the sober realities of science, and have received his annunciation of facts with scepticism only to be removed by demonstration . . . This memoir . . . is, in all respects, the most absurd production we have been obliged to read in the discharge of our professional duty. Such writings, in general, are treated by this journal with the neglectful silence their insignificance merits. It is only in cases where the authority of a *name* might mislead the unwary, that we condescend to notice folly, which would otherwise waken no deeper feeling than pity, no stronger emotion than contempt."

This excommunicatory diatribe is worth preserving for its nonconformist rhetoric and provincial over-emphasis no less than for the modicum of justice contained in its condemnation of Magendie's incapacity for self-criticism. Old errors of judgment, which he never renounced, and which at first escaped notice because of real successes, were beginning to catch up with him.

In claiming that "Magendie's foramen" was merely "Bichat's fissure" the *Lancet* was taking the same stand as the Paris Faculty of Medicine. Even four years later the official text book of anatomy [31] still stated that Bichat had discovered the opening from the subarachnoid space into the ventricle of the brain, although it added that this had been challenged in 1830 by Dr. Martin Sainte-Ange.[32] By the time Magendie published his monograph on the cerebrospinal fluid in 1842, the controversy was cleared up and

[31] Cloquet, H., *Traité de l'anatomie descriptive*, 1831.
[32] Sainte-Ange, M., *J. hebdom. de méd.*, Jan. 23, 1830.

Bichat was "victoriously refuted." Bichat's supposed opening was farther forward than Magendie's and was entirely an artifact. Bichat's directions for finding his opening are to pass a probe under the brain and direct it upward, whereupon the probe will pass through the opening. There is no opening whatever at this point, but a thin spot in the membrane, and Bichat's fissure was the hole torn by his own probe. Magendie's foramen, the median one, is not always present in the human brain, but it is absent in only two per cent of the cases examined. It has since been found that there are two other openings in this same region, which are, however, located at the sides, so that Magendie's conten-tion that an opening serves for the circulation of cerebrospinal fluid between the subarachnoid space and the fourth ventricle in this neighborhood is true even for the residual two per cent of cases.[33]

Another criticism of Magendie's idea of the circulation of the cerebrospinal fluid arising from the persistent influence of Bichat's work was that the direction of flow was contrary to that demanded by the latter's law for serous membranes, which stated that fluid secreted by a hollow organ is always secreted toward the interior of the organ, not toward its exterior. When the famous German physiologist, Tiedemann, came to Paris, he visited Magendie, who offered to demonstrate to him that cerebrospinal fluid passed in the subarachnoid space through the foramen into the ventricles of the brain. Tiedemann at once exclaimed that that was impossible, since it was contrary to Bichat's law. Magendie replied that, impossible or not, he would demonstrate it to Tiedemann's satisfaction. He did so, and his account of the process was accepted in Germany on Tiedemann's authority.[34]

Magendie's view that cerebrospinal fluid was a secretion

[33] Cruveilhier, J., *Traité d'anatomie descriptive*, 1877, v. 3, p. 360.
[34] Bernard, C., *Pathologie expérimentale*, 1880, p. 515.

from the arachnoid membrane and that the direction of flow is from the subarachnoid spaces to the ventricles has only recently been seriously questioned. We now believe that there is sufficient evidence to warrant the view that the fluid comes from the villous projections of the vascular choroid plexuses in the ventricles of the brain, and that it then passes through the foramen of Magendie and the lateral openings of Luschka into the subarachnoid space. Circulation is slow, but secretion is continuous, and the fluid is eventually absorbed, mainly, it is thought, by the arachnoid villi, which are specialized portions of the epithelial membrane lining the subarachnoid space. This is just the reverse of Magendie's picture of the formation and circulation of cerebrospinal fluid, but we do owe to him the demonstration of the foramen named for him and the first clear description of the nature of the fluid.[35]

Later in the year 1828, Flourens presented before the Academy of Sciences two articles on the semicircular canals. In his customary manner he indicated the continuity of this work with what he had already done by referring to his important memoir of 1824. He now found that if he cut the different semicircular canals in birds they exhibited forced movements of the head. When he tried a similar experiment on rabbits he found that they rolled over and over. He claimed that these movements were different from those obtained after lesions of the cerebellum (which he referred to lack of coordination), ignoring Magendie's earlier demonstration of rotational movements after cutting a peduncle of the cerebellum. The similarity of the behaviour of Flourens' rabbits to that of Magendie's animals in the earlier experiment was pointed out by Cuvier and Duméril, who had been appointed to report to the Academy on Flourens' paper, and this similarity suggested to them that there must

[35] Best, C. H., and Taylor, N. B., *The Physiological Basis of Medical Practice,* 1939, p. 1512.

be an intimate relation between the peduncles of the cerebellum and the eighth nerve (one branch of which con-
veys sensation to the brain from the semicircular canals).
They therefore urged Flourens to continue the work which,
they said, had been so well begun by Bell, Magendie and
Flourens himself.[36]

[36] Cuvier, G., and Duméril, A.-M.-C., *Procès-verb. Acad. d. Sc.*, 9:148,
1828.

10

MARRIAGE, APPOINTMENT TO PROFESSORSHIP AT THE COLLÈGE DE FRANCE, THE CHOLERA EPIDEMIC
1830-1832

*"Je n'ai jamais rien vu qui pût me faire soupçonner
que le choléra fût contagieux."* [1]

HARSH criticism and petty annoyances could not dampen Magendie's spirit, and the year 1830, moreover, brought changes which were propitious to his fortunes. To begin with, he married in April of that year. For ten years he had been living in bachelor quarters at No. 30, rue de Seine. Since his residence was located in the parish of Saint-Germain-des-Près, his banns were read in this church, and the civil marriage took place at the mairie of the sixth arrondissement, in which the rue de Seine was situated, on April 10. The groom was described simply as François Magendie, doctor of medicine; the bride had borne the maiden name of Henriette Bastienne de Puisaye, was 28 years old, a "woman of property" (if one may translate the French "propriétaire" in a Galsworthian manner), the widow of Nicolas Théodore Audinot and in residence at 17, rue de Vendôme, a rather more aristocratic neighborhood than the rue de Seine on the Left Bank. Five days after the civil cere-

[1] *Phén. phys.*, 1842, v. 1, p. 66.

mony the religious one was performed in the church of Sainte Elizabeth, on the other side of Paris, near the Temple. According to the record there, the witnesses included Magendie's younger brother, Jean-Jacques, now a naval captain, officer of the Legion of Honor and chevalier of the royal military Order of St. Louis; Amedée François Lancaux, professor at the Royal College of Music; Jean-Baptiste d'Heuneville-Fanction, officer of the Legion of Honor and Intendant du Fête de la Cour; and Pierre Louis Anselme Dufaisey, evidently like most of the others a friend of the bride, since he lived on the same street as she. Magendie seems to have been supported only by his brother. La Marquise du Pelleport inscribed her name, almost illegibly, in the lower left hand corner of the page in the Register.

On July 25, 1830, when he signed the famous ordinances, Charles X took a step too far in the direction of autocracy for a France which had by no means forgotten the days of 1793, and he was obliged to flee the country. The medical students of Paris played an active part in the Revolution of July; they fought during the "three days" at the barricades, occupied the Hôtel-de-Ville, and were, in fact, at the centre of the insurrection.[2] Liberalism triumphed and the citizen-king, Louis-Philippe was placed on the throne of France. Mgr. Frayssinous was deposed from his office as Grand-Maître of the University, and the medical students, eighteen hundred strong, headed by their new dean, Antoine Dubois, marched through the streets to the Palais-Royal to thank the new king in person.

The effect of this political upheaval on Magendie's career is very neatly shown by the change of front exhibited in two articles published in a new journal, La Gazette Médicale de Paris, the first issue of which appeared early in 1830. The editors of this journal proposed to devote several columns of each number to criticism, favorable or adverse as the

[2] Triaire, P., Récamier et ses contemporains, 1899.

case might be, of leading French physicians, and they began
with Magendie as one of the most outstanding. In the first
article in the issue of June 12 it was stated that Magendie's
chief aim was the introduction of chemistry into medicine,
and that in this respect he reverted to the philosophy of the
eighteenth century and was out of touch with that of the
nineteenth. Although the writer did not mention Rousseau's name, it was Rousseau's principle, "study nature,
imitate nature," which Magendie was charged with foster-
ing. He was accused of believing that physiology was a
mere frame (a very strange one from the standpoint of
theology) to be filled with scientific expressions, experiment, observations and the like. It was claimed that he
argued in a vicious circle, for if vital laws were regarded as
being different from or opposed to physical laws it was
only because legitimate observation of phenomena had led
to this conclusion. If observation had induced Magendie to
take his stand against vital laws, observation had also induced his opponents to take theirs for them. The real bone
of contention was whether vivisection could after all shed
any light on normal processes in the living body. Magendie
claimed that this was the only way to gain knowledge of
vital processes; the editors of the journal had no hesitation
in saying that Magendie's experiments "had plunged us into
fearful darkness and augmented confusion." Their admiration for his skill, ardor and inventive genius was not going
to prevent their giving a thorough and detailed analysis of
his scientific work.[3]

It would appear that the question of whether living
organisms obey other laws than those which govern physical and chemical reactions was acute at this period. Cuvier
stated in 1831 that the medical schools especially held to
the doctrine that "the primordial causes of phenomena of
organization are of quite another nature from those which

[3] *Gaz. méd. de Paris,* 1:212, 1830.

preside over the inorganic world." There was still firm adherence to Bichat's idea that the vital principle in living
things actually resists the forces governing brute matter, and
Magendie had stated his opposition to this view once more
in his recent annotated edition of the "Treatise on Membranes." He was, as we have seen, in other ways at outs
with the orthodoxy of the medical profession, and this attack came from the camp of the orthodox, equally of medicine and religion.

However, in its September issue, the *Gazette*, apparently
bowing to the political changes of the past two months,
made a volte-face, and its second and final article on
Magendie was a brief one. While declining to withdraw
anything which they had already said in their first article,
the editors announced a change of policy. They were now
definitely for Magendie, but no further analysis of his work
would be undertaken in justification of their opinion of him
as a physiologist. There followed a passage in which each
slap was accompanied by a caress:

"No doubt Magendie is often wrong, even oftener than others
are, for his writing and his investigations cover a great deal of
ground . . . Although there may be objections to his theories,
this does not destroy the public esteem accorded him. . . . In
spite of false systematic views, this physician is the most skilful
physiologist of the age."

The article concluded with the statement that grave wrong
had been done Magendie in 1827 when he was denied the
chair of medicine at the Collège de France, and that he
ought to have it now, for he was exactly the man for the
post.[4]

All holders of public office were compelled after the July
Revolution to take the oath of allegiance to the new government: "Je jure fidelité au roi des Français, obéissance à la

[4] *Gaz. méd. de Paris*, 1:326, 1830.

charte constitutionelle et aux lois du royaume." For many
years an oath of allegiance had not been required of University professors, but before the month of August was out
Louis-Philippe had the form sent to the President of the
Collège de France for its professors to sign. Fifteen days of
grace were allowed, and all who refused to sign at the end
of that period were automatically to be dismissed. Récamier
refused to attend the meeting for signing the oath, which
had been delayed until the last day of September, sending
a note to explain his reasons for absenting himself. The note
was forwarded to the new Minister of Public Instruction,
Montalivet, who on the last day of the year announced that
the dismissal of Récamier had received the royal signature
ten days before. It was requested that there should be
presented the name of a candidate for the chair of medicine
at the Collège de France, now declared vacant.

Even before the signing of the decree, which everyone
knew would mean the bestowal of the chair upon Magendie,
advancement had already come to him at the beginning of
December in the form of an appointment as physician at
the Hôtel-Dieu, the oldest and most famous of the Paris
hospitals, and the scene of Bichat's triumphs. He was placed
in charge of the ward Sainte-Monique, which contained 74
beds for women patients. This appointment placed him on
an equal footing with the more orthodox members of the
medical profession, who had shown disapproval of his attempts to make medicine more scientific, and at the same
time it brought him into direct relation with the official
curriculum for medical students who would in future attend
his clinical lectures at the Hôtel-Dieu. Among his colleagues
there were Dupuytren, now surgeon-in-chief, and Récamier,
physician-in-chief. Dupuytren enjoyed the reputation of being the most famous living French surgeon. He had been a
great favorite of both Louis XVIII and Charles X and had

been made a baron under the Restoration.[5] Both he and
Récamier were hostile to Louis-Philippe, who was in their
eyes a mere usurper.

As soon as Récamier's dismissal was made official the
Academy of Sciences voted, on January 31, 1831, that
Magendie should have the chair of medicine at the Collège
de France; the section on medicine and surgery first pro-
posing that he be the sole candidate, and then the Academy
as a whole casting 46 out of 47 ballots for him. In March the
Collège de France was informed of his appointment and
on April 4 came the certificate signed by Louis-Philippe
giving Magendie the chair of "Récamier, démissionaire."

Récamier in his lectures at the Collège de France had
been little more than an expositor of Bichat, the close friend
of his youth. Bichat's extraordinary influence on French
medicine is shown in the way in which his disciples won
renown for themselves by following up work which their
young master had begun. Roux and Béclard continued his
anatomical studies; Roux, his favorite, prepared the postu-
mous fifth volume of his Descriptive Anatomy, and Béclard
brought out a new edition of the General Anatomy with
additions of his own, and furnished the manuscript from
which Bichat's last course of lectures was published as the
Pathological Anatomy. Richerand took over his physiology,
and we have already seen that Magendie, while rejecting
the doctrine of vital properties, was stimulated to much of
his early work by his desire to examine the details of
Bichat's theory in the light of experiment. Récamier was
the inheritor of the materia medica. He built his whole
edifice of medical doctrine on Bichat's interpretation of

[5] When Charles X fled to Holyrood, Dupuytren wrote to the exile that he
possessed three million francs; he offered one to Charles, one was destined
for his daughter's *dot* and the third was to be reserved for his own old
age. The gesture might have been made more magnificent and it was
eminently safe, for when Dupuytren died five years later, his fortune
amounted to five millions.

vitalism with only a superficial alteration of the descriptive terms. For *organic* and *animal* life Récamier substituted *common* and *special* functions, for *organic sensitivity* he used *latent and confused sensation,* for *animal sensitivity* he put *evident and distinct sensation,* etc. Following Bichat, he held that the proportions of "vital force" and physical causes determined a state of health or disease, and he revived the mediaeval doctrine of the four humors, assigning to each temperament, sanguine, choleric, melancholic and phlegmatic, a characteristic derangement of function according to the preponderance or lack of "vital force." His whole conception of fevers was merely an elaboration of that of Bichat. Such an exposition of medical theory was, of course, intolerable to Magendie, and it is not difficult to understand the verdict of Magendie's pupil, Claude Bernard, that Récamier's teaching left no trace on the Collège de France, that he was not scientifically minded, but allowed his imagination to run away with him, building up unstable theories with no foundation. Bernard's words were a curt dismissal: "His presence at the Collège de France was only an accident, and lasted but a short time." [6]

Magendie conducted his new courses at the Collège de France according to the methods which he had already used with great success in his private courses in physiology. He had recourse to a discussion centering about some clinical observation, often with the pathological specimen displayed before his audience, or a description of some physiological process illustrated by demonstrations on living animals. In experiments of this sort the unexpected sometimes happened, or even the reverse of what he had ventured to predict, but this did not disconcert the professor, who would join in the general laughter and take advantage of the incident to tell a story from his rich repertoire.[7] Digressions

[6] Bernard, C., *Diabète*, 1877, p. 29.
[7] *Phén. phys.*, 1842, v. 1, p. 51.

Table in the U. S. Army Medical Museum, (neg. no. 49595) Washington, D. C., bearing the following inscription:

"This Operating Table was made for François Magendie in 1831. It was used by Magendie in the Physiological Laboratory of the College of France from 1831 to 1854; and by Claude Bernard from 1854 to 1861. In 1861 it was given by Claude Bernard to Austin Flint, Jr. Upon this Table Magendie frequently demonstrated the Properties of the Roots of the Spinal Nerves, discovered by him in 1822, and Bernard discovered The Functions of the Spinal Accessory Nerves, in 1844, The Glycogenic Functions of the Liver, in 1848, The Digestion of Fats by the Pancreas, in 1848, The Influence of the Sympathetic Nerves upon Animal Heat, in 1851. Feb. 10th 1878."

were a matter of course, and there was not much system in his selection of topics. More often then not, he began his lecture with fresh pathological material brought from the Hôtel-Dieu by his assistant, Dr. Constantin James, or, later, Claude Bernard. He had to obtain special permission to carry away these pathological specimens from the Hôtel-Dieu across the Seine to the Collège de France and the document giving him this permission is still extant. It is dated May 25, 1831, and states that "pieces of anatomy" shall be obtained only on written demand, and that unless absolutely necessary no pieces demanded by the family of the deceased shall be available for study, and, finally, that the holder of the permit must not abuse his privileges. It must be remembered that the lectures at the Collège de France were not part of the official curriculum for medical students (who might nevertheless attend them voluntarily). Magendie was therefore not restricted in his choice of subject matter by responsibility for the systematic instruction of these students in either medicine or physiology. With his appointment at the Collège de France came the end not only of his private courses, but also of his *Journal*, the recent issues of which had contained almost no articles by the editor himself.

Magendie, at this period, devoted very little time to original experimental work. He seems to have been completely occupied with his duties as a physician and as professor, and he left to others the final solution of problems on which he had worked with such enthusiasm a decade earlier. He was particularly disgusted with the position which Bell continued to hold in the matter of priority of discovery of the different functions of the two roots of the spinal nerves. Bell's book, "An Exposition of the Natural System of Nerves" (1824), in which he had set forth his claims two years after Magendie's announcement of his discovery in 1822, had had a widespread influence. It had been translated into French, and in Germany the proposition that the dorsal roots are for sensation and the ventral roots for motion was known as "Bell's Theorem" or "das Bellsche Gesetz." Between 1822 and 1831 many workers tried without success to "prove" the absolute validity of this "law," using, as had Bell and Magendie, mammals as experimental material. Among them was Johannes Müller, who was soon to gain the reputation of being the greatest teacher of physiology of his generation. In April, 1831, he thought of trying experiments on a frog instead of a mammal and was so successful that, as it has been picturesquely put, he "achieved immortality on a frog's back." [8] For the next fifty years the frog became the physiologist's standby in all his experimentation, and Claude Bernard described this animal as "the Job of physiology." Müller's report appeared under the title, "Confirmation of Bell's Theorem," [9] but it is not quite clear whether the encomium was meant for himself or Bell when he stated, not only in his original article, but also in his famous Handbook of Physiology (1834), which spread the doctrine throughout the scientific world, that Bell's Law was one of the greatest discoveries in the realm of physiology. He credited Bell with the idea, but stated that Magendie was the first to put it to the test of physiological experiment.[10]

In the autumn following his successful experiments on the spinal nerve roots of the frog, Müller, accompanied by his brilliant young friend, Jacob Henle, came to Paris, and on September 13, in their hotel room near the Jardin des Plantes, they gave a demonstration before Alexander von Humboldt, Dutrochet and several others among Magendie's friends. Both the place for the demonstration and the

[8] Robinson, V., *The Life of Jacob Henle*, 1921.
[9] Müller, J., Bestätigung des Bellschen Lehrsatzes, *Frorieps Notizen*, No. 646, 647, May, 1831. Cf. *Ann. d. Sc. Nat.*, Ser. 1, 23:95, 1831.
[10] Müller, J., *Handbuch*, 1835, p. 649.

absence of Magendie on such an occasion seem odd. It is just possible that it was feared that he might not at the moment get on too well with Müller. Although there is no record of the two men having met in 1831, Müller on his next visit to Paris in 1838 recorded in a note-book that he had called on Magendie.

Towards the close of his first year at the Collège de France, Magendie made a second visit to England and again got his name into the English newspapers. In 1830 cholera morbus had broken out in Russia. Although pressure was brought to bear on the Paris Academy of Sciences to do something in the face of the terrific ravages of the disease, it was felt that in view of the attitude of the Russian ambassador, the Academy could take no initiative in this matter. The Tsar, Nicholas I, a firm believer in the divine right of kings, would not recognize Louis-Philippe, and had given orders to the ambassador at Paris to refuse passports to French subjects who wished to enter Russia.[11] The Paris Academy, however, decided to ask for information concerning the epidemic from the St. Petersburg Academy, requesting at the same time that a certain number of French physicians might be sent to act with a committee of Russian physicians. They did this in the hope that the Russian government would see in the proposed visit nothing more than the philanthropic mission it was intended to be. A committee consisting of Portal, Duméril, Magendie, Dupuytren and Serres was appointed, February 28, 1831, to deal with all matters pertaining to the question of cholera. The principal point upon which information was sought was whether the disease was contagious; the majority of the medical section of the Academy, including Magendie, thought that it was not. The Academy of Medicine also appointed a committee to report on cholera, upon which, needless to say, Magendie was not invited to serve. Just after the appointment of the

[11] Lucas-Dubreton, J., Louis-Phillippe, 1938, p. 173.

former committee Magendie received a letter from Moscow saying that the epidemic was over.

In late October cholera again appeared, this time much nearer home. The seaport town of Sunderland, near Newcastle, on the north east coast of England (*not* Ireland, as Claude Bernard's uncertain geography has led all French authors after him to state) reported several undoubted cases of cholera morbus. By the first week in December there had been a hundred deaths, chiefly in the poorer districts. "Nothing can exceed such scenes where death, in its most terrific form, unites with squalid poverty," wrote the correspondent of the London *Times*. The epidemic spread to Newcastle and surrounding towns,[12] and the death toll rose rapidly. Londoners opened their morning papers to read such gruesome accounts as the following:

"A long trench, capable of holding twelve coffins, two abreast, had been dug, and while the clergyman was reading the service this evening over the first two occupants, four other corpses arrived. Six coffins were deposited in the trench before six minutes had expired."

On November 21 Magendie had asked the Academy of Sciences to send him to Sunderland to obtain firsthand information with regard to the epidemic. Flourens reports his dramatic appeal:

"I am a physician, gentlemen; my profession summons me to the threshold of the disease. I leave for Sunderland; may I be able, by studying cholera where it has appeared, to bring you back some light."

12 Also to Edinburgh and Glasgow. From Glasgow it was carried to Belfast and Dublin. This was the great period of Irish emigration to the United States of America, so that the disease reached this country in 1832 and depopulated various communities in the new world to the estimated extent of $\frac{1}{20}$ to $\frac{1}{3}$ of their inhabitants. *Vide* Chambers, J. S., *The Conquest of Cholera*, 1938.

The Academy acquiesced. Magendie went at once to London to make the necessary arrangements for a visit to the stricken seaport. He was accompanied by Dr. Natalis Guillot, who was later to become a distinguished member of the Paris Faculty of Medicine. They arrived in Sunderland on December 2 and the next day Magendie wrote to the President of the Academy of Sciences:

'Here I am at last in Sunderland: in spite of all my efforts to arrive quickly, and in spite of the admirable manner in which one travels in this country, I had to stay in London nearly three days, in order to get in touch with the council of health and some members of the government; I received everywhere the most cordial welcome and everyone laid himself out to facilitate my mission.

'The noise that the cholera has made in England does not follow the law of the propagation of sound; its intensity is, on the contrary, directly proportional to the distance. In London everyone spoke to me of the cholera, asking me whether or not it was contagious, what means there were to insure not getting it, etc., etc. They regarded me as a brave man, since I was going to face so great a danger, and I was myself not without some internal satisfaction in listening to these words of praise. But everything was changed as soon as I began the journey. I had covered only a hundred miles when I no longer heard exclamations over my journey, when I had gone two hundred miles I passed as the merest traveller; and at last at Sunderland, where I have been since yesterday morning, no one remarked upon my arrival; I have received not a single compliment, regarding the object of my visit. I except always the doctors, who gave me the most fraternal reception.

'It is, however, not a case here of a false alarm. Seeing the evil close at hand does nothing to combat the idea of it which we had made for ourselves. Far from that, it would be impossible, I think, for the most lively imagination to create an adequate picture of it. Perhaps I shall transmit my impression to you by saying that a person in the best of health, when he is smitten by the cholera, is in an instant transformed into a corpse! There is the same state of the eyes, the same aspect of the face; the same coldness of the limbs; the same color of the skin, etc. Were not the intelligence left, so to speak, intact, were there not a remnant of the voice, even though almost imperceptible, one would proceed to burial at the actual moment of the attack. Such is the cholera which is here called Asiatic, spasmodic or malign; it does not appear to be modified by any treatment. In a few hours all is over; and nearly always the issue is fatal; and how terrible the disease is at its inception, and with what destructive power it strikes the organs is proven by the cadaver being exactly like the patient: the circumstance of death has added nothing to what existed before. To put it all in one word, the disease which is under my eyes in an instant *cadaverizes* the person whom it attacks.

"Happily, the cholera does not always have this frightening intensity. In two-thirds of the patients, I am told, it is much less severe, but as I have not yet seen these privileged cases, I shall not speak of them today.

"Has the disease been imported, or did it arise in this unhealthy country, teeming with poor and ill-housed inhabitants? Is it contagious or not? There are so many questions which disturb them but little here. The capital point is that no quarantine has been imposed, and everyone is of the opinion that if the English government had ordered isolation by a cordon of troops, the population of Sunderland, which is about 40,000, instead of being tranquil as it is today, appearing not to give, or actually not giving any attention to the disease, would soon be troubled and in despair, and that there would follow events even graver than the disease itself. I add that the propagation of the disease, supposing it to be of a nature to propagate itself, would not be retarded; perhaps it would be accelerated.

"People are satisfied with distributing food to the poor of the city; they give them flannel to cover their bodies; they exhort them to cleanliness; these are the only sanitary measures.

"There, my dear sir, is what I can tell you positively today with respect to the cholera in Sunderland. If you think it proper to communicate my letter to the Academy, add, if you please, that everywhere I dine I receive a toast to the Institut de France.

"I hope not to make a long stay in this sad country where the cold, the fog, the smoke and the cholera are a menace to the inhabitants and consequently to the curious traveller, like your affectionate

Magendie." [13]

About December 17 he was back in London. When asked there what he thought of cholera, he is said to have replied epigrammatically: "I think that it is a disease which begins where others end, with death." On his way back from London to Paris he stopped at Boulogne, and was entertained in honor of his safe return to the shores of France. He was told that the fear of the spread of cholera was so great that a foreign boat which had attempted to come into port without submitting to the customary sanitary measures had been fired upon. Magendie said: "Gentlemen, if anyone could bring you cholera, it is I; for I have come from places where it is rampant. I am even wearing the same clothes I wore while visiting the sick. Therefore all of us here are due for the quarantine." For a moment there was consternation, then, since it was to the interest of each one present to prevent this being known, the company swore to secrecy. They cautioned Magendie to keep silence, for if rumors began to circulate in the city his person, they assured him, would not be safe.[14]

He arrived in Paris in time for Christmas, and the next day made his verbal report before the Academy. Notes of this speech reached London in time for the issue of the *Times* for December 30. Magendie had been struck by the horrible state of poverty of the lower orders in Sunderland, and by the fact that the cholera was confined to the lower town, where its 17,000 inhabitants and 14,000 paupers were

[13] *Gaz. méd. de Paris*, 2:444, 1832.
[14] *Phén. phys.*, 1842, v. 1, p. 75.

crowded into rooms less than ten feet square in houses
lining alleys only four feet wide, while in the better houses
on the heights there was not a single case. He said that he
had never seen such "a picture of wretchedness, filth and
poverty, which, accustomed as he had been from his professional duties to visit the abodes of human misery, he
could not have believed to exist in the present age in any
part of civilized Europe." He did not scruple to call attention to the fearfully crowded conditions of the houses of
the poor, the inmates of which were subject to yearly epidemics of typhus, scarlet fever and the like. He spoke very
feelingly of not having been allowed to perform a single
autopsy on a cholera victim. He said that he approved of
the British government having placed but few restrictions
by way of quarantine on boats in the port, as he thought
that the restrictive measures taken on the continent only
tended to augment the fatal effect of the disease. This aspect
of his speech was attacked by M. Moreau-Jones who had
consistently maintained that cholera was contagious and that
quarantine should be rigidly enforced. Magendie replied,
and when M. Moreau-Jones rose to speak again the Academy unanimously passed to the order of the day and he was
not allowed to make any further protest. There could be no
doubt that Magendie was the hero of the hour among his
confrères in the Academy of Sciences.

In England, on the contrary, his outspoken references to
the squalid conditions of Sunderland were not altogether
welcome. A medical journal said that he "drew a picture
of that unhappy town, which, however satisfactory and con-
soling for the learned Academicians, would be anything but
ornamental to our pages, or agreeable to our readers." [15]
Moreover, he was rebuked in the *Times* for his conclusion
that the quarantine of vessels was slack on the ground that
he "did not visit any one of the quarantine establishments

[15] *London Med. Gaz.*, 9:565, 1832.

during his stay in this country, at all of which the strictest precautionary measures are enforced."

Reports of his attitude aroused so much feeling that Magendie visited the English ambassador in Paris to disclaim any desire to foment prejudice against British commerce. The note which he wrote on the day after this visit was printed in *Le Moniteur Universel*, the official French journal, on January 20. It was as follows:

"To the English ambassador at Paris,

"Your excellency,

"I had the honor of telling you yesterday, and I repeat to you today in writing that in the verbal and abridged report which I made before my colleagues of the Academy of Sciences (in private sitting) of my journey to Sunderland, I spoke solely of things which I had seen, and since I devoted so brief a time to the study of quarantines, only those of the city of Sunderland could be in question.

"I authorize you, sir, to use this declaration in any way you see fit.

"I have the honor to be, etc.

Magendie

"January 18, 1832.   Academy of Sciences."

Two months later, under the most dramatic circumstances, cholera appeared in Paris. On March 29, in the midst of the mi-carême revels, the disease struck the inhabitants of the crowded quarters of the *Cité,* and masked dancers were carried in a moribund state direct from the balls to the nearby Hôtel-Dieu. The slums of Paris, at this time were quite as regrettable as those of Sunderland. Some streets were only six feet wide, yet the houses rose to a height of five stories. The plumbing followed the stairways and from leaks in the pipes the sewage trickled down the steps. The worst buildings housed rag-pickers and street-sweepers who were sheltered for five sous a night, whole families of them crowded into corners, surrounded by their gleanings of foul

rags and bones, unmindful of horrifying odors. To expedite
the removal of dead bodies of cholera victims and of offal
from the streets, the municipal government sent out a fleet
of small carts, and this aroused the rag-pickers to pitched
battle with the cry that the government was depriving them
of their livelihood. Their cause was taken up by *La Tribune*
which, furthermore, in order to inflame the republicans and
revolutionists against the new government, accused the
President of the King's Council, Perier, of conspiring with
the physicians and the priests in an attempt to decimate the
population of Paris by poisoning them in the hospitals.
Magendie reported having had to make his way up the
steps of the Hôtel-Dieu through infuriated crowds in the
midst of brandished fists and cries of "Death to the poison-
ers!" These events had a strange sequel. On April 1 Louis-
Philippe accompanied by Perier went to the Hôtel-Dieu to
visit the cholera patients. The opposition immediately proclaimed that the object of this visit was to gloat over the
miseries of the people. Five days later, Perior was stricken
with cholera and died.

The epidemic had not been foreseen and there were no
facilities to cope with the situation. The nursing sisters
were not only frightened but inadequately trained. There
was supposed to be no lack of medical students to help out,
since Orfila was commissioned to bring 120 each day to the
Hôtel-Dieu, but they preferred to remain outside in the
open space before Nôtre-Dame to watch the unloading of
stretchers. Magendie's staff was reduced to himself, his internes and special disciples, and a few aides who were
personally devoted to him. He gave the highest praise to
his head nurse, Mère Saint-Paul. This small squad of the
faithful watched the patients, turn and turn about. Unlike
other physicians who made a single daily visit, Magendie
passed entire days and nights at the hospital, walking up
and down his wards for hours on end. He could not trust

the hospital attendants, whom he accused of being more bent on robbing the patients than on trying to help them, and the "women of the town" who came into the ward on the pretext of caring for the sick were also more accomplished as thieves than nurses and extracted from the pockets of the patients what little remained in them. Alongside his disapproval of the attendants' behaviour Magendie put the fact that they were paid only ten francs a month and were badly fed besides.[16] His own energies were entirely devoted to the poor, for he said, "The wealthy will not lack physicians," an expression which Aléxandre Dumas puts into the mouth of his doctor in "Mémoires d'un médicin." There could no longer be any complaint on his part of an insufficient number of cases to study. Moreover, he could perform as many autopsies as he could find time for, since in less than a month there were more than 10,000 deaths, chiefly in the quarters near the Hôtel-Dieu.

He studied his patients' symptoms with care and reported his findings to the auditors of his course at the Collège de France, for he made cholera the subject of his first series of lectures in his new chair. There are several references to his experiences with cholera in later lectures also, but aside from more detailed descriptions of symptoms and his mode of treatment, little was added to what he had said in his letter from Sunderland after his first inspection of cholera cases. He did, however, put forward what he evidently regarded as a rationalization from all the observed symptoms. He said: "Cholera consists in a complete arrest of arterial circulation . . . The heart no longer beats, nevertheless the patient speaks, reasons, replies rationally to questions addressed to him, is in possession of all his senses and all his faculties." [17] He added: "Often I opened great arterial trunks; never did I find any liquid . . . I recall a fact which

16 Le choléra, 1832, pp. 198, 235.
17 Phén. phys., 1842, v. 3, pp. 114-115.

made a great impression on those who attended my clinical lectures at the Hôtel-Dieu. A doctor recently arrived from Poland where he had observed the cholera said that in that country bleeding from the temporal artery was thought to have great virtue, almost as if it were a specific cure. Immediately I took a scalpel and cut across this artery in one of my worst cases of cholera. Not a single drop of liquid fell."

Here, as upon occasion elsewhere, Magendie's observation was not carried far enough. If circulation had really stopped, the patient could not have survived more than five or six minutes. The heart was undoubtedly exceedingly feeble, for this is characteristic of the disease, but it must still have been beating. It has since been found that, as a result of dehydration of the body, due to vomiting and diarrhea, the volume of blood is brought so low that if *small* veins and arteries are cut the blood will not flow, and the pulse and heartbeat may be so feeble as to be virtually imperceptible. Whatever we may think now of Magendie's observation, for a time it was accepted literally, and Claude Bernard, in order to account for the phenomenon, evolved a theory that such patients were in a state of suspended animation comparable to the hibernating state in certain animals, in which the tissues were receiving no oxygen whatever. Magendie, having noticed that the blood was dark, actually tried to remedy the assumed lack of oxygen by making his patients swallow oxygenated water and giving them inhalations of gaseous oxygen.

His guess as to the origin of the epidemic was influenced by the age-old superstition regarding "bad air," for he proposed in the Academy of Sciences that analyses of samples of air from different parts of the city might afford a clue. The Academy evidently thought seriously of carrying out this suggestion, and at once appointed two of the most celebrated chemists of the day, Gay-Lussac and Thénard, to act with Magendie in the quest. It was undoubtedly this particular attempt to solve the mystery of the origin of cholera which influenced Bernard in a later epidemic to collaborate with Pasteur in an attempt to isolate the cholera germ by collecting air in the cholera wards of the hospitals.

The epidemic of 1832, the first of the six great cholera epidemics of the nineteenth century, was, in fact, utterly baffling to the whole medical profession. There was great difference of opinion between the English and the French both as regards contagion and treatment. One English medical journal reported sarcastically that at the Hôtel-Dieu on March 26, only four and one half days after the arrival of the first patient, the physicians of that hospital said they had "observed no circumstance which authorizes us to suspect that the disorder is contagious." [18] English medical opinion held firmly to the idea that cholera was contagious and spread in accordance with known laws of contagion. In this the English were right and the French wrong, for the route of the first epidemic, which came from India along the Caspian Sea to Tiflis, then to the Caucasus and on up the Volga to Russia, and thence to Europe, demonstrated the transportability of cholera along lines of travel.

As to treatment, within the Hôtel-Dieu itself there was considerable divergence of opinion and practice. Dupuytren bled 2-3 ounces and ordered rubbing with dry flannel, administration of a decoction of poppy heads, acetate of lead and mint infusion. Magendie prescribed his famous "punch," 1 pint of infusion of camomile, 2 ounces of alcohol, 1 ounce sugar and lemon juice to taste, and with it frictions with camphorated spirit, ammonia or turpentine, hot beds and hot sand bags. Récamier ordered cold affusion at 16 degrees,[19] then an infusion of mint, opium and ether with

18 *London Med. Gaz.*, 10:29, 1832. Cf. 11:31, 1832.
19 Récamier always prescribed cold baths after the occasion upon which he had reduced his own fever by immersion in a cold tub in the face of

mucilage. Breschet gave ammonium acetate in camomile tea, ether, canella and quinine, laudinum injections and frictions with ammonia. The most drastic treatment was the application of heated irons down each side of the spinal cord, with turpentine rubs.

Magendie's "punch" was perhaps the most discussed remedy of all, and there was a very lively difference of opinion between him and certain members of the Academy of Medicine on the use of stimulants. These polemics reached the public in the form of cartoons. In one, two couples sit at tables back to back; the first pair, with smiling faces, have a bowl of punch before them, the other two contemplate some ice with less satisfaction. Another pictures two patients in the hospital; one says to the other, "Say, number 2, how do you find M. Magendie's punch?" Number 2 replies, "I wish the cholera morbus would last a long time, and that afterwards the typhus would come along, for they say that it's the same treatment for both." [20]

Magendie claimed the greatest number of cures. In his lectures at the Collège de France in May he said: "Of 600 cholera patients admitted to the ward of Sainte-Monique at the Hôtel-Dieu, which was under my care, with the exception of 38 who died in their litters, all became warm, and in all the circulation appeared after the employment of the means already mentioned . . . In my private practice I have been fortunate enough not to lose one, even of those who had reached the very advancd stages of the disease." The *London Medical Gazette* pointed out that elsewhere in these lectures Magendie had said: "594 cholera patients were admitted into my wards and underwent my mode of treatment: 364 were cured; 208 died." There is certainly some lack of precision in this arithmetic, but if we make

consternation on the part of the physicians attending him. Carnot, P., *La clinique médicale de l'Hôtel-Dieu*, 1927.

[20] Delaunay, P., *Med. internal*, Oct., 1931.

allowance for relapses after a degree of response to the treatment, the two reports are perhaps not really contradictory, and we need not subscribe to the Gazette's biting comment: "These discrepancies are sufficient to prevent us from attaching much importance to the views of the writer." [21]

Magendie's efforts cannot be dismissed in this fashion. He had given his services unsparingly throughout the whole epidemic. His treatment was at least as good as any of the others, and he had made an attempt at analysis of the symptoms. It must be conceded that he was almost absurdly mistaken in thinking that circulation had completely ceased, but, having made up his mind that this was the difficulty to be met. he set about remedying it in the best way he knew. It was not until Koch discovered the spirillum of Asiatic cholera in 1883 that the methods of inoculation, to be initiated even later by Pasteur, could be applied to the cure of cholera. The physicians of Magendie's day could treat only the symptoms of the disease. They were powerless against its source. To alleviate the extreme dehydration of the body, due to the violent diarrhea and vomiting, the patient should be given plenty of liquids, even injections of fluid under the skin in extreme cases; he should also be kept warm, and stimulants, such as brandy, are often useful; opium and astringents help to check the diarrhea. The measures taken by the physicians at the Hôtel-Dieu, regarded as treatment of the symptoms, were excellent, and they cannot be held for more.

Flourens says that the French government rewarded Magendie's services by bestowing upon him the cross of the Legion of Honor and that Magendie remarked with satisfaction, "I believe it was well bestowed." As a matter of record, Magendie was so honored on October 9, 1829, two years before the cholera struck western Europe. Even if the

[21] *London Med. Gaz.,* 11:213, 1832.

gratitude of France was not expressed in this way, Magendie at least had the consolation of receiving a letter from Garibaldi in the name of Italy, thanking him for his kindness to a committee of physicians sent from Rome to Paris to study the disease.[22]

[22] Letter from Garibaldi, May 31, 1834.

11

PROFESSORIAL ACTIVITIES, PUBLISHED LECTURES, RECURRENT SENSITIVITY
1833-1840

"Il n'est peut-être pas inutile de dire un mot sur le mode d'enseignement qui distingue aujourd'hui le Collège de France." [1]

By HIS appointments at the Collège de France and the Hôtel-Dieu Magendie was finally established in his career. At the age of 47 he had arrived where he wanted to be. His lectures and demonstrations in experimental physiology, so long carried on privately, were made official at the Collège de France, and his post at the Hôtel-Dieu, where he gave instruction to internes and externes both at the bedside in his ward and at autopsy, gave him his place in medical education. The actual alteration in the routine of his life was, perhaps, not great, but the official authorization of his activities did not diminish the satisfaction which he derived from them.

Monday was still reserved for the meetings of the Academy of Sciences, where his attainments had first been recognized and where he continued to find an environment at once stimulating and congenial, for the record of attendance shows that his absences were rare. It must be remembered that the Academy met every week, exception being made only if Monday fell either on the day before Christmas or

[1] *Phén. phys.*, 1842, v. 2, p. 1.

on Christmas day itself. There were three six-month semesters during which Magendie did not miss a single session,
and others which show only one absence. He continually
acted on committees to judge the merits of memoirs on
medical and physiological topics, and he retained his membership on two of the Montyon Prize Committees. Beginning
with 1839, he was permanently on the committee to award
the Manni prize for memoirs on apparent death.

One of his assignments, for March 10, 1834, is of particular interest to American physiologists. With Duméril and
Serres, he was charged with the investigation of the recent
work of a Dr. Williams (sic) Beaumont, the English title of
which translated into French became, "Expériences sur
l'état gastrique et sur la digestion." They were to find out if
it might not be profitable to bring to Paris the French-
speaking person with the artificial opening in his stomach
who had been the subject of these experiments. There is no
record that the committee met with any success in consequent negotiations, and any student of the history of physiology who knows the difficulties which Beaumont himself
had with the recalcitrant Alexis St. Martin can readily imagine that physiologists on the other side of the Atlantic
who wished to probe through the famous fistula would have
even less chance of laying their hands on the experimental
subject than the physician who saved his life.

The great figure in the Paris Academy of Sciences, Baron
Cuvier, died in 1832. Although Magendie did not attend
Cuvier during his last illness and was not present at the
autopsy performed by Bérard, he was convinced that Cuvier
was a victim of the cholera, a verdict in which other physicians did not concur.[2] Cuvier's masterly yearly summaries of
notable advances in science, which always included generous praise of Magendie, came to an end, and Flourens
succeeded him as permanent secretary. In 1836 Magendie

2 *Le choléra*, 1842, 4th lecture.

was chosen vice-president, and the presidency came to him in the following year. In the latter half of January, at the very beginning of his presidency, he complained of a bad attack of "la grippe" which kept him away from his lectures at the Collège de France for three weeks, and he was again ill in the middle of May, but he did not let these indisposi- tions interfere with his presiding at the Academy, for he did not miss a single Monday throughout the entire year.

Magendie was, almost in spite of himself, a physician at heart, and although he did not frequent the discussions of the Academy of Medicine, which also met on Monday, he always reported to the Academy of Sciences the more inter- esting, or at all events the more curious, of his cases at the Hôtel-Dieu, as well as those of other physicians which came to his attention. He thought it worth while to mention, for instance, a woman, thirty-four years of age, whose head, thorax, hands and feet were gigantic and still increasing in size (undoubtedly a case of pituitary disturbance);[3] a girl who was a nymphomaniac before the age of puberty;[4] and a child with no cerebellum.[5] He still used the galvanic current to restore lost powers of sensation and two of his most successful cases were officers of the Polish army. One of these officers had been knocked unconscious in a battle with the Russians, and when he revived he found that he had lost the sense of taste, his hearing and the ability to speak. After trying cures in Vienna and Trieste he came to Paris and consulted Magendie. Two or three applications of the electric current were sufficient to restore taste.

The needle-electrodes had been inserted so that they touched the chorda tympani nerve where it runs across the back of the eardrum. Magendie concluded that this nerve must be a branch of the fifth cranial nerve, since it was

[3] *Procès-verb. Acad. d. Sc.*, 10:462, 1834.
[4] *American J. Med. Sc.*, 21:228, 1837.
[5] *Syst. nerv.*, 1839, v. i, p. 217.

plainly sensory, and not a branch of the seventh, which he considered to be purely motor. This conclusion was immediately challenged by Roux, surgeon at the Hôtel-Dieu, who insisted that both the findings of anatomists and his own observations on patients showed that the chorda tympani must come from the seventh. Here the matter rested until 1839, when the question of the origin and function of this small nerve became the subject of the first paper published by Claude Bernard.

Magendie was able to restore not only his patient's sense of taste, but his hearing as well; and the first sound of which the Polish officer was conscious was the beat of the drums at sunset in the Luxembourg Gardens. There still remained his inability to speak, and Magendie at the time of his report of this case hoped to restore his patient's voice by application of the galvanic current to the appropriate nerves.[6]

Another Polish officer came to him, having been rendered deaf and dumb by a fall from his horse in a cavalry charge, and he also was benefited by this treatment.[7] These cases make one wonder if the difficulty was not psychological rather than physical, and the cure essentially the result of suggestion. In still other patients Magendie stopped the pangs of neuralgia by means of the galvanic current, and he restored the sight of a totally blind man so that he was able to walk about the streets unaccompanied.[8]

Being always on the lookout for new chemical compounds for use in treatment of disease, he went with Duméril to the Hospital St. Louis to see Dr. Lugol's (1786-1851) treatment of scrofula by the application of iodine compounds. Together they presented to the Academy a glowing report of the success of this treatment even in advanced cases, and today the term *Lugol's* is so common that one almost forgets

[6] *Comp. rend. Acad. d Sc.*, 5:855, 1837.
[7] *Comp. rend. Acad. d. Sc.*, 2:447, 1836.
[8] *Comp. rend. Acad. d. Sc.*, 5:856, 1837.

that this iodine-containing solution preserves the name of a nineteenth century physician.[9] Magendie himself tried out ammonium nitro-sulphate, newly prepared by his friend, Pelouze, in typhoid fever cases.[10] With Dupuytren he investigated the efficacy of cold water on burns. On presenting the eighth edition of his "Formulaire" (1834), he called the Academy's attention to the therapeutic action of the new drug codeine. When he heard of a new method of the quantitative estimation of sugar in diabetic urine by means of the polariscope, he immediately had one of these instruments installed at the Hôtel-Dieu.

In 1833 Magendie acquired his estate [11] at Sannois, now a suburb of Paris, but at that time open country. It was part of his wife's *dot,* and the documents of transfer show that the previous owner was M. Nicolas Audinot, Mme. Magendie's first husband, who is further described as director of the theater "l'Ambigu-Comique." The property consisted of a farm, four hectares in extent, with a small but elegant chateau of brick and stone, dating from the Regency and going by the name of le Petit Cernay.[12] Magendie equipped a small pharmacological laboratory for his investigations of drugs, and in connection with it he maintained a modest dispensing pharmacy for the benefit of the poor of the neighborhood. It was said that any fees for consultation passed in a reverse direction and impecunious patients departed with small sums of money jingling in their pockets.[13] Magendie also stocked the farm with all sorts of

[9] *Procès-verb. Acad. d. Sc.,* 9:562, 1831.

[10] *Comp. rend. Acad. d. Sc.,* 1:80, 1835.

[11] Magendie's estate is now cut up into small building lots. The street which originally separated his property from the town, rue de Magendie, bears his name, and another street parallel with it, rue du Chateau, passes in front of the chateau Petit Cernay, only half of which was standing in 1938.

[12] Cornilleau, R., *Progrès med.,* 15:76, 1938.

[13] Flourens, M., *Éloge,* 1858, p. 29.

domestic animals and carried on experiments in animal breeding and in horticulture. In 1838 he told in a lecture of killing on a Sunday morning in early spring one of his very fat English pigs whose blood refused to coagulate. Some years later (in 1844), when one of his milkmaids complained of pimples on her hand, Magendie examined the teats of his cows and found on one animal pustules and scabs indicating the presence of cow-pox. He announced this circumstance in the Academy and offered to put the cow at the disposal of any of his colleagues who wished to work on vaccines. He even persuaded the local vaccination officer to try out the efficacy of pus from this cow as a vaccine on seven children. As the regularly appointed time for public vaccination fell on a fête day, the experiment was deferred until the following day. Vaccine from Magendie's cow took on only one small boy, named Henri, whom Magendie conducted to the chateau in order to examine the results more carefully.[14]

With modern train transportation Sannois today cannot be reckoned as being far from the Collège de France, but in the 1830's a country residence fifteen kilometres outside Paris demanded the maintenance of a city house as well. For a short time after his marriage Magendie lived in an apartment at 5, quai Malaquais, just around the corner from his old bachelor quarters in the rue de Seine, and convenient, as they had been, to the Institut and the Collège de France, although the situation was more open, with a fine view across the river to the Louvre. It was a neighborhood with both literary and commercial traditions. Racine had lived and died in a house close behind no. 5; next door was Honoré Champion's book shop; and just along the quai on the other side of the rue Bonaparte was the book shop of Anatole France's father. For the last twenty years of his life, however, Magendie maintained an establishment in

[14] *Comp. rend. Acad. d. Sc.*, 18:986, 1844.

the fashionable rue d'Anjou St. Honoré, the street in which the aging comtesse de Rumford (1758-1836), widow of Lavoisier, had held her salon, the meeting place of some of the most distinguished scientists of that day, baron von Humboldt, comte de Laplace, baron Cuvier and others. The house which Magendie began to occupy in 1835 was no. 8. Today it bears an inscription on a plaque which may be translated:

'General Lafayette, defender of liberty in America, one of the founders of liberty in France, born September 6, 1767, at the chateau de Chauagnac in Auvergne, died in this house, May 30, 1834."

There is no mark on the house to record Magendie's tenancy, which apparently immediately followed that of Lafayette.

It is rather probable that Mme. Magendie was responsible for the gravitation from the Left Bank to the Faubourg St. Honoré. There is not much evidence of the part which she played in a scientific milieu probably at first distinctly foreign to her. There seems to have been hospitality extended to students at Sannois, and when the professor took his guests for country walks, he improved the occasion by having them stuff their pockets with frogs from the nearby swamp to be used later for experimental purposes. There are even reports of the existence of a handsome billiard table for indoor amusement. We are assured that Mme. Magendie presided over all this very graciously, and letters from old students always include her in kind remembrances. There is one such letter, written in 1832, expressing gratitude for Magendie's intervention on behalf of the writer in what seems to have been a political scrape. The young man wrote that he regretted having been arrested and carried off to prison from the society of "The Friends of the People." He added that although he would not wish to alter his hatred of tyrants and his love of the people, nevertheless he was distressed at the pain his parents would experience if they were ever to hear of their son's arrest. He was grateful to Magendie for having procured his release and he "really did not know how to thank Mme. Magendie for her great kindness" to him. This is one of the letters preserved by Magendie in the portfolio which is now in the Musée Gilbert. The signature does not belong to any of the pupils who afterwards distinguished themselves, but the letter may stand as a witness to the evergreen quality of Magendie's liberal principles in politics and to a kindly disposition to youth in distress which seems to have been shared by his spouse.

At the Collège de France he gave two lectures a week in a winter course beginning late in December and ending early in April, and a summer course continuing from April through July. His cholera lectures had been published in 1832. From 1835-1840 his lectures were taken down verbatim by some of his pupils, and from 1838 they were edited by Dr. Constantin James, who at this time was serving his interneship at the Hôtel-Dieu under Magendie.

The lectures of the four semesters between April 1836 and April 1838 were published in separate volumes as each course was concluded, and in 1842 they were republished under the general title, "Physical Phenomena of Life." The title is significant of how far Magendie in thirty years had been able to carry his revolt against the vitalism of Bichat. In 1809 he had merely wished to assert the principle of determinism against the instability which was presumed to be characteristic of vital phenomena. Now he felt that he had himself explored vital processes sufficiently to be able to show that in some of their aspects at least physical laws were operative. It is the modesty of his claim which is striking. As a practising empiricist, he seems not even to have wished to assert that vital phenomena were completely under the sway of physical law. His position was made quite clear in the opening sentences of his introductory lecture:

"Gentlemen, The study of the functions of the nervous system has been the subject of the semester which has just passed. We limited ourselves to reviewing various phenomena appreciable to our senses and amenable to experiment, phenomena designated generally under the head of vital, without trying to relate them to the laws which govern inert bodies. What relations, indeed, could we have established between the contractility of a living fibre and the simple elasticity of inorganic bodies? There is no analogy whatever between these properties . . .

"I propose this semester to study with you that other order of phenomena essentially distinct from vital phenomena, which, when submitted to the general laws of physics, become accessible to our explanations.

"I know that certain minds would regard as audacious the idea of relating the laws which preside over the play of our organs to those laws which govern inanimate bodies; but, although novel, this truth is none the less incontestable. To hold that the phenomena of life are entirely distinct from the general phenomena of nature is to commit a grave error, it is to oppose the continued progress of science. Therefore I think that it would be a great step forward to establish the teaching of vital physics, properly so-called." [15]

[15] *Phén. phys.*, 1842, v. 1, pp. 5-6. Cf. v. 2, p. 15: "I see in the lung a bellows, in the trachea a vent tube, in the glottis a vibrating reed. And this admirable hydraulic machine destined to cause the circulation of the blood in our tissues, is it not a marvellous mechanism? One could conceive that even in the absence of vital laws the phenomena of circulation would be carried out in a cadaver, if one could artificially put in play this system of pumps and tubes represented by the heart, the veins and the arteries. So true is it that here physical phenomena have the largest part! But do not on the other hand fall into the opposite excess of seeking to explain everything by the laws which hold sway over inorganic matter. If I can analyze the progress of the luminous cone across the media of the eye, I would try in vain to understand how the retina sends to the brain the impression of exterior objects. Nature has not up to the present permitted man to raise the veil which hides from him the understanding

The general subject which Magendie decided was most amenable to this treatment was circulation and the blood, to an account of which he applied, none too successfully, the physical concepts of elasticity, mechanical absorption and hydraulics. Aside from the description of early quantitative measurements of blood pressure by means of Poiseuille's haemodynamometer there is little in the four volumes of these lectures to interest a modern physiologist. The explanation which Magendie gave for the heart sounds differed from that put forward by Laennec, and was, unfortunately, wrong, although Magendie thought that he had given experimental proof of his view. The emphasis which he placed on the therapeutic applications of physiology was perhaps even more conspicuous in these lectures than in those on the nervous system, although in all his teaching as professor of Medicine at the Collège de France, he took the medical implications of the title of his chair more seriously than, for instance, his immediate successor, Claude Bernard.

The lectures on circulation and the blood were translated into English, appearing *seriatim* in the London *Lancet*. Those belonging to the last of the four semesters were published in Philadelphia under the title "Lectures on the Blood and the changes it undergoes during disease." Magendie's contemporaries were not too complimentary. An American reviewer, whose report ran to 36 pages, protested against certain deductions, among them, the erroneous opinions regarding the origin of heart sounds.[16] At Montpellier a medical student obtained his degree upon presentation of a thesis, dedicated to his own professor of physiology, which was a wholesale condemnation of the "Physical

---

of vital phenomena." The artificial putting in play of pumps and tubes has been admirably carried out by one of Magendie's countrymen, Alexis Carrel. (Carrel, A., and Lindbergh, C. A., *The Culture of Organs*, 1938.)
[16] Condie, D. F., *Am. J. Med. Sc.*, 25:135, 1839.

Phenomena of Life." The student had found the Parisian professor's lectures to be utterly lacking in order and full of contradictions. Naturally the very title would have involved a contradiction in the eyes of one brought up in the tradition of Barthez, and we are not surprised that the young man concluded that Magendie had failed to find a mechanism to account for the facts which he presented. "A rational interpretation of such facts," the young critic maintained, "can only be given by admitting the intervention of occult powers for their accomplishment. Vital force alone can surmount the obstacles presented by the regularity of their appearance." [17] This seems to be the converse of the usual argument.

The parts of these lectures which reflected Magendie's immediate research interest centered about the new piece of physiological apparatus invented by Jean-Louis Poiseuille (1799-1869). This young man had had an excellent training in mathematics and physics at the École Polytéchnique before taking his doctorate in medicine in 1828. The thesis which he had presented for the degree was a remarkable one, for in it he described a method of registering blood pressure in an experimental animal which has ever since been the standard of laboratory procedure the world over. Magendie had been proud to publish this thesis in his *Journal*. It seems probable that the suggestion which led to the construction of the haemodynamometer, as the instrument used in Poiseuille's new technique was called, came from Magendie's contention in 1817 that propulsion of blood through the arteries is accomplished by the force of the heartbeat in conjunction with the elasticity of the arterial walls, an idea which its proponent never had any hesitation

---

[17] Grandvoinet, J. A., *Examen critique de l'esprit et des propositions principales de l'ouvrage intitulé Leçons sur les phénomènes physiques de la vie,* 1838.

in claiming as his own, and which he was constantly having to defend.[18]

The pioneer in measuring blood pressure was, of course, Stephen Hales (1677-1761), the famous rector of Teddington. Hales had used a straight glass tube connected directly with the aorta of the experimental animal;; but this necessitated the use of a tube some eight feet in length and, in addition, the blood soon clotted. Poiseuille got around these difficulties by substituting for the long tube a short U-shaped one containing mercury. The mercury served to counterbalance the pressure of the blood and coagulation was prevented by introducing a solution of sodium carbonate between the blood and the mercury, which made possible observations of changes in blood pressure over long periods of time. It was found that the column of mercury rose to practically the same height when the tube was connected with the carotid, iliac, radial or any other large artery, and this made Magendie more sure than ever of the correctness of his view regarding the purely passive role played by the artery wall in the propulsion of the blood. This is undoubtedly true for arteries of large calibre, but it remained for Claude Bernard to show that Magendie and Poiseuille were wrong in viewing the whole circulation of the blood as if there were nothing involved but mechanical hydraulics, for with his discovery of the vasomotor system Bernard was able to show that the diameter of the smaller blood vessels could change under the influence of the nervous system.[19]

Poiseuille collaborated with Magendie throughout the 1830's and continued the same type of work for the remainder of his life. In 1835 he entered his paper on the causes of movement of blood in the capillary vessels for the Montyon prize. The 10,000 frances was divided between him and M. Gaudichaud who had submitted a paper on a

[18] *Phén. phys.*, 1842, v. 1, p. 173; cf. v. 2, p. 111.
[19] Bernard, C., *La chaleur animale*, 1876, p. 224.

botanical subject. Although not at this time Magendie's official préparateur he nevertheless continued to assist the latter in his lectures at the Collège de France, demonstrating the use of his instrument and lending notes of experiments which he had just performed to be read by Magendie from manuscript.[20] Magendie was exceedingly careful to give the younger man full credit for his contributions and any of his mechanical devices used was explicitly described as "Poiseuille's apparatus." One of the discoveries which is credited to them jointly is the effect of respiratory movements on blood pressure.[21] This, however, had been noted earlier by Magendie,[22] but the new instrument afforded ocular demonstration of its truth. Poiseuille's experiments eventually became more physical than physiological, and his finest work is that on the movement of liquids in tubes of small diameter. This paper was read before the Academy of Sciences, December 14, 1840, and in it are to be found the experimental results on which is based the law relating velocity of flow to the sectional area of the tube and the pressure gradient, which finds a place both in physics and physiology and which is named after Poiseuille.[23] In 1843 Poiseuille submitted papers in competition for two of the Academy prizes, that in experimental physiology and that in medicine and surgery. The committees in charge of awarding these two prizes always included Magendie. He was evidently unable to do anything for Poiseuille in regard to the prize in experimental physiology, but although none of the forty-one contestants was considered to be worthy of the prize in medicine and surgery, he managed to obtain 700 francs in recognition of Poiseuille's work on circulation time in mammals, where the calculations were based on the time taken

---

[20] *Phén. phys.*, 1842, v. 3, pp. 36, 274.
[21] Schafer, E. A., *Textbook of Physiology*, 1898, v. 1, p. 122.
[22] *Phén. phys.*, 1842, v. 2, p. 335.
[23] Bernard, C., *Substances toxiques*, 1857, p. 72.

for potassium ferrocyanide to pass from one jugular vein to the other.

While working with Poiseuille, Magendie abandoned the nervous system and turned his attenton entirely to the circulatory system. In this connection it was natural that as Laennec's successor at the Collège de France he should take up the question of heart sounds. The immediate stimulus for embarking on this new subject for research was, however, not the work of Laennec himself, but of one of his followers, James Hope.[24] Laennec's revolutionary method of diagnosis of diseases of the heart and chest by means of auscultation had brought several young graduates of the Edinburgh medical school to Paris in order to familiarize themselves with the use of the stethescope. Some were so fortunate as to attend Laennec's clinic at the Charité,[25] but James Hope (1801-1841), the author of the treatise which aroused Magendie's interest, came too late to receive instruction directly from Laennec.[26] He had been in Paris from the summer of 1826 to that of 1827, serving as clinical clerk under Chomel at the Charité, but Magendie could not have known him, since he assumed that the English physician

[24] Hope, J., *A treatise on the diseases of the heart*, 1832.

[25] E.g., C. T. B. Williams (1805-1889) who returned to England to become an eminent chest specialist and eventually, in 1839, successor to John Elliotson, Magendie's friend, as professor of Medicine and physician to University College, London University.

[26] Even in his student days, when British physicians were inclined to ridicule the new-fangled French contrivance, Hope had prophetically remarked to a friend, "Depend upon it, George, the intrinsic value of the instrument is so great and self-evident, that in a short time you will no more see a physician without his stethoscope, than you would fifty years ago have seen him without his gold-headed cane, or a major without his boots." (Mrs. Hope, *Memoir of the late James Hope, M.D.*, p. 338.) Hope became famous as a heart specialist and in February, 1835, was drawn into a controversy with C. T. B. Williams over the subject of vivisection in connection with experiments done for his treatise. V. Hope's *Treatise*, 3rd ed., 1839, pp. 32-24, and preface to the 4th ed.

had made a long stay in Paris in 1830-1831.[27] Magendie
read passages from Hope's "Treatise" to his audience at the
Collège de France, translating directly from the English
text. He performed a number of experiments before his class
upon a variety of animals, large dogs, geese and even a
swan, to show the alteration in heart sounds when the
chest wall was cut away so that the heart could not touch
the wall as it contracted. Under these conditions it is true
that the heart sounds are so diminished that with the early
form of stethoscope they might seem to have disappeared
altogether. Magendie concluded from his experiments that
the first heart sound must be due to the apex striking the
chest wall in systole and the second to the striking of the
anterior face of the heart on the chest wall in diastole.
This idea was utterly at variance with Laennec's original
explanation, which, according to Magendie, was not based
on direct observation, but only on inference, and it was also
contrary to Hope's conception, which again, according to
Magendie, was merely theoretical.[28] These experiments
were the basis of the memoir read before the Academy of
Sciences in 1834 and published four years later.[29] There
was much opposition to Magendie's point of view, and he
did not hesitate to strike back at those physicians for whom,
in his opinion, "an assertion expressed with assurance is
equivalent to a demonstrated fact." He added, "Laennec
shared this absurd prejudice up to a certain point; so complete was his confidence in his own opinion that he permitted neither doubt nor discussion; like many another he
believed blindly in the product of his imagination."[30] This
was a charge to which Magendie himself was at least
equally open, for it is now recognized that heart sounds

[27] *Mém. Acad. d. Sc.*, 14:155, 1838.
[28] *Phén. phys.*, 1842, v. 2, p. 263.
[29] *Mém. Acad. d. Sc.*, 14:155, 1838.
[30] *Mém. Acad. d. Sc.*, 14:158, 1838.

arise from the heart itself and are merely magnified by the presence of surrounding structures. Magendie himself showed that placing a piece of cardboard on the exteriorized beating heart will augment the sounds. No physiologist then or now could subscribe to his point of view as regards the origin of either of the two heart sounds, and both Laennec and Hope were nearer the truth than he. He here, as too often before, allowed a single set of experiments to bias his judgment, having given way to his wonted elation when he thought that his results could be used to cast doubt on an existing theory.

In 1839 he returned to the subject of the nervous system in his lectures at the Collège de France, and again Constantin James edited the two volumes which appeared at the end of the year. These were the last lectures to be published in book form. Occasional series or parts of series are to be found in medical journals, and from 1849 to 1853, the year he ceased lecturing, *L'Union médicale* gave résumés of each course. The two volumes on the nervous system are of greater interest than any of the others. He was more at home with this part of the mammalian body, and here the simple operation of nerve-cutting or the removal of successive slices from the brain lead to striking results, and he was undeniably a skilful operator.

It was inevitable that the question of Bell's share in the discovery of the functions of the dorsal and ventral roots of the spinal nerves should be brought up in these lectures. Magendie went over the whole story, explained the part which each of the protagonists, including "Schaw" (*sic*), had played, and gave demonstrations on both the spinal roots and the fifth and seventh nerves.[31] There were in his audience two young men for whom these lectures were to serve as an impetus to continue the exploration of the functions of the nervous system. Both won permanent places

[31] *Syst. nerv.*, 1841, v. 2, p. 61, seqq.

in the history of physiology for their discoveries, and both their names are always linked with Magendie's. The more famous of the two, Claude Bernard, is actually mentioned in the lectures of May 29 and 31, 1839, as having skilfully prepared a dissection of a rabbit's head to show the relations of the fifth and seventh cranial nerves. The other, François-Achilles Longet (1811-1871), makes his first appearance in a rather less favorable light in the report of the meeting of the Academy of Sciences for the following Monday. Bernard was still an interne at this time, but Longet had taken his medical degree in 1835, and himself gave a course in experimental physiology at the École pratique. He had as yet published no work of his own, and he seems to have been very much bent upon correcting the mistakes which he discovered in this course of Magendie's which he was attending.

The affair of Longet and recurrent sensitivity is a curious one. It created something of a furore at the time because the discovery was thought to be of first-rate importance. It seemed at first that an exception to the Bell-Magendie rule might have been established. To reach an understanding of the situation there are at least four sources of information which have to be consulted, the records of the Academy of Sciences, Magendie's lectures, Longet's account and Bernard's account as an eye witness.

Magendie had repeated before the class his demonstration that the dorsal roots of the spinal nerves were exceedingly sensitive and that the ventral roots were "scarcely so." He found, however, that the ventral roots were distinctly sensitive, provided that the corresponding dorsal roots were intact, but became insensitive after the corresponding dorsal roots had been cut. His method of stimulation was pinching or pricking the nerve and his criterion of sensitivity was a cry or struggle on the part of the animal, i.e., evidence of pain. This peculiar influence of the dorsal or sensory root on the ventral or motor root puzzled him, and in his Wednesday lecture, May 8, 1839, he frankly confessed himself unable to suggest any experiment to clear up the mystery.[32] At the Friday lecture, two days later, he said that after he got home from the previous lecture he had suddenly thought of a way of solving this problem, and so anxious had he been to try out his idea that he sent Constantin James and his nephew, Dr. Charles Depuisay, back to the Collège de France to perform the experiment on the dog which had survived the class demonstration. The experiment consisted in cutting a ventral root and then pinching the two cut ends. If the end next the spinal cord was sensitive, the sensitivity must come from the spinal cord; if, on the other hand, only the peripheral end were sensitive, the sensitivity must come from the dorsal root. The two young men reported that "the animal was very exhausted and unmanageable," but they were sure that the peripheral end of the ventral root only was sensitive. This observation Magendie proceeded to confirm before his class then and there, performing the operation himself. On May 20 he reported these findings briefly at the Academy and gave the phenomenon a name which is always translated into English as "recurrent sensitivity." His last experiment had, of course, made it clear that no exception to the Bell-Magendie rule was involved.

Magendie began on May 24 to lecture on Bell's work on the fifth and seventh cranial nerves, Bernard performing some of the dissections, and here again he thought that he had come upon something important which he should at once announce to the Academy, *viz*, that in rabbits the upper and lower branches of the seventh nerve are insensitive, but the middle branch derives its sensitivity from the fifth. He considered that this was further proof of his former conviction that the seventh was entirely motor, a conviction which he had already expressed in 1836 when he restored

[32] *Syst. nerv.*, 1841, v. 2, pp. 82, 89.

the sense of taste to the Polish officer by galvanism of the chorda tympani nerve. Now he was more outspoken and gave it as his opinion that operations to relieve neuralgia involving the cutting of the seventh nerve would only cause facial paralysis and leave the pain untouched. In this respect he was right, but still he had by no means proved the seventh nerve to be wholly motor. When, because of Magendie's dispute with the surgeon Roux over the origin of the chorda tympani, Claude Bernard came to work out the anatomy of this nerve and show that it really came from the seventh cranial nerve, he was still so much under Magendie's influence that he wrongly maintained that the Chorda tympani must of necessity be purely motor. We now know that it contains taste fibers from the anterior two-thirds of the tongue as well as the vaso-dilator fibers which Bernard later discovered; therefore it is both sensory and motor.

At the close of the session of the Academy at which Magendie made this announcement regarding the fifth and seventh nerves, among the correspondence was read a letter from Longet, claiming that the idea of recurrent sensitivity was his own and not his professor's; that in Magendie's presence he, the pupil, had pinched the ventral root whose corresponding dorsal root had been cut and had got no evidence of sensitivity, while the ventral root on the other side of the body was sensitive. "This result is not new to the Academy," he said, "since this skilful physiologist, who, I am sure, will not contest my priority, has taken care himself to communicate the fact in the meeting of May 20,— but I wish to lay bare the facts exactly as they are and to inform the Academy that I am at this moment trying to determine by experiment the consequences of a finding which is my own." [33] Magendie replied at once that Longet did indeed perform this particular experiment under his eyes

[33] Longet, F. A., *Comp. rend. Acad. d. Sc.*, 8:881, 1839.

at the Collège de France, but that the young man had done
nothing new; certainly his experiment was not the same as
Magendie's own of dividing the ventral root and stimulating
each cut end. One must agree with the professor that although Longet's experiment was suggestive, it lacked the
decisive character of Magendie's. In any case, it seems rather
bizarre for a pupil to intervene during a demonstration by
his professor to make an observation and then lay claim to
a discovery of his own.

Longet, however, was not to be silenced. Next week another letter from him was read in which he contended that
his experiment did prove recurrent sensitivity; that Magendie's experiment was done on the day following the
one upon which the professor had seen Longet's experiment;
therefore, Magendie's experiment was merely confirmation
of his own.[34]

The result of this communication was a rather undignified
squabble over the exact dates of these happenings. In the
meantime, the affair was brought up in the Academy of
Medicine, evidently in a manner damaging to Magendie,
for he wrote a sarcastic letter which was incorporated into
the official *Bulletin* of this Academy. "Sometimes," he said,
my work is discussed in the Academy of Medicine with a
good will to which I am most responsive, but at others
with a license of criticism which I find excessive. One of my
honorable colleagues went so far as to state that I was a
hand directed by a head other than my own, which while
flattering to my hand was less so to my head." [35]

When Longet came to repeat his experiment by himself,
he could not find any trace of sensitivity in the ventral
roots whatsoever! He then attacked Magendie in the medical press for having said in 1822 that the ventral roots
were virtually insensitive and in 1839 that they were dis-

[34] Longet, F. A., *Comp. rend. Acad. d. Sc.*, 8:919, 1839.
[35] *Bull. Acad. de la Méd.*, 3:965, 1839.

tinctly sensitive (when the dorsal roots were left intact), ignoring both the point of the 1839 experiments and the lack of consistency in his own results over a much shorter interval of time. "Let the reader," he wrote, "make his choice, if he dare, among the contradictory assertions put forward by Magendie. . . . He should at least tell us, in order to extricate us from our embarrassment, which experiments were properly done, those of 1822 or those of 1839." As a further aggravation to the object of his attack, Longet included his own version of the old Bell-Magendie controversy, giving, as might be anticipated, all the credit to Bell. His crowning effrontery was to present all this in competition for the Montyon prize, disregarding the circumstance that Magendie was always one of the judges. Two members only of the committee went to see Longet's demonstration and he complained of the delay in rendering a decision to the Academy. The prize was finally awarded to him, but one member of the committee had refrained from voting, which one, although no names were mentioned, it would not be difficult to guess. Since Longet in his demonstration maintained his second position, *viz,* that the ventral roots were insensitive, it would appear that the award was made on the ground of his having refuted Magendie's theory of recurrent sensitivity in the ventral roots when the dorsal roots were left intact, and not on the ground of priority in observing the phenomenon in question.

With regard to the charge of inconsistency, Magendie stubbornly maintained that if his results were different in different experiments that was not his fault. He had truthfully reported what he saw, and was willing to leave it at that; but Claude Bernard, who had been a witness of the demonstration at the Collège de France, was not satisfied. He prevailed upon Magendie to repeat the experiments with him in 1847. They found that the ventral roots were entirely insensitive. Was Longet perhaps right after all?

True to Magendie's teaching, Bernard could not distrust his own senses, but, unlike Magendie, he was not willing to let the matter rest until he had found a satisfactory explanation for the discordant results. He eventually found that recurrent sensitivity must be due to sensory fibers from the dorsal roots passing into the ventral roots for a short distance, then turning around in a loop and proceeding outwards again towards the periphery. For Magendie's demonstrations the dogs had been prepared an hour or two before the lecture, and the exposure to the air of the meninges of the cord made them particularly susceptible to painful stimuli. The sensations were presumably carried in pain fibers from the meninges doubling back in the ventral roots in the manner described. In the later experiments, the tests were made immediately after the operation, i.e., before this extreme sensitivity had developed.[36] The discovery of recurrent sensitivity, which is now considered merely a curious and unimportant deviation in the pathway of certain dorsal root fibers, was given a temporary importance because Bernard made use of this phenomenon as a technique for showing the motor and sensory aspects of the individual cranial nerves. This is why, when he succeeded Magendie at the Collège de France and gave his own lectures on the nervous system, he devoted one whole semester to recurrent sensitivity.

Longet successfully played the part of gadfly to Magendie during the whole of the 1839 course of lectures, for he seemed to delight in picking flaws in the experiments. When Magendie did his demonstration of the rotating rabbit, Longet this time did not interfere during the demonstration, but repeated the experiment by himself and found that his rabbits rolled toward and not away from the side of the cerebellar lesion. Did Magendie not know his right

[36] Bernard, C., Pathologie expérimentale, 1880, p. 516; Introduction à l'étude de la médecine expérimentale, 1865, p. 305.

hand from his left? Again Claude Bernard came to the rescue and showed that Magendie had injured the anterior half of the cerebellar peduncle, Longet the posterior half.[37] Hence, the observations of both Magendie and Longet were upheld.

The feud, however, did not end with these irritations. Longet's best-known book is his large treatise on the "Anatomy and physiology of the nervous system in man and animals," published in 1842. Here he actually accused Magendie of plagiarizing Bell,[38] and made a careful list of every mistaken idea which Magendie had entertained with regard to the nervous system, for instance, that the pineal gland acts as a valve; [39] and that the fifth nerve serves for olfaction and influences sight and hearing.[40] He stigmatized Magendie's work on the corpora striata and immobility of horses as misinterpretation of experiments,[41] and his conclusions regarding the cerebellum as error.[42] Almost the only thing of which Longet did approve was the work on cerebrospinal fluid,[43] but even here there was opportunity for a later imbroglio.

Longet had seen Magendie in 1839 demonstrate his method of extracting this fluid in the living animal and the disturbances following its removal.[44] The procedure was to cut through the neck muscles in order to disclose the occipito-atlantoid membrane which could then be pierced without injury to the nervous tissue beneath. Constantin James in transcribing the notes of this particular lecture interjected the observation that as the liquid dripped away the animal staggered and finally fell down in a state of

---

[37] Bernard, C., *Physiologie opératoire*, 1879, p. 45.
[38] Longet, F.-A., *Anatomie et physiologie du système nerveux*, 1842, p. 22.
[39] *Ibid.*, p. 490.
[40] *Ibid.*, p. 250.
[41] *Ibid.*, p. 521.
[42] *Ibid.*, p. 434.
[43] *Ibid.*, p. 183.
[44] *Syst. nerv.*, 1839, v. 1, p. 76.

immobility. Six years later Longet reported to the Academy of Sciences that he had made a new discovery, *viz*, that after withdrawal of cerebrospinal fluid the disturbances in locomotion were not due to loss of this fluid, but merely to the cutting of the neck muscles to facilitate arrival at the occipito-atlantoid membrane.[45] Magendie's reply was that Pinel had shown this twenty years before, and that he himself had repeatedly demonstrated the fact in his lectures. Again Bernard tried to come to the rescue, but, unfortunately, he has given us two versions which do not exactly coincide. In one [46] Magendie is said to have discovered his own mistake in thinking that the disturbance in locomotion was due solely to withdrawal of cerebrospinal fluid. The occasion was an interrupted experiment. After cutting the neck muscles of the animal, Magendie was called away for a few moments and on his return found the animal staggering about as if intoxicated. Bernard then says that Longet later rediscovered this phenomenon. The other version [47] is that some other experimenter was interrupted while repeating Magendie's experiment, observed the phenomenon and was then able to correct Magendie. Bernard's own contribution here was to prove that the collection of cerebrospinal fluid in birds could be made without injury to the neck muscles and that loss of fluid did not result in disturbance of locomotion.

Longet was not alone in indulging in belittlement of Magendie in print during 1842. In this year Flourens brought out the second edition of his monograph on the nervous system, adding an entirely new section on "the admirable conception of Charles Bell" regarding the function of the spinal nerve roots. In a foot-note he gave grudg-

[45] Longet, F.-A., *Comp. rend. Acad. d. Sc.*, 19:1742, 1845.
[46] Bernard, C., *Système nerveux*, 1858, v. 1, p. 496.
[47] Bernard, C., *Introduction à l'étude de la médecine expérimentale*, 1865, p. 320.

ing acknowledgment that the idea of one root serving for
sensitivity, the other for motion, "fruit of an analysis as profound as it was precise," had been "taken up and confirmed,
at first in France by M. Magendie, then in Germany by M.
J. Müller, etc., and" (this concluding phrase was the final
effrontery) "quite recently in France once again, and with
great skill, by M. Longet."

Magendie's general reputation as an experimental physiologist was well enough established to stand up against attacks like these which grew out of the Bell-Magendie
controversy. The earliest honors which came to him from
abroad after his classic papers of 1882 were conferred by
such apparently dissenting strongholds as Edinburgh and
Dublin (1823), and from points on the periphery of the
scientific world, Tunis and Salvador (also 1823). His work
on cerebrospinal fluid and his emergence from political disapproval seem to have been accompanied by some of the
more important of the continental recognitions, *viz*, Brussels (1829), Hamburg (1830) and Berlin (1834). He was
elected to membership in the Academy of Medicine of
Mexico in 1839, and in 1840 was made a member of the
Royal Medical and Chirurgical Society of London. When
Leopold of Belgium created his Royal Academy of Medicine in 1842, Magendie's name appeared on the list of
foreign corresponding members, which may perhaps be
taken as an index of professional renown, along with those
of his critic, Flourens, and of Breschet, Orfila, Roux and
Velpeau.

12

GOVERNMENT COMMITTEES AND COLLABORATION WITH CLAUDE BERNARD

1840-1845

"Ne nous arrêtons pas complaisamment sur ce qui a été fait; ce qui reste à faire doit surtout éveiller notre sollicitude et diriger nos recherches." [1]

SIR CHARLES BELL visited the Paris hospitals on his way to Italy in 1840. Roux received him with open arms at the Hôtel-Dieu and dismissed his class with the words, "It is enough, you have seen Charles Bell!" Bell was delighted with his reception and amused by the French pronunciation of his Christian name, which sounded to him like "Sharley." There is no record of his having gone to visit Magendie's ward or to inspect the new laboratory for animal experimentation and the demonstration amphitheatre then being constructed at the Collège de France. Magendie had inherited from Récamier a mere closet in which to conduct his experiments. He had finally prevailed upon the authorities to give him adequate quarters not only for his experiments but also for his lecture demonstrations, and if we have no report from Bell on this unique installation, we do have an American physician's impressions of Magendie's course for that very year. This worthy young man felt a

[1] *Phén. phys.*, 1842, v. 2, p. 348.

natural distaste equal to Bell's for vivisection, but, unlike Bell, he was able to appreciate the didactic value of Magendie's demonstrations. His report may be quoted in full, bearing, as it does, the unmistakeable marks of being the impression of an eye witness. He wrote:

"This surgeon's spring course of experimental physiology commenced in the beginning of April. I seldom fail of "assisting" at his murders. At his first lecture, a basketful of live rabbits, a glass receiver full of frogs, two pigeons, an owl, several tortoises and a pup were the victims ready to lay down their lives for the good of science! His discourse was to explain the function of the fifth pair of nerves. The facility was very striking with which the professor could cut the nerve at its origin, by introducing a sharp instrument through the cranium, immediately behind and below the eye. M. Magendie drew the attention of the class to several rabbits in which the fifth pair of nerves had been divided several days before. They were all blind of one eye, a deposition of lymph having taken place in the cornea, from inflammation of the eye always following the operation alluded to, although the eye is by this section deprived of all its sensibility. Monsieur M. has not only lost all feeling for the victims he tortures, but he really likes his business. When the animal squeaks a little, the operator grins; when loud screams are uttered, he sometimes laughs outright. The professor has a most mild, gentle and amiable expression of countenance, and is in the habit of smoothing, fondling and patting his victim whilst occupied with preliminary remarks, and the rabbit either looks him in the face or 'licks the hand just raised to shed his blood.' During another lecture, in demonstrating the functions of the motive and sensitive fibers of the spinal nerves, he laid bare the spinal cord in a young pup, and cut one bundle after another of nerves. The phrenological developments of the professor belie those of physiognomy. His skull is enormously broad between and behind the ears. Living dissection is as effectual a mode of teaching as it is revolting, and in many cases the experiments are unnecessarily cruel and too frequently reiterated; but so long as the thing is going on, I shall not fail to profit by it, although I never wish to see such experiments repeated." [2]

There is an implied charge of sadism in the description of Magendie's manner at the demonstration table which should not be allowed to pass unchallenged. It may be suggested that the "grins" and "laughs" were automatic reactions caused by a desire to reassure spectators, whose discomfiture at evidences of pain or fright displayed by an experimental animal Magendie understood only too well. The writer remembers witnessing a demonstration at a Swiss university in which a blood pressure apparatus, similar to Poiseuille's, was attached to the carotid artery in a series of rabbits without the use of an anaesthetic. In one instance only did an animal utter a protesting squeal. The operator immediately turned to the spectators with a reassuring smile, or "grin," remarking, "That rabbit cannot be a native of our canton." It was perfectly evident that this mildly facetious comment on the capacity of the rabbit to "take it" was meant to counteract uneasiness in the audience and involved no malevolence toward the experimental subject.

Another cinematographical glimpse of Magendie in the same year, 1840, may be derived from the verbatim transcription in the proceedings of the Academy of an exhibition of temper on his part over a report submitted by Breschet (1784-1845) and Rayer (1793-1867) in behalf of a committee investigating questions of equine hygiene at the request of the Minister of War. Magendie had been associated with this committee since September, 1836, when the Minister of War preferred a request through the Minister of Public Instruction that someone be appointed from the Academy of Sciences to supervise experiments on a treatment for horse glanders proposed by M. Goly of the Paris School of Pharmacy. There was great concern over the

[2] *Medical Times,* 2:77, 1840.

prevalence of glanders in horses, particularly in army horses, for the incidence of the disease was proportionally greater in France than in other countries. Magendie was presiding at the Academy as Vice-president when the matter came before that body and he was himself proposed as the member to undertake the investigation. Three years passed without any report being presented, when on February 10, 1840, Breschet and Rayer anticipated Magendie with a paper of their own. The report was read by Breschet, who was doubly a colleague of Magendie, since he was surgeon at the Hôtel-Dieu and had succeeded Dupuytren as a member of the Academy of Sciences, but it was Rayer, the younger man, who was chiefly responsible for the work. After Breschet's reading of the memoir, Magendie demanded the floor. He said:

"Our honorable confrère has just made a pronouncement on certain questions of the greatest importance in a manner so positive and final, that wishing to reply to him and believing that I can do so to some effect, I have no other course than myself to employ brief and trenchant terms which can be matched without disadvantage with those which he has employed.

"I shall say to my honorable confrère without any oratorical preliminaries: when you say chronic glanders is the same disease as acute glanders, you are wrong!

"When you say that chronic glanders is contagious, you are again wrong!

"When you say that horse glanders is transmitted to man by contagion you express merely an opinion and that is no proof. If this idea were spread abroad on the authority of your word, it would have the most harmful consequences."

Magendie brought his speech to a close with biting sarcasm:

"Our confrère holds that the alleged glanders in man, newly brought to our attention today, has always existed and that all that has been lacking was observers to recognize it. The earth turned, he tells you, before Galileo so taught the world.

Regarding this brilliant but rather strange comparison, in which we have suddenly before us a Galileo of human glanders, I would make only a simple comment; to discover the movement and rotation of the earth about the sun, the genius of a great man was required; but to perceive that by living with horses one catches their diseases, that the nose runs, that one dies with the face disfigured, one must certainly have the mind of the most innocent of stable boys." [3]

Breschet answered very briefly, maintaining his position and asserting that Magendie was wrong in regard to the transmissibility of the disease. At the next meeting of the Academy Magendie was the first speaker of the day, demanding proofs from Breschet that chronic glanders was contagious, and promising himself to furnish proof that it was not. As a matter of fact, he was wrong on every count in regard to chronic glanders. Although rare in man, it is known; it is transmissible from horse to man, being practically always fatal. In spite of Magendie's protest, the evidence which Rayer had presented three years before this episode in his book, "On glanders and farcin in man," has been accepted and constitutes its author's chief claim to fame.

Magendie's idea of contagion seems to be a decidedly peculiar one for a practising physician to hold even in pre-Pasteurian days. It was almost as if he would refuse to consider a disease contagious if a single individual could be found who had been in contact with a disease without having contracted it. For example, he would defend his stand that cholera was not contagious by pointing out that he was right in the midst of the cholera and never caught the disease. In fact, he allowed his narrowly sceptical conception of what constituted proof to put him in an impossible position, and having taken up the position he defended it with an irascibility varying directly with the opposition

[3] *Comp. rend. Acad. d. Sc.*, 10:223, 1840.

encountered. His bad temper on the occasion just described was probably augmented by resentment at what he no doubt regarded as trespass by Breschet and Rayer on territory which he had preempted.

Magendie was inclined to take his appointments to committees very seriously. Even M. Dubois, who had in general very little approbation to bestow upon him, commended the energy and ability which he displayed while acting on committees of the Academy dealing with the public health. In particular, he considered that Magendie had derived considerable prestige from his widely read report, submitted in 1841 on behalf of the so-called "Gelatine Committee," of which he had at that time been a member for ten years. As long before as the Revolution of 1793, certain chemists, chief of whom was d'Arcet (père), had conceived the idea of extracting from bones a gelatine which they claimed possessed not only as high a nutritive value as meat, but had the added virtue of making use of an otherwise waste product. The government of the day had received this pronouncement with great acclaim, and in order to encourage and popularize the use of so cheap a food, passed an order containing extravagant recommendation of it. When d'Arcet died he bequeathed his obsession to his son, who invented a method of extracting gelatine from bones by means of steam. His slogan was, "Five beeves out of four!" This naturally appealed to those in charge of feeding the poor in such institutions as the public hospitals, and bouillon soon became the chief item on the patient's bill of fare. However, the bouillon made from gelatine ordinarily had so nauseating an odor that the patients rebelled.

In the summer of 1831 a memoir was presented before the Academy of Sciences on the value of gelatine as a food, and Magendie, together with Chevreul, who was well known for his researches on the chemistry of fats, and d'Arcet, was appointed to look into the matter. Once it was known that the Academy was investigating gelatine there was a stir among the manufacturers of this commodity and samples were sent in for testing. D'Arcet, seeing that the opinion of his fellow members on the committee was against him, withdrew. In November the Hôtel-Dieu abandoned the practise of administering gelatine to its patients, and a long report signed by 137 members of the staff, including Magendie, Récamier, the baron Dupuytren and Breschet, stated that gelatine from bones was not only disgusting to the taste but produced indigestion, gurgling, flatulency and diarrhea. Upon the withdrawal of d'Arcet, the Academy committee had been enlarged to include Dupuytren, Flourens and the chemist Thénard. In spite of urgent requests from each succeeding president of the Academy of Sciences no report was forthcoming. In 1834 Thénard reported that the committee had taken the matter up, but Magendie complained that so far as he knew no one had been delegated to do any experiments. In 1835, however, at the Collège de France, experiments on dogs were carried on of a type very reminiscent of those which Magendie had employed in his studies on protein-free diets.

Three more years passed in silence, when Arago, who had visited the Hospice Saint-Nicolas at Metz, reported to the Academy that patients there were fed twice a day, five days a week, on soup containing one-fourth of a litre of bouillon made partly from bones and partly from meat. The authorities there were satisfied and wanted no change. Magendie at once rose to protest; such a report should not have been made in public session before the whole Academy, but should have been handed over to the Gelatine Committee. Arago replied with the taunt that at least here was something definite, and that was more than the Gelatine Committee had been able to produce in seven years. When this reply was read at the following meeting as part of the minutes, Magendie, Dumas and Thénard all protested, but in spite of their professed good intentions it was actually a full ten years after the inauguration of the committee when Magendie finally made the first report on its behalf. Although this report occupied nearly sixty pages, it can be very briefly summed up: gelatine from bones could not take the place of meat; furthermore, animals died of starvation rather than eat the stuff.[4] There was no attempt to decide whether or not gelatine was actually harmful; it was merely stated that it was virtually useless as a food. A further report was promised for a later date. The resulting debate was heated. Some still maintained with d'Arcet that gelatine was a good food, others demanded that the Minister of the Interior have the use of gelatine suppressed.

In 1844 a letter from Holland was read in the Academy which thoroughly upheld Magendie's report and the newspapers played the matter up strongly. D'Arcet was not to be downed. He obtained other letters from Holland to bolster up his own contrary views. Magendie became utterly disgusted with the whole affair and on April 1, 1844, withdrew from the committee. When asked his motives for withdrawal he intimated that there was nothing more to be done; the answer to the problem had already been given. "In my opinion," he said, "it (gelatine) is a simple chemical product and by no means can it be considered food." Here the matter rested for a quarter of a century until besieged Paris tried to extract nutriment not only from bones but from even less promising material, and the Academy of Sciences again debated the food value of gelatine.

It was in 1841 that Claude Bernard became Magendie's préparateur at the Collège de France. The story of the choice of this particular interne from his ward at the Hôtel-Dieu for the post is told in detail by all biographers of Bernard, and its chief point seems to be the disconcerting effect of the elderly professor's brusqueness of manner.

[4] *Comp. rend. Acad. d. Sc.*, 13:237, 295, 1841.

Magendie is said to have suddenly noticed the skilful dissections made by this student and then, although he hardly knew the young man's name, to have shouted across the room, "Here, I'll take you for my préparateur!" This as it stands is not entirely credible, for in 1839 Bernard had not only attended Magendie's lectures at the Collège de France, but was mentioned by name as having made dissections for demonstrations, the references occurring both in James's lecture notes and in a communication by Magendie before the Academy.[5] Further, Bernard in describing the old laboratory at the Collège de France which served Magendie until 1840 said it was "a sort of small closet where *we two* could scarcely fit ourselves in." [6] It is probable that there has been a telescoping in the story of Magendie's first awareness of Bernard and the considerably later appointment at the Collège de France after Bernard had served for some time as a voluntary assistant there, and in the second year of his interneship at the Hôtel-Dieu. Van Tieghem says that as an interne Bernard had been discouraged by Magendie's uncompromising and even uncomplimentary manner, and although more interested in research than in the practice of medicine had almost decided that he could hope for nothing better than being a country doctor in the neighborhood of his birthplace, Saint-Julien. Rayer, on whose service Bernard had also acted, recognized that he was an exceptional student, and out of regard for his future intervened with Magendie on his behalf, and so smoothed the way for the appointment at the Collège de France. It will be observed that this account implies that Rayer bore Magendie no grudge for the rudeness with which the latter had attacked his joint report with Breschet on the subject of glanders. Evidently most people had acquired the habit of taking Magendie with a grain of salt.

[5] *Comp. rend. Acad. d. Sc.*, 8:865, 1839.
[6] Bernard, C., *Physiologie opératoire*, 1879, p. 63.

Bernard was not, however, the only medical student to be put off by Magendie's manner. J. Devasse has left us a revealing account of his externeship under Magendie in 1843.[7] The round of visits to the patients on the ward Sainte-Monique began at daybreak. Magendie himself was always punctual and demanded punctuality in others. First came the roll-call of students, then the professor, followed by a cortège of attending physicians, internes and students, passed from bed to bed. Magendie addressed his questions in a brusque voice, less with the intention of eliciting information from the patient as to her symptoms than with a view to disconcerting his medical colleagues, whom he twitted unmercifully regarding their mode of treatment. His lip seemed permanently curled in scorn, but beneath his sarcasm there was an essential kindness, and he exerted most meticulous care with regard to the patients' food and drink. The only medicaments which he would prescribe were simple tisanes and poultices, or, under exceptional circumstances, mustard plasters and blistering agents; he rarely prescribed pills, forbade "apozemes, baumes et julips" (decoctions, ointments and sweetened drinks). From his own "Formulary" he retained only morphine, quinine and Sedlitz salt. He, too, had a pet remedy, galvanism, which was always used in cases of nervous diseases. Not only the old mixtures of polypharmaceutical days —thériaque, discordium, opodeldock—were anathema to him, but the current remedies as well. Diet and plenty of fresh water were his chief remedial agents.[8] Although he

---

[7] Milcent, A., *Jean-Paul Tessier, esquisse de sa vie*, 1863.

[8] Magendie's heretical views regarding hospital regimen were publicized as far away as San Francisco. Soon after his death, the San Francisco *Evening Bulletin* for Sept. 16, 1856, reprinted from the June number for that year of the *American Medical Gazette* the impressions retained by an American medical student in Paris of one of Magendie's lectures, which read, in part: "Let me tell you, gentlemen, what I did when I was the head physician at the Hôtel-Dieu. Some 5000 or 4000 patients passed through

had a horror of the universal practice of bleeding, nevertheless a small sacrifice of 2-3 ounces of blood was frequently collected for use in his lectures at the Collège de France. Devasse at one period had charge of autopsies and he complained that although he spread out the choicest bits for the inspection of Magendie and his accompanying train, the elderly physician was not much interested.[9] He wanted only spinal cords for his current work on cerebrospinal fluid at the Collège de France. Devasse had entered the Faculty of Medicine with high aspirations and humanitarian, if somewhat vague, ideals, but when he was taught that medicine was a tissue of contradictions and errors, he was revolted and gave up his medical studies, only to return to them later when he realized that Magendie was right but in advance of his time. Nevertheless, the original impression had been so strong that even after his return to the wards he

---

my hands every year. I divided the patients into two classes; with one, I followed the dispensary and gave them the usual medicines without having the least idea of why or wherefore; to the other I gave bread pills and colored water, without, of course, letting them know anything about it—and occasionally, gentlemen, I would create a third division to whom I gave nothing whatever. These last would fret a good deal, they would feel they were neglected (sick people always feel they are neglected unless they are well drugged, the fools) and they would irritate themselves until they really got sick, but nature invariably came to the rescue, and all the persons in this third class got well. There was little mortality among those who received but bread pills and colored water, and the mortality was greatest among those who were carefully drugged according to the dispensary."

[9] From the same source as that of the preceding note we have: "Why, gentlemen, at the school of Montpellier (God knows it was famous enough in its day) they discarded the study of anatomy and taught nothing but the dispensary, and the doctors there knew just as much and were quite as successful as any others. I repeat it, nobody knows anything about medicine." Since the writer cannot parallel this extension of Magendie's scepticism to the efficacy of anatomy as a basis of medicine with anything equally drastic from the published lectures, it should be remembered that the American student did not profess to quote but only to reproduce a general impression.

seemed to see lurking in their corners "the mephistophelian smile of the old professor."

At the Collège de France Magendie almost at once turned over to Bernard the supervision of such matters as procuring meat for the dogs, hiring laboratory servants and purchasing laboratory apparatus. The laboratory accounts had more than once been a source of friction with the administrative officials of the Collège before Bernard's advent, and they continued to be so after it. A dispute over unpaid bills which was carried as far as the Minister of Public Instruction at the beginning of 1843 indicates that Bernard was responsible for the details of expenditure but Magendie's signature was a necessary preliminary to actual disbursement. The administration was rather plaintive in its correspondence with the Minister over this affair. The professor had originally had a budget of 1000 francs for his course and this had been increased at his request to 1300 francs, but he did not hesitate to spend what he wanted and the feeding of the dogs kept in the cellars of the laboratory ran into money. The administration washed its hands of financial responsibility for M. Magendie and could only suggest that "forbidding experiments on living animals and dissections would bring down the expenses of the course, which would then take a direction more theoretical than practical." While awaiting the Minister's decision in these matters, the administration would caution the professor not to spend any more money.

As regards their joint experimental research it would appear that at the beginning of their association Bernard acted strictly as assistant to Magendie. There are tales that Magendie objected to the use of his new and comparatively commodious laboratory quarters by his skilful and ambitious pupil for independent work and Bernard was obliged to maintain a humble working place at his own expense. It is probable that as long as he was merely the professor's préparateur he refrained from using the official laboratory for anything except actual collaboration on Magendie's projects. From the beginning each man wrote his papers independently of the other and no paper bears their names conjointly. The usual sources of information about the results of their work together are Magendie's contemporary reports before the Academy of Sciences and Bernard's published lectures of later years. Until 1844, when Bernard, having secured his M.D., was finally liberated from the routine of the medical course, the initiative was retained by Magendie, but from then on the younger man took the bit in his teeth and not only did the volume of his own publications increase rapidly, but even his collaboration was constructive and critical. This has already been pointed out in regard to Magendie's controversy with Longet in which Bernard supported his master by the more careful analysis of disputed experiments.

One of Bernard's earliest duties as research assistant was to collect cerebrospinal fluid for the investigations which were eventually reported in Magendie's second monograph on this subject, issued in 1842, in which the author acknowledged that many of the new experiments were undertaken with the help of M. Bernard, his préparateur at the Collège de France. Bernard's internship at the Hôtel-Dieu overlapped his appointment as préparateur by about a year and it was convenient for him to collect cerebrospinal fluid for Magendie's experiments from cadavers at the hospital. He told afterwards [10] of the method he devised for making these collections, and in his monograph Magendie mentioned as an improvement a change in the site of the incision for collection, which was now from the lower end of the spinal cord near the site of the modern lumbar puncture. His earlier method of cutting the neck muscles to arrive at the atlanto-occipital membrane had caused his experi-

[10] Bernard, C., Système nerveux, 1858, v. 1, p. 495.

mental animals to stagger and circle about. The symptoms which he now described in animals deprived of cerebro-spinal fluid, with avoidance of injury to the neck muscles, were immobility as if "overcome by astonishment," falling and inability to rise again. Increase of pressure by injection of additional fluid caused unconsciousness, and in one strik-ing experiment he returned the fluid after cooling it and found that the dog shivered violently as if in a severe chill. This pamphlet has the additional interest of being beau-tifully illustrated by the famous lithographer, H. Jacob, and so pleased was Magendie with the plates drawn from nature that he made especial mention of them in his preface.

Although there are no contemporary reports of results, there is evidence in later lectures of both Magendie and Bernard [11] that they made experiments on animal heat to-gether as early as 1842, subjecting various animals to extremes of both heat and cold. In a related experiment, they endeavored to find the lower limits of oxygen supply compatible with life by means of an ingenious system of tubes containing sulphuric acid and calcium chloride to remove water and carbon dioxide (in reality a closed cir-cuit respirometer). They found that reduction of oxygen to 3-5% was fatal for a rabbit.[12]

They also undertook an investigation of the old question of the seat of oxidation in the animal body. Before the Revolution, Lavoisier had concluded that combustion must take place in the lungs where the blood comes into contact with the oxygen of the air, and that this combustion must be the source of body heat. Only a short time before Ma-gendie and Bernard began their experiments, Becquerel and Breschet [13] had for the first time used electric ther-

[11] *Union méd.*, 14:183, 1850.
[12] Bernard, C., *Substances toxiques*, 1857, p. 115.
[13] Becquerel, A. C., and Breschet, G., *Ann. de Sc. nat. Paris Zool.*, 3:257, 1835; 4:243, 1835.

mocouples to register differences in temperature of the blood in the aorta and in the inferior vena cava. They found that blood leaving the heart was about one degree higher in temperature than that entering it, a finding which supported Lavoisier. Magendie and Bernard, on the contrary, thrusting long thermometers directly into the chambers of the heart itself, found that blood in the right ventricle was slightly warmer than that in the left, i.e., blood on the way to the lungs had a higher temperature than that leaving them, so that combustion in the lungs could not be the source of body heat.[14] A little later Magendie made measurements of the amounts of carbon dioxide in arterial and venous blood, and found that although this gas was present in both, there was more in venous than in arterial blood, a further argument against the lungs being the seat of oxidation. This result is to be found in a comment by Magendie at the Academy of Sciences in support of a paper which Gay-Lussac had presented in refutation of a recent publication by the German physiologist, Magnus.[15] Magendie and Gay-Lussac planned to carry out a series of experiments on this subject, but the work was never completed.

The animals used in the experiments involving introduction of thermometers into the heart were horses which were available to Magendie through his connection with the now permanent committee on equine hygiene, of which he was appointed president in 1843, continuing to hold this office until 1852. He was responsible for a great many experiments in connection with this committee, among them some spectacularly dangerous ones on mad horses carried out with the assistance of Bernard and Rayer at the veterinary college at Alfort. Ever since his early work on rabies he had retained a lively interest in "animal dementia." He had edited a section in Pierquin de Gembloux' two-volume trea-

[14] Bernard, C., *La chaleur animale*, 1876, p. 40.
[15] Gay-Lussac, J. L., *Comp. rend. Acad. d. Sc.*, 18:554, 1844.

tise on "Folie des animaux," where is to be found material ranging from strange tales of demented cats to a discussion of "immobility" in horses and its suggested cure by application of blistering agents to the forehead and neck.

In 1843 the subject under discussion by the equine committee was the nutritive quality of different kinds of hay, green grass and other forage. Dumas and Boussingault in their famous essay of 1841 had contended that animals could not synthesize fats or any other organic material in their own bodies, but had to obtain these substances directly from the vegetable world. Liebig of Germany sent a letter to the Paris Academy of Sciences in protest against this conclusion, claiming that fat could be made by herbivorous animals out of sugars and starches. Magendie spoke in support of Liebig and cited figures obtained by his committee on the proportions of ether-soluble substances in dry hay and in horse feces, *viz* 2% as against 6½%. Where could the fat have come from, if not from the animal itself? Both Boussingault and Payen, who were on Magendie's committee, stated that Magendie was mistaken in his figures. His reply to this accusation was a flight of Gallic oratory which contributed nothing to the scientific aspect of the question. Two weeks later, however, he apologized nicely, admitting that his figures were wrong; the fat in hay was 4½% and he considered himself silenced. It was a pity that he gave way so meekly on this occasion, for he was on the right track. Bernard was presently to show how wrong Dumas and Boussingault were. In one of his most striking experiments he proved that a dog fed exclusively on a diet of lean meat is able to form and store up in its liver glycogen, an animal starch closely allied to that made by plants.[16]

Since the investigations of the committee on equine hygiene at this time centered about digestion, Magendie

[16] Bernard, C., and Barreswill, C., *Comp. rend. Acad. d. Sc.*, 27:514, 1848.

turned wholeheartedly to this branch of physiology. The first formal memoir of the committee on this topic was read before the Academy in 1845. It contained the statement that saliva from the parotid gland of the horse had no action on starch, while mixed saliva from the other salivary glands had this property.[17] This was another case where Magendie stopped his experiment too soon. Although saliva leaves the parotid gland of the horse in an inactive state, the enzyme becomes active on mere contact with the air.[18] Bernard later described the method which they had used for obtaining saliva directly from the parotid duct [19] and it is evident that in their experiments parotid saliva would not be mixed with air, while the mixed saliva collected from the mouth would.

Bernard prepared for demonstration at the Collège de France pigeons and mammals with the pancreatic ducts ligated and was able to clear up the difference in results which had previously been obtained by Brodie and by Magendie on tying off bile ducts. Magendie had used dogs, and because of the anatomical arrangement in this animal had succeeded in tying off the bile duct alone. Brodie, using cats, had included the pancreatic ducts as well.[20] In the heated discussion which followed Bernard's explanations in the Société philomathique it was evident that the old conception of vitalism was not dead, since Dr. Gerdy, a surgeon at the Charité, refused to believe that Bernard's account was an explanation and held that Brodie and Magendie were probably both right. In Dr. Gerdy's opinion, the very fact that the experiments were performed on living animals precluded the possibility of constant results.[21]

[17] *Comp. rend. Acad. d. Sc.*, 21:902, 1845.
[18] Goldschmidt, H., *Zeit. f. physiol. chemie*, 10:273, 1886.
[19] Bernard, C., *Physiologie opératoire*, 1879, p. 505.
[20] Brodie, B. C., *J. de physiol. expér. et path.*, 3:93, 1823.
[21] Bernard, C., *Introduction à l'étude de la médecine expérimentale*, 1865, p. 322.

Sometimes the results of Bernard's experiments brought him into conflict with Magendie himself. Magendie had been one of the first to obtain pure pancreatic juice. Since this juice was coagulated by heat, he concluded that it must contain a protein.[22] Bernard repeated his experiments and obtained coagulation, but he found that he could account for this phenomenon on other grounds and concluded that pancreatic juice did not contain protein in solution. When he presented his facts to Magendie, the latter handsomely acknowledged his error in a lecture, saying: "I, who believed that one should never go beyond the evidence of his senses, had nevertheless passed the boundaries of brute fact in my experiment on pancreatic juice; and that is why I was mistaken. In short, I saw only one thing, that pancreatic juice was coagulated by heat; and instead of simply stating this result, I said: pancreatic juice must contain protein. If I had been satisfied with saying: pancreatic juice is a liquid coaguable by heat, I could not have been attacked." [23]

Magendie's lectures at the Collège de France for 1846 had as their principal subject the aspects of digestion in which he and others had been interested for the last few years, and many of the experiments were reproduced for this course. He had been particularly struck by the investigations of Bernard and his friend, the chemist, Barreswill, on the transformation of starch and sugar in the animal body as tested in the urine by Barreswill's new copper reagent. They found that a starving herbivore has urine characteristic of a carnivore since it is virtually living on its own tissues. Magendie injected starch into the veins of a fasting rabbit, and to his surprise found that the starch disappeared and sugar took its place in the blood within a very short time. He then thought that by feeding starving animals a

[22] Bernard, C., *Physiologie expérimentale*, 1880, p. 482.
[23] Bernard, C., *Pathologie expérimentale*, 1880, p. 484.

diet of starch he could improve upon the injection experiment, since he regarded the introduction of starch into veins as an unnatural process ("en dehors des phénomènes réguliers de la vie"). A dog fed on potatoes and lard not only had the urine of a herbivore but its blood contained sugar. He also found sugar in the blood of a horse fed on oats. Up to this time the presence of sugar in the blood had been considered to indicate a pathological condition. Magendie's results showed that sugar in the blood was a normal phenomenon, and he did not exaggerate when he said that he thought this discovery an important one for the study of diabetes mellitus.[24]

The collaboration of master and student is shown by the story of these experiments to have come round full cycle, for we here have Magendie pushing further a problem arising out of Bernard's independent research. This time there was no jealousy and resentment as had happened earlier when the work of Flourens and Longet had overlapped with his. Bernard was proud to have served his apprenticeship under Magendie, and he was sensible alike of the distinction and keenness of the older man's intelligence,[25] and of the great and salutary influence which he had exercized in the medical sciences by his introduction and sponsorship of the experimental method.[26] It is true that Bernard on one or two occasions felt obliged to apologize for the extremes to which the cult of experiment was carried by Magendie, who was fond of saying that he had only eyes and ears but no brain when he was experimenting,[27] with the variant that he had eyes (for facts) but no ears (for theory).[28] He seemed to be afraid of planned experi-

---

[24] *Comp. rend. Acad. d. Sc.*, 23:189, 1846.
[25] Bernard's own phrase is "un esprit d'élite et de premier ordre."
[26] Bernard, C., *Substances toxiques*, 1857, pp. 1-2.
[27] Bernard, C., *Pathologie expérimentale*, 1880, p. 482.
[28] Bernard, C., *Substances toxiques*, 1857, p. 30.

mentation as if the bias of a preconceived idea must inevitably invalidate his observation. He said: "Let the results of haphazard experiments collect and they will speak for themselves." [29] Bernard was well aware of the dangers of this procedure. He had resolved too many of the "contradictions" for which Magendie was almost notorious to be content with an empiricism too narrow to satisfy the demands of reason. However, he realized that Magendie's attitude was "instinctive and unconscious" (and perhaps pedagogical) rather than the result of any rigid and systematic conviction that experience was the only source of knowledge.[30]

We can add to our gallery of student portraits of Magendie as he appeared in the wards of the Hôtel-Dieu and at a lecture demonstration at the Collège de France another, contributed by Bernard, which shows him in the research laboratory. It is evident that it was not too easy for the reserved and serious young investigator to accustom himself to the vagaries of the chief arbiter of his fortunes. Bernard wrote:

"There was no resemblance between M. Magendie as a casual acquaintance and M. Magendie in the laboratory; in these two settings he was two quite different people. All who knew M. Magendie remember how affable and kindly he was with the world at large. But in the laboratory and in his scientific relationships his character changed completely and automatically took on the color of his peculiarities as a scientist, that is to say, of his deep antipathy for all argumentative discussion. When a young man, full of youthful enthusiasm, came to consult M. Magendie about ideas, about plans for work on which perhaps he based the highest hopes, he always suffered at M. Magendie's hands complete disillusion. This advisory frankness was often taken very ill. M. Magendie, however, believed that

[29] Bernard, C., *Physiologie opératoire*, 1879, p. 7.
[30] Bernard, C., *Pathologie expérimentale*, 1880, p. 515.

it was a useful test which prevented later and more painful disappointments. For if a man could allow himself to be discouraged by mere words, he had no right to enter on a career of experimental physiology, the realities of which so often overthrow our logical expectations. If someone else approached M. Magendie, not with ideas or plans, but with a fact, with an experiment of which he described the results, the first reaction of M. Magendie was always a contradiction: What you tell me is impossible, he would say; you are mistaken. This was a sort of ordeal to which M. Magendie seemed to subject all those whom he did not know. If, however, you opposed him and, sure of the truth of what you were telling him, tried to make him see it, he did not refuse to listen; on the contrary, he wanted persistence, and if you performed a good experiment proving clearly what you had told him, he was the first to acknowledge it cheerfully, and congratulate you, and thereafter you had his respect and sympathy." [31]

Bernard remarked in another place that he had had a long association with Magendie but had not come to understand him until quite late.[32] It would appear that their personal relationship ripened a good deal more slowly than their scientific one. The dedication of Bernard's thesis for his degree of doctor of medicine to Magendie in 1843 was probably a gesture of scientific homage, although such early dedications are apt to be the expression of personal attachment. Magendie had dedicated his, as we have seen, to his surgeon father. When Bernard married in 1845 both Magendie and Mme. Magendie were among the sponsors whose names appeared in the marriage contract. A little later, in 1849, when Bernard was made Chevalier of the Legion of Honor, his first reaction on receiving the announcement was to exclaim: "I am sure that it is to Magendie that I owe this." However, in spite of their great mutual esteem and good will for one another, it is to be doubted whether

[31] Bernard, C., *Substances toxiques*, 1857, pp. 28-29.
[32] Bernard, C., *Pathologie expérimentale*, 1880, p. 516.

Magendie and Bernard were at any time really intimate. By the time the younger man had overcome his flinching from the older one's brusqueries, the latter had become a little afraid of his pupil's solemn and undeviating devotion to his scientific calling. Much as Magendie respected Claude Bernard, he probably really liked Constantin James better.

James (1813-1871), who was the same age as Bernard and who had taken his doctor's degree in 1840, seems to have been a friendly soul, in later life full of anecdotes about his more illustrious associates, with a passion for travel and an amateur's taste for the bizarre in scientific investigation. He had edited Magendie's lectures at the Collège de France from 1838-1840, and after obtaining his medical degree had continued the work which he had begun under Magendie, publishing in 1841 a paper on a cure of facial paralysis and on neuralgias and their treatment. In 1843 James and Magendie took a trip together to Italy. They were particularly interested in the Cave of the Dog near Naples, and did a number of experiments on the properties of the gas floating over its floor. James described the reactions of the dog which the keeper had used daily for three years to demonstrate the effects of the gas. When the visitors appeared, it became very agitated in expectation of what was coming. Its master tied its legs and put it in the middle of the cave. The dog gasped and within a few minutes seemed to be dying, but revived completely upon being brought out into the fresh air. James and Magendie also performed careful autopsies on rabbits killed by the gas, and they were particularly astonished at the behaviour of a frog which the gas made leap more vigorously than it seemed possible for a frog to leap. They decided that the gas must irritate the skin. James himself got down on his knees and thrust his head into the cushion of gas. The results were vertigo and a severe pain in the chest, but recovery was rapid.[33] He

[33] James, C., *Gaz. méd. de Paris,* 11:781, 1843.

wrote an account of this "scientific journey to Naples with
M. Magendie," a veritable busman's holiday, and included
in it mention of experiments by the latter on varnishing the
hair of certain mammals, a procedure which without interfering with respiration led to a marked lowering of body
temperature and eventually to death. This experiment has
found its way into text-books of physiology, where James's
account of his trip is given as the reference.[34] Later Magendie was influential in having James sent by the Government to examine mineral springs and spas in France and
other countries, and the last recorded adventure of this
wandering disciple seems to have been a narrow escape
from being murdered on a railway train in 1871 on his way
back to Paris from Egypt.

[34] Schafer, E. A., *Text-book of Physiology*, 1898, v. 1, p. 727.

Photograph said to be of Magendie in his old age, found in Claude Bernard's album of small photographs of his intimate friends and presented to the author by M. Devay, Bernard's great-nephew.

13

SEMI-RETIREMENT, COMMITTEE ON
PUBLIC HYGIENE, LAST YEARS
1845-1855

*"Je persiste à soutenir la théorie que j'ai proposée, car
elle est basée sur les recherches nombreuses et un
examen consciencieux."* [1]

In 1845 Magendie retired from active duty at the Hôtel-
Dieu and began to spend more time at Sannois. He was
still carrying on experiments in the laboratory of the Collège de France, being, as we have seen, especially interested in the work of Bernard and Barreswill on carbohy-
drates. For his interesting experiment of 1846, in which he
showed that sugar was a normal constituent of the blood,
Magendie had a new collaborator, M. Ferrand, to whom he
referred as his préparateur at the Collège de France.
Whether or not Bernard still held this title also is not quite
certain, but in the same paper in which Magendie spoke of
the assistance rendered by Ferrand he also said that he had
asked Bernard to prepare a pigeon with blocked pancreatic
ducts for a similar blood-testing experiment. At all events,
in 1847 Bernard acquired the new title of "suppléant"
(deputy) to Magendie at the Collège de France, when he
began in May of that year to replace the professor in the
lectures of the summer course. Magendie himself continued
to give the winter course for another five years.

As Magendie grew older he became more conservative.

[1] *Phén. phys.*, 1842, v. 1, p. 247.

He, who in his youth had been indefatiguable in searching out new chemical compounds for use in medicine, now appeared as the active opponent of the introduction of one of suffering humanity's greatest boons, anesthesia. Ten years before, in March, 1837, he had injected into the veins of a dog "oenanthic ether," then recently discovered by Liebig and Pelouze in the distillate of wine lees. The dog was overcome and exhibited all the symptoms of alcoholic intoxication. The laboratory aide who prepared the solution for injection breathed the fumes and staggered as he brought the mixture into the lecture room. Magendie grasped the point that this substance could act on the mental faculties by mere inhalation, but said that he did not know whether it "stimulated the brain, altered the blood or modified the solids of the body." [2] His failure to follow up the implications of this observation is a perfect example of his lack of scientific curiosity about the answers to questions which he himself had raised. If another experimenter had suggested that these fumes produced a peculiar effect upon the nervous system, the chances are that Magendie, scenting encroachment upon his own preserves, would have carried the matter further and so have stood a very good chance of being the first to make anesthesia available for surgery.

This was not, however, the course followed by events. The first reports of the successful use of (sulphuric) ether in operations on human patients in the United States and England began to appear in French newspapers early in January, 1847. Magendie was absent from the meeting of the Academy of Sciences when the announcement was made of Jackson's discovery and Morton's use of it, and consequently he did not hear the enthusiastic report of Velpeau and the more cautious statement of Roux on their own use of this new agent in operations. At a subsequent

[2] *Phén. phys.*, 1842, v. 2, p. 20.

meeting of the Academy, Velpeau again reported excellent results from painless operations "by the aid of this precious discovery." Magendie was immediately up in arms. Such advertisement, in his opinion, "savored of the daily press which panders to the insatiable and avid taste of the public for the miraculous and impossible." It appeared to him that "for some weeks a certain number of surgeons have set themselves to experiment on man, and for an undoubtedly praiseworthy purpose—that of performing operations without pain—they intoxicate their patients to the point of reducing them, so to speak, to the state of a cadaver which one can cut and slice at will without causing suffering." The protest against rash experimentation on human subjects came rather oddly from a physician who many years before had experimentally scratched the retina of an unsuspecting patient! Magendie held that pain was necessary to prevent the surgeon from going too far. There was no need, moreover, "to make a man drunk for a little operation like excision or cauterization of hemorrhoids. Pain? Pain is one of the prime movers of life. As for myself, I should never allow my body to be handed over to a surgeon in a defenceless state." [3]

His main objection was sound; the use of ether was still in the experimental stage and wide-spread press notices might do more harm than good. However, to bolster up his argument he brought in the question of public morals. Might not some criminal take advantage of a defenceless female in this state of intoxication? Instantly there was a furore in the Academy and Magendie was shouted down. However, he was in earnest and wrote a strong letter to the *Journal des Debats* complaining of the way in which his objections had been treated in the press, and claiming that his attention had been called to cases which justified his apprehensions.

[3] *Comp. rend. Acad. d. Sc.*, 24:134, 1847.

The Academy met as usual on the following Monday and ether was the topic of the day. Flourens and Serres both read papers on its action on the nervous system. Roux demanded that Magendie cite these untoward cases at which he had hinted in his letter to the press. Magendie rose in reply. He said that what he had in mind was something of almost too delicate a nature to broach even in the bosom of the Academy of Sciences, but what he really was disturbed about was the erotic hallucinations evoked by ether. "Females thus inebriated had been seen to hurl themselves upon the operator, with gestures and propositions so expressive, that in this singular and novel situation, the danger was not for the patient but for the surgeon." And then poor Magendie was disconcerted by a hilarious burst of laughter from the Academicians assembled. The minutes state in parenthesis: "prolonged hilarity, interruptions." Magendie was perfectly serious and went on to say: "I should be very unhappy if my wife or my daughter had been involved in scenes of this kind." [4] Then he told of a case at the Charité in which a man went to the hospital for the simple operation of having his tonsils removed. Ether was inhaled, the operation was performed; subsequently, the patient was unable to stand, cried out, trembled, became pale and eventually had to remain overnight in the hospital, instead of walking home at once as he would ordinarily have done after so simple an operation.

At the next meeting of the Academy it was revealed that it had been Constantin James who had told Magendie about the tonsil case at the Charité, and that, furthermore, the operation had been performed by the famous surgeon, Velpeau. The latter was now up in arms and produced letters

[4] This is the only reference to a daughter. The name, Martine Gabrielle de St. Maurice, appears on the reverse side of Magendie's tombstone. The date of birth (1826) suggests that the inscription may refer to a daughter of Mme. Magendie by her previous marriage, and Magendie was perhaps here speaking of a stepdaughter.

from his internes to show that everything which Magendie had said had been grossly exaggerated. Moreover, James, Magendie's informant, had written Velpeau a letter as follows: "I do not know to whom you were alluding yesterday when you spoke of persons attending your clinic in a spirit of malevolence and hostility. All that I can say is that in being present at your rounds I had no other end in view than to become instructed in the properties of ether" (and here Velpeau, in reading the letter, interjected, "I hesitate to read the phrase which follows, but you will understand that I must do so.") "in the school which I believe to be the best for surgical talent." Magendie stuck to his guns; he would rather believe what Constantin James had told him than anything which Velpeau's three internes might say. He added:

"Furthermore, I avow that after having devoted so many years to work, which, if I am not deceived, has not been sterile in ideas redounding to the good of mankind, I should not have expected that anyone would represent me as the apostle of pain, and as spurning a useful discovery for the sole reason that I had not made it myself. What does it matter? It was on my conscience to fulfill a duty by putting my colleagues and society on guard against an innovation, which, if some day it has real usefulness, has already brought in its train disastrous consequences and can hereafter be the occasion of deplorable abuses."

Roux tried to calm the old gentleman by admitting that such erotic hallucinations as he had described would be a serious objection to the use of ether; he had seen nothing of this sort himself; besides, physicians worthy of the name might witness such behaviour without consequences which would besmirch the reputation of their profession.

Unfortunately, at the following meeting of the Academy of Sciences, February 22, Flourens in reading his account of the action of ether on the spinal cord attributed to Charles Bell the discovery of the functions of the dorsal and ventral roots of the spinal nerves. Magendie could hardly wait until Flourens sat down to shout that he had incontestable rights to this discovery.[5] He added that if he had not known of his honorable colleague's good will toward him, he might have mistaken his intentions and construed them as most unkind. He hoped that before committing his memoir to print Flourens would rectify his error. There was a further interchange of several short, sharp passages, which were nevertheless phrased in polite terms. Finally Magendie demanded that Flourens produce his evidence that Bell was to be credited with the discovery. Flourens complied at the first meeting in March. His whole argument was that Bell's 1811 pamphlet contained the complete discovery. He also brought up the circumstance that already in 1833, in the *Journal des Savants*, he had made a similar statement, and that Longet, who had received the Academy's prize in experimental physiology in 1842 for his work on the spinal nerve roots, had done the same, and Magendie had not protested.

Magendie's reply was that he had not protested in Longet's case because, as the report stated, he had refused to take part in the judging on the ground that the subject matter of Longet's memoirs was too close to his own work. He went on to speak of Bell, and this final pronouncement on their controversy was mildness and generosity itself. He said:

"Charles Bell had before me, but without my knowledge, the idea of cutting separately the spinal roots; he had likewise the merit of discovering that the anterior root influences muscular contraction more than the posterior. In regard to these points I have acknowledged his priority from the first. However, as to the establishment for these roots of distinct properties and

[5] *Comp. rend. Acad. d. Sc.*, 24:258, 1847.

functions, that the anterior preside over movement, the posterior over sensation, *this discovery belongs to me.*" [6]

This declaration, so dramatically made in the face of all his
scientific confrères, has the complete concurrence of the
writer. Magendie's outstanding trait of character was his
downright honesty. He could never be prevailed upon to
deviate from what he considered to be the path of truth,
although he was sometimes mistaken in his identification of
this path. Flourens, nevertheless, was not convinced, and
after Magendie's death, eight years later, he actually appended to the eulogy of his distinguished confrère, which
it was his duty as permanent secretary of the Academy of
Sciences to compose, some twenty pages of notes in fine
print, reviewing in great detail events relative to the discovery. Here he once more reiterated his unshaken belief
that Bell should have all the honor. It is almost impossible
not to feel, in the light of a careful consideration of the
actual wording of the original documents and subsequent
alterations of it, that Flourens was less than fair.[7] One
suspects that he had resented the close parallelism of some
of Magendie's work on the nervous system with his own,
and that he had allowed his resentment to warp his judgment in the Bell-Magendie controversy.

Flourens' introduction of Longet's name into the debate
provoked Magendie or, more probably, incited Bernard to
urge Magendie, to publish an additional paper on recurrent
sensitivity, a discovery which, he said, had been condemned
twice by the Academy, since memoirs in which it was described as an error had twice received the Montyon prize.[8]

[6] *Comp. rend. Acad. d. Sc.*, 24:320, 1847.
[7] It is unlikely that any great number of the members of the Academy of
Sciences were acquainted at first hand with the rare pamphlet of 1811,
written, not only in English, but in a style notably deficient in precision
and clearness.
[8] *Comp. rend. Acad. d. Sc.*, 24:1130, 1847.

This paper was written with the acknowledged help of his "customary collaborator, Dr. Bernard," and in it we find explanation of the appearance and non-appearance of the phenomenon in different experiments, to which allusion has already been made.[9] It was succeeded by two others (one being a general description of results and the other giving details of the data upon which conclusions were based) which supplement it by describing the effect on blood pressure of stimulation of the dorsal and ventral spinal nerve roots. It had been long observed that sensations and emotions, such as pain and fear, affect the heart. By means of a new cardiometer, an improvement on Poiseuille's original hemodynamometer, Magendie and Bernard were now able to register differences in pressure as low as one millimeter of mercury. They found that stimulation of a dorsal root in the lumbar region caused variations in blood pressure of as much as 20 millimeters; the same was true for a ventral root, provided the corresponding dorsal root was intact.[10] This is, of course, another manifestation of the phenomenon of "recurrent sensitivity," the only difference being that painful impulses were here indicated by their vascular effects, rather than by contortion of skeletal muscles. The reports of these final investigations of this subject by Magendie were the last formal papers to bear his name, and even in them the work was acknowledged by the older man to be essentially that of his collaborator. Magendie, who was now sixty-four, continued to comment on various papers and to give his reports as chairman of committees, but never after this did he present to the Academy any new experimental work of his own.

A rather sordid incident took place at this time, which perhaps arose out of mistaken reliance upon his reputation for kindness to those of lowly estate. He was called in 1847

[9] Cf. chap. 11, above.
[10] *Comp. rend. Acad. d. Sc.,* 25:875, 926, 1847.

to give testimony as an expert witness in the trial of a Mme. Laurens. The application of leeches was still a favorite practice in medicine and Magendie had recognized this long before in a lecture when he warned his auditors against the application of leeches to a woman's face if she cared anything for her beauty. Unscrupulous vendors sometimes tried to palm off already gorged leeches on purchasers, although in this condition they were, of course, useless. The charge against Mme. Laurens was that she had sold gorged leeches. Before the trial she came to Magendie urging him to use discretion in his testimony, and on her departure she left on the table an envelope which she said contained memoranda for his guidance. The envelope proved to contain 3000 francs and a letter begging him to procure dismissal of the case. When the trial opened, Magendie told of the attempted bribe. Mme. Laurens put forward the rather lame defence that it was a mistake to have written the letter, that she really had not intended to leave it behind and that she could not imagine how the money had got into the envelope; it must have occurred by accident, certainly without her knowledge. This sorry exhibition had no effect upon the tribunal except to bring about a sentence for the accused of one month's imprisonment and a fine of 300 francs. The unaccepted bribe was confiscated to be paid into the account of the Paris Infirmaries.

In the span of his sixty-four years Magendie by 1848 had witnessed the Revolution of 1793, Napoleon's spectacular rise to power and equally spectacular fall, the Restoration of the Bourbons in 1814 and the deposition of Charles X in the Revolution of 1830, and now he was to see the dethronement of Louis-Philippe in the Revolution of 1848 and the establishment of the second French Republic with Louis-Napoleon as its president. Neither this last political upheaval nor its sequel, the coup d'état of 1851 which ushered in the second empire, seem to have had any repercussions on Magendie's career. His work on the Committee of Equine Hygiene, which was responsible to the Minister of War, was uninterrupted by the changes in the Government, and he continued to take pride in its reports, five volumes of which appeared between his first appointment and his final resignation in 1852 at the age of sixty-nine. He considered it a great credit to the work of the Committee that the mortality of army horses had been reduced from 97 to 64 per 1000 in 1849 and to 52 per 1000 in 1851.

It happens that among the private papers in Magendie's portfolio, preserved in the Musée Gilbert, there is a letter, dated July, 1848, from a Danish physiologist in Copenhagen, apparently a former student, which gives not only a brief glimpse of a pleasant personal relationship, but illuminates for a moment the troubled state of all Europe in this turbulent year. Some of its expressions seemed curiously pertinent once more in 1941.

Copenhagen, July 9, 1848.

My ever dear master,

I was very glad that you sent M. M— to me. I have done everything I could for the success of his affair and it has gone very well. My wife and I have tried to make his stay in Copenhagen a little more agreeable for him. In these days when anything can happen, perhaps M. and Mme. Magendie will make their way through Germany to devote a few days to a little visit to Copenhagen. I have not got a fine country house with a billiard table, etc., etc., but we are very comfortable. Mme. E— says that it is a very long time since we have seen M. and Mme. Magendie. I asked M. M— when he arrived if you were still working away at physiology. He replied that you certainly were and he had a good deal to say about your cardiometer and recurrent sensitivity and the roots of the spinal nerves. I had my doubts about the latter, whereupon he asked me to try the experiment myself and see the thing. I find this very reasonable and I shall have done it before M. M— leaves, if he does not go off in too great a hurry. You do not hear anything about my work, perhaps, nevertheless I am not idle. Unfortunately I write in a language foreign to you. I have only a short memorial of Jacobson which I have translated into French and which I am sending you. He was not a friend of mine, but he was a distinguished man, and I appeared before our Academy to present this memorial. For the last few years I have been engaged on an extensive piece of work on the colossi of our seas, the great cetaceans, in which I have found much that is important for physiology. I hope to give you a detailed account of this some day or other. Ah, my dear M. Magendie, what a time of civil war and confusion we live in! One cries out, let us be at peace, let us be united, and that means, accept my views and act in concert with me or I will give you—! To become rich, we want to pillage the rich; to make our own country respected, we want to humiliate other countries, and man becomes a destructive animal. The Prussians and Germans in general have overrun our country. This is costing us a great deal, much more than the most magnificent provision for the arts and sciences would have cost. Mme. E— wishes to send to Mme. Magendie a small example of Danish work. She has chosen a little Amor from the group of the Graces by our Thorvaldsen. Mme. E— thinks that it would do very nicely on Mme. Magendie's dressing table.

Adieu, my dear master and friend,

Your E—

Perhaps the significance of this utterly unimportant scrap of paper which happens to have survived the years is to bear witness once again how little after all great events disturb the lives of those who do not happen to be drawn directly into their maelstrom.

Magendie seems to have received his appointment as president of a new "Advisory Committee on Public Hygiene" in 1848 under the auspices of the new Government, for it was in the autumn of that year that an epidemic of cholera, the problem first placed before the Committee, again made its appearance in France. The disease was as yet confined to the district around Dunkerque, and the Minister of Commerce requested Magendie, because of his experiences in Sunderland nearly twenty years before, to visit the town and make a first-hand study of conditions. This time he did not have to travel by stage-coach, which at his age may have been just as well, as it was late November, but he was able to begin his report from Dunkerque to the Minister in Paris with the assurance that he had proceeded as fast as the railway to the north could take him. He saw only victims who were recovering and concluded that the epidemic was over and so light that it could not really have been the true Asiatic cholera which had proved so devastating in 1832.

Both Flourens and Dubois commend the energy and sagacity which Magendie displayed in presiding over the Committee on Public Hygiene. Flourens thought that his influence was wholly salutary. Dubois is inclined to cavil and suggest that Magendie wasted time in parading his scepticism and pet prejudices. His views on contagion furnish a case in point. He still clung to his conviction that cholera was not contagious, although by now few French physicians agreed with him. We have already seen how his narrowly sceptical attitude to contagion in general had brought him into conflict with Breschet and Rayer regarding the communicability of horse glanders to man. He was proud of his scepticism because he considered it to be scientific. A solitary apparent exception, while not constituting disproof, nevertheless left the case non-proven. "Doubt," he had said rhetorically in one of his lectures, "and I do not speak of that scepticism which questions even what has been proved, doubt which is applied only to facts still obscure, to suppositions bare of proof, doubt, I say, is the seal of true wisdom." [11] In his opinion, the verdict in the case of cholera even in 1848 must still be "non-proven." He was

[11] *Syst. nerv.*, 1839, v. 1, p. 17.

therefore particularly scornful of the sanitary measures taken by the government in the attempt to prevent the spread of such diseases, and he did not hesitate to condemn outright the laws of 1822, for which Pariset had been responsible, providing for severe quarantine, detention in lazarets and the like. As far back as 1836 he had said in his lectures at the Collège de France that the sanitary code recognized five contagious diseases, typhus, cholera, yellow fever, leprosy and the pest, with the death penalty for infringement of the rules laid down to prevent their introduction into French territory, but in his opinion four of these five diseases were not contagious and should be written off the index; typhus alone he would let stand.[12] He pointed out that not only had he had months of intimate experience with typhus and cholera in their most virulent epidemic form without himself being stricken, but he had with impunity gone to Marseilles to study the pest and he had done experiments on injecting into dogs the black vomitus of yellow fever patients. Leprosy was the only one of the five diseases of the code with which he had had no first hand experience. The difference in his attitude toward typhus and cholera may have arisen from the results of the circumstance (unknown, of course, to him) that ordinary cleanly measures might protect one from the cholera, while in the case of typhus nothing but chance is a protection from the errant flea. He had been particularly struck by his observation that medical students would succumb to the typhus after only one visit to an infected ward, and that they did not transmit their infection to other occupants of their own lodging. He concluded that the disease had been communicated by means of the confined and polluted air of the ward.

His general theory was that infection occurred when "putrefying animal atoms" from a person suffering from the

12 *Phén. phys.*, 1842, v. 1, p. 63.

disease were "imbibed" through the pores of the skin, as he presumed to be the case in syphilis, or by the pulmonary epithelium, as he thought happened in typhus. Since "imbibition," a type of absorption, was to him a physical process, the transmission of communicable disease was to be regarded as a physical, as opposed to a "vital," phenomenon. A good deal of the controversy which raged about the subject was on this theoretical ground. Magendie once remarked, with sarcastic intention, that to avoid all contact with the "atoms" of infection it would be necessary not only that travelers from infected regions be restrained from entering an uninfected country, but that letters and merchandise be excluded as well. His logic was perfect, but his sarcasm is lost on us for whom such procedures are now a commonplace.

His opposition to the sanitary measures of his day as being not merely useless but ridiculous eventually bore fruit, and it was chiefly his reports which brought about a modification of the quarantine laws. Some have praised him for his success in ameliorating the difficulties which travelers experienced on entering France in the middle years of the nineteenth century; [13] others have blamed him for being responsible for the rescinding of "the sanest and most intelligent sanitary laws ever decreed." [14] In any case, so potent was his influence that it was not until six years after his death that the code was once more stiffened.

In 1848-1849 he gave his winter course as usual at the Collège de France and chose as his topic the role of sugar in the animal body. Before the course was over, Claude Bernard had discovered that puncturing the floor of the fourth ventricle of the brain caused sugar to appear in the urine. So enthusiastic was Magendie over this discovery that he could not wait for Bernard to publish his results in a

[13] *London Med. Times and Gaz.*, 11:558, 1855.
[14] Triaire, P., *Récamier et ses contemporains*, 1899.

formal report, but himself announced the discovery *viva voce* on March 26, 1849, as soon as the Academy had taken their seats. He was generous in his praise of Bernard, and he was also active in bringing the matter of the young scientist's nomination as Chevalier of the Legion of Honor in acknowledgment of his achievement before the Minister of Public Instruction at once. Dr. Constantin James is the source of the story that Magendie arranged to have the preliminaries kept quiet so that Bernard might enjoy the surprise of the actual accomplishment of the affair, and that Bernard's first thought on being apprised of his honor was that he was indebted for it to Magendie.

Magendie's voice continued to be heard from time to time in the Academy of Sciences, oftenest on his old topics for debate. The question of the manner in which cholera was spread was revived by the epidemic of 1849, and it was claimed that the effluvium from the vomitus and excreta of victims gave rise to the disease in other subjects, but Magendie persisted in his own view that the cholera was not contagious, unmoved by the fact that it was no longer shared by the majority of his colleagues. In 1850 a paper was read on the diet of Belgian miners and his contribution was to remind the Academy of the work of the Gelatine Committee and of his own experiments on the necessity for foods containing nitrogen. Upon occasion he could drive home the expression of a characteristic shrewd scepticism with a witty comment. The attention of the Academy was directed in 1851 to the case of a toad which was supposed to have emerged uninjured from a pebble in the heart of a willow tree where it had been imprisoned for centuries. Magendie was not impressed by the solemn report of Flourens, Duméril and others who had examined the credibility of the sworn statement of the only eye witness of the event, a workman who had cut down the tree. He said that he would have expected the toad to have been at least a little stiff after so long a sojourn in a pebble, or perhaps to show some characteristic distinguishing it from contemporary toads.[15]

Although relieved now for the most part of his formal teaching at the Collège de France, he still had a coterie of devoted disciples, who surrounded him with respect and deference, and hung on his every word. Visiting foreign scholars made a point of asking to be introduced to him. M. Dubois[16] thought that all these attentions, well-deserved as they may have been, had nevertheless rather spoiled the elderly scientist. Great prestige had changed a naturally obliging and generous disposition. Magendie had ceased to be the young professor whom everyone had known as being full of courtesy and kindness, whose manners had been polished and elegant. He was still good-natured enough when he wanted to be, but he was apt to indulge in the eccentricities of those crusty old scholars who seem to think that haughty abruptness and habitual rudeness are the "necessary consequences of their position." Nevertheless, M. Dubois insisted that Magendie had "never harbored malice against any man." Only in public and when acting in an official capacity did he assume disconcerting mannerisms. In his own house, or among his friends, he was once more an agreeable person, even-tempered and courteous.

The Academy did not cease to pay tribute to Magendie's reputation as a physician and still commissioned him to bring it news of its illustrious invalids. At its request he journeyed to Limousin to see Gay-Lussac who was suffering from "ossification of the aortic valves." He also called on Mirbel, but poor reports were soon to be made of his own state of health.

The winter course of 1851-1852 was his last at the Collège de France. At his opening lecture the audience, which

15 *Comp. rend. Acad. d. Sc.*, 33:115, 1851.
16 Dubois, F., *Mém. Acad. Imp. de Méd.*, 22:1, 1858, p. xxix.

consisted largely of physicians with a sprinkling of students
and ladies, gave him a loud ovation, for the newspapers
had just announced his elevation to the rank of Commander
of the Legion of Honor. This was among the last of his
official distinctions. A month later Spain made him Chevalier of the Royal Order of Charles III. His announced subject
for the course was contagious diseases, sanitary measures
and experimental toxicology, but the published notes suggest
that he did not stick to his text, but rambled from Bernard's
work on sugar to ferments and thereafter to an anecdote of
how, when Dubois-Reymond came to Paris to demonstrate
that contracting muscles developed a current of electricity,
he, with Becquerel, assisted in the experiments. He did not
hold with Dubois-Reymond's explanation, but thought that
merely putting the needles into the animal and bringing
them into contact with the body fluids might cause the gal-
vanometer to register. Again his scientific scepticism had led
him astray. He was right as far as he went, for "currents of
injury" are important phenomena, but "currents of action"
are no less real. This reminiscence was made the excuse for
cautioning his hearers to be wary of drawing hasty conclusions and to multiply experiments, advice which he would
have done well more than once in his lifetime to have followed himself. He told of having touched the human retina
without evoking pain, of experiments on animal heat, of the
futility of bleeding, of the effect of diet on the blood. "There
is still plenty to do," he said. "Let our successors trouble
themselves over the future. I bequeathe to them the thyroid,
the thymus, suprarenal capsules, the sympathetic nerve, etc.,
whose functions are totally unknown."

When Magendie was about seventy he began to be
troubled with shortness of breath. His appearances at the
Academy of Sciences became infrequent and he remained
for only a brief time when he did attend a meeting. He
complained that the hall was badly built; it lacked air.

There still exist his letters to the administration of the Collège de France making the same complaint regarding his quarters there. He said that there was lack of light and air in his amphitheatre, and the dampness in the laboratory had given his substitute painful rheumatism. He requested that more windows be inserted, and that the cellars be connected by drains with the street to allow the liquids from the animals to drain off. We have also a letter written February 26, 1853, showing his solicitude for Bernard's welfare by a request to the administrator of the Collège de France that he endeavor to find 1000 francs out of his 1852 budget "in favor of M. Bernard, for many years my collaborator, who has performed inestimable services in my laboratory and now replaces me in my course. He has made eminent discoveries and does honor to the Collège de France." It is probable too that Magendie's influence was of importance in securing for Bernard the award of the Academy's prize in experimental physiology four times, in 1847, 1850, 1851 and 1854. The fact that this prize involved a sum of money as well as scientific recognition could not have been without importance to Bernard at this stage of his career. In 1854 Magendie was chairman of the nominating committee for membership of the Academy of Sciences, and Bernard was elected in that year, after an earlier rebuff.

Magendie's health grew steadily worse and he suffered great pain, which he bore with fortitude. His symptoms point definitely to what now would be diagnosed as coronary sclerosis. Dubois said that Magendie had a "strange illusion" about his condition; that in another person he would have at once recognized such symptoms as denoting the presence of "one of those material lesions which afford an impediment to the free circulation of the blood," but in his self-diagnosis he blamed a "gouty product which, after circulating about the tissues in various forms, was finally deposited in the organs of circulation and respiration." Dubois seems to have been no nearer the truth than Magendie himself. If by "material lesion" he meant valvular trouble, as seems reasonable, because the emphasis in cardiac disease at that time was on the valves, this would have been picked up in listening to Magendie's heart sounds, an aspect of examination which would certainly not have been omitted in the case of this particular patient. In the absence of such murmurs, Magendie may be pardoned for thinking that some deposit in the tissues of his circulatory system was at the root of his troubles, although he was rather far afield when he extended his suspicions also to his respiratory organs.

With advancing age and illness he seemed to lose his habitual harshness. His colleagues began to forget his former gruffness, and he himself said, "You must understand that my severity increased in proportion to the value which I recognized in those against whom it was directed." When Bernard saw him for the last time, Magendie bequeathed to him his professorship at the Collège de France. "At least," he said, "I know that it won't fall to a molly-coddle."

Those who came to see him toward the end were struck by the grief of the old servant who had been with him for thirty years and who, according to Flourens, had made himself into a grotesque but convincing copy of his master. As Magendie lay dying, the old servant exclaimed, "Come back, my good master! Please, come back! We'll grumble together again."

Magendie died October 7, 1855, at the age of 72, at his country home in Sannois. The official report made at the Mairie the next morning states that the witnesses to his death were his nephew (by marriage), Dr. Charles Depuisay, and Dr. Charles Leconte, a friend of the family, giving his address as the Collège de France. The funeral took place on October 11 in the Madelaine, the corners of the canopy over the coffin being supported by Serres, Flourens, Dubois (d'Amiens) and Villermé, representing respectively the Academy of Sciences, the Collège de France, the Academy of Medicine and the Committee on Public Hygiene. Among the mourners was Claude Bernard, his pupil and immediate successor at the Collège de France. After the religious ceremony at the Madeleine, the funeral procession wound its way through the Paris streets to the famous old cemetery, Père Lachaise, where Andral delivered the funeral oration written by Serres, and both Dubois and Villermé spoke. It was eminently fitting that François Magendie should find his last resting-place only a few paces from that of the very man who had not precisely inspired, but rather provoked, his scientific début, and whose views had so often furnished a background against which his own could be set forth, Xavier Bichat.

REFERENCES

ANONYMOUS. Private Correspondence. *The Morning Herald*, March 27, 1823.

—— Acte d'accusation contre Edme-Samuel Castaing prévenu de l'empoisonnement et le soustraction de testament. *Moniteur universel*, p. 1336, Nov. 15, 1823.

—— M. Magendie from his Journal. *Lancet*, 1:439, 1823.

—— New Remedies. *Medico-chirur. Rev.*, 1:47, 1824.

—— Recent discoveries on the physiology of the nervous system. *Edin. Med. and Surg. J.*, 21:141, 1824.

—— To Richard Martin, Esq., M.P. for Galway. *The Times*, July 3, 1824.

—— Lord Byron. *The Times*, July 5, 1824.

—— Society for the Prevention of Cruelty to Animals. *The Times*, June 17, 1824.

—— New Institution for the Prevention of Cruelty to Brute Creation. *The Morning Herald*, June 17, 1824.

—— Hydrophobia. *The Times*, Sept. 20, 1824.

—— Dr. Hale's experiment on himself. *The Times*, Oct. 9, 1824.

—— Untitled (Magendie's reply to Dr. Lefort regarding immobility in horses). *Arch. gén. de méd.*, 15:292, 1827.

—— Magendie as a physiologist! *Lancet*, 9:71, 1828.

—— Abstract of a course of lectures on physiology delivering in Paris by M. Magendie. *Lond. Med. Gaz.*, 1:205, 1828.

—— Magendie's memoir on the brain. *Lond. Med. Gaz.*, 2:552, 1828.

—— Fragmens d'histoire et de biographies médicales contemporaines. *Gaz. méd. de Paris*, 1:212, 1830; 1:326, 1830.

ANONYMOUS. Cholera morbus. *The Times,* Dec. 30, 1831.

—— Magendie's Report. *Lond. Med. Gaz.,* 9:565, 1832.

—— French medical reasoning. *Lond. Med. Gaz.,* 10:29, 1832.

—— (Review) Leçons sur le choléra morbus faites au Collège de France par M. F. Magendie. *Lond. Med. Gaz.,* 11:213, 1832.

—— (Review) Nymphomania before puberty. *Am. J. Med. Sc.,* 21:228, 1837.

—— Sketch of Magendie by an American. *Med Times,* 2:77, 1840.

—— Célébrités médicales et chirurgicales contemporaines. *A chacun selon ses oeuvres.* Paris, Deloges éditeur, 1841.

—— Recueil des Travaux de la Société médicale d'Émulation de Paris, 30:——, 1850.

—— Memoir of Magendie. *Lond. Med. Times and Gaz.,* 11:558, 1855.

—— Magendie's Lectures. *San Francisco Evening Bulletin,* Sept. 16, 1856.

—— Final Report of the Commission on Medical Education. N. Y., 1932.

BARD, P. *Macleod's Physiology in Modern Medicine.* St. Louis, C. V. Mosby, 1938.

BARTHEZ, P.-J. *Nouveaux élémens de la science de l'homme.* Montpellier, 1806 (2e éd.); Paris, Baillière, 1858 (3e éd.).

BECQUEREL, A.-C. and BRESCHET, G. Premier mémoire sur la chaleur animale. *Ann. d. Sc. nat. zool.,* 3:257, 1835. Second mémoire sur la chaleur animale. *Ann. d. Sc. nat. zool.,* 4:243, 1835.

BELL, C. On the nerves; giving an account of some experiments on their structure and functions, which lead to a new arrangement of the system. *Philos. Trans. (Roy. Soc., London),* 111:398, 1821.

On the nerves which associate the muscles of the chest, in the actions of breathing, and expression. Being a continuation of the paper on the structure and functions of nerves. *Philos. Trans. (Roy. Soc., London)*, 112:284, 1822.

Second part of the paper on the nerves of the orbit. *Philos. Trans. (Roy. Soc., London)*, 113:289, 1823.

An exposition of the natural system of the nerves of the human body with a republication of the papers delivered to the Royal Society, on the subject of nerves. London, Spottiswoode, 1824.

On the nervous circle which connects the voluntary muscles with the brain. *Philos. Trans. (Roy. Soc., London)*, 116:163, 1826.

Lectures on the nervous system. *London Med. Gaz.*, 1:617, 1828.

The Anatomy and Philosophy of Expression as Connected with the Fine Arts. London, Bohn, 1865 (5th ed.).

Letters of Sir Charles Bell, K.H., F.R.S.L. & E., selected from his correspondence with his brother George Joseph Bell. London, J. Murray, 1870.

BÉRARD, F.-J. *Doctrine médicale de l'école de Montpellier et comparison de ces principes avec ceux des autres écoles d'Europe.* Montpellier, 1819.

BERNARD, C. Recherches anatomiques et physiologiques sur la corde du tympan, pour servir à l'histoire de l'hémiplégie-faciale. *Ann. méd.-psychol.*, 1:408, 1843.

Leçons sur les effets des substances toxiques et médicamenteuses. Paris, Baillière, 1857.

Leçons sur la physiologie et la pathologie du système nerveux. Paris, Baillière, 1858. 2 vols.

Introduction à l'étude de la médecine expérimentale. Paris, Baillière, 1865.

Rapport sur les progrès et la marche de la physiologie générale en France. Paris, Impr. impériale, 1867.

Leçons sur la chaleur animale. Paris. Baillière, 1876.

Leçons sur le diabète et la glycogenèse animale. Paris, Baillière, 1877.

Physiologie opératoire. Paris, Baillière, 1879.

Leçons de pathologie expérimentale. Paris, Baillière, 1880.

BERNARD, C., and BARRESWIL, C. De la présence du sucre dans le foie. *Comp. rend. Acad. d. Sc.,* 27:514, 1848.

BEST, C. H., and TAYLOR, N. B. *The physiological basis of medical practice.* Baltimore, Williams & Wilkins, 1939.

BICHAT, X. Mémoire sur la membrane synoviale des articulations. *Mém. d. Soc. méd. d'émulation,* 2:350-370, 1799.

Dissertation sur les membranes et sur leurs rapports généraux d'organization. *Mém. d. Soc. méd. d'émulation,* 2:371-385, 1799.

Mémoire sur les rapports qui existent entre les organes à la forme symétrique et ceux à forme irrégulière. *Mém. d. Soc. méd. d'émulation,* 2:477-487, 1799.

Recherches physiologiques sur la vie et la mort. Paris, Brosson, Gabon et Cie., An viii (1800). 4e éd. Revue et augmentée de notes par F. Magendie, 1822. 5e éd. Revue et augmentée de notes pour la deuxième fois par F. Magendie, 1829.

Traité des membranes en général et de diverses membranes en particulier. Paris, Richard, Caille et Ravier, 1800. Nouvelle éd., revue et augmentée de notes par M. Magendie, 1827.

Anatomie générale, appliquée à la physiologie et à la médecine. Paris, Brosson, Gabon et Cie., 1801.

BING, F. C. A forgotten contribution to nutrition by Magendie. *Science,* N.S., 74:456, 1931.

BOURDON, I. *François Magendie. La Dictionnaire de la Conversation.* Paris, Fermin Didot, 1868.

BRODIE, B. C. Expériences sur l'usage de la bile dans la digestion. *J. de Physiol. exp. et path.,* 3:93, 1823.

BUSQUET, P. Chaussier (François). *Les Biographies médicales*, 1:37, 1927.

Duméril (André-Marie-Constant). *Les Biographies médicales*, 1:133, 1927.

Guillaume Dupuytren (Le Baron). *Les Biographies médicales*, 3:1, 1929; 3:17, 1929.

Bichat (Marie-François-Xavier). *Les Biographies médicales*, 3:33, 1929.

Boyer, Alexis (Le Baron). *Les Biographies médicales*, 3:165, 1929.

CARNOT, P. *La clinique médicale de l'Hôtel-Dieu et l'oeuvre de Pr. Gilbert*. Paris, Baillière, 1927.

CARREL, A., and LINDBERGH, C. A. *The Culture of Organs*. New York, Hoeber, 1938.

CHAMBERS, J. S. *The conquest of cholera*. New York, Macmillan, 1938.

CHEREST, J. Recherches historiques sur la Société, son origine, ses fondateurs, ses travaux. *Recueil des travaux de la Soc. méd. d'émulation de Paris*, 30:5, 1850.

CLOQUET, H. *Traité de l'anatomie descriptive redigé d'après l'ordre adopté à la Faculté de Médecine de Paris*. Paris, Crochard, 1831-1832.

CORNILLEAU, R. Un "médecin de banlieue" d'autrefois: Pierre-Paul Retoli. *Progrès méd.*, 15:76, 1938.

CORVISART, J. N. Nouvelle méthode pour reconnaître les maladies internes de la poitrine par la percussion de cette cavité, par Auenbrugger, ouvrage traduit du latin et commenté par J. N. Corvisart. Paris, Migueret, 1808.

COUDIE, D. F. (Review) Leçons sur le sang, et les alterations de ce liquide dans les maladies graves. Par Prof. Magendie. *Am. J. Med. Sc.*, 25:135, 1839.

COUSIN, V. *De l'enseignement et de l'exercise de la médecine et de la pharmacie*. Paris, Baillière, 1850.

CRUVEILHIER, J. *Traité d'anatomie descriptive.* Paris, P. Asselin, 1877.

CUVIER, G. Analyse des travaux de la classe des sciences mathématiques et physiques de l'Institut, pendant l'année 1809. *Mém. de l'Inst. de Fr.,* —:51, 1810.
Analyse des travaux de la classe des sciences mathématiques et physiques de l'Institut, pendant l'année 1811. *Mém. de l'Inst. de Fr.,* —:79, 1812.

CUVIER, M. le Chev., Analyse des traveaux de l'Académie Royale des Sciences pour les années 1813, 1814, 1815. Partie physique. *Mém. de l'Inst.,* pp. cxvii-ccxxxvi.

CUVIER, G., and DUMÉRIL, A.-M.-C. Rapport. *Procès-verb. Acad. d. Sc.,* 9:148, 1828.

DALTON, J. C. Magendie as a physiologist. *Internat. Rev.,* 8:120, 1880.

DAWSON, PERCY M., M.D. A biography of François Magendie. *Med. Libr. Hist. J. (of Brooklyn),* 4:45-56, 1906.

DELAUNAY, P. Le corps médical et le choléra en 1832. *Médecine internat. illustrée,* Oct., 1931.

DELHOUME, L. *Dupuytren.* Paris, Baillière, 1935.

DELILLE, R., and MAGENDIE, F. Examen des effets de l'upas antiar et de plusieurs substances émétiques. *Procès-verb. Acad. d. Sc.,* 4:242, 1809; 4:275, 1809.

DESMOULINS, A. *Anatomie des systèmes nerveux des animaux à vertèbres, appliquée à la physiologie et à la zoologie.* Paris, Méquignon-Marvis, 1825. 2 vols.

DUBOIS, F. Éloge de M. Magendie. *Mém. Acad. Imp. de Méd.,* 22:1, 1858.

FLINT, A., JR., Considerations historiques sur les propriétés des racines des nerfs rachidiens. *J. de l'Anat. et Physiol.,* 5:520, 1868.

FLOURENS, P., Nouvelles expèriences sur le système nerveux. *Mém. Acad. d. Sc.,* 9:478, 1830.
Recherches expérimentales sur les propriétés et les fonc-

tions du système nerveux dans les animaux vertébrés. Paris, Baillière, 1842 (2ᵉ éd.).

Éloge historique de François Magendie. Paris, Firmin Didot Frères, Fils et Cie., 1858; also *Mém. Acad. d. Sc.*, 33:1, 1861.

FOURIER, M. LE BARON. Éloge historique de M. le Marquis de Laplace. *Mém. Acad. d. Sc.*, 10:81, 1831.

FULTON, J. F. *Selected Readings in the history of physiology.* Springfield, Ill., Thomas, 1930.

GAY-LUSSAC, J. L. Observations critiques sur la théorie des phénomènes chimiques de la respiration. *Comp. rend. Acad. d. Sc.*, 18:546, 1844.

GENTY, M. Bichat et son temps. *La Médecine internat.*, vols. 42-43, 1934-1935.

Magendie (François). *Les Biographies médicales*, 9:113, 1935; 9:129, 1935.

GODMAN, J. D. Mémoire physiologique sur le cerveau, par M. Magendie. *Am. J. Med. Sc.*, 3:157, 1828.

GOLDSCHMIDT, H. Zur Frage: Ist im Parotidenspeichel ein Ferment vorgebildet vorhanden oder nicht? *Zeit. f. Physiol. Chemie*, 10:273, 1886.

GOLTZ, F. Der Hund ohne Grosshirn. *Arch. f. d. Ges. Physiol.*, 51:570, 1892.

GRANDVOINET, J. A. Examen critique de l'esprit et des propositions principales de l'ouvrage intitulé Leçons sur les phénomènes physiques de la vie. Thèse défendue à Montpellier. Montpellier, 1838.

GROEBBELS, F. *Der Vögel.* Berlin, Borntraeger, 1932. 2 vols.

GUIZOT, F. *Essai sur l'Histoire et sur l'État Actuel de l'Instruction Publique en France.* Paris, Maradan. 1816.

Mélanges Biographiques et Littéraires. Paris, Michel Lévy Frères, 1828.

GUNTHER, R. T. *Early Science in Cambridge.* Oxford University Press, 1937.

HAWKINS, B. Medical Statistics. *Lond. Med. Gaz.*, 1:713, 1828.

HOEFER, ——. *Nouvelle biographie générale.* Paris, Firmin Didot Frères, 1863.

HOPE, MRS. ANNE (FULTON). *Memoir of the late James Hope, M.D.* London, J. Hachard & Son, 1844. 3rd ed.

HOPE, J. *A treatise on the diseases of the heart and great vessels; comprising a new view of the heart's action, according to which physical signs are explained.* London, W. Kidd, 1832.

HUNTER, W. Anatomical Notes taken from a course of Dr. Hunter's lectures by W. D., January 20, 1775. MS in the Sutro Branch of the California State Library, San Francisco.

JAMES, C. Grotte d'ammoniaque. Recherches et expériences pendant un voyage à Naples avec M. Magendie. *Gaz. méd. de Paris*, 11:781, 1843.

KELLEY, E. C. Medical Classics. *Science, N.S.*, 87:167, 1938.

KOPPANYI, I. The rise of Pharmacology. *Sc. Monthly*, 41:316, 1935.

LEFORT, ——. Du fluide encephalo-rachidien. *Arch. gén. de Méd.*, 15:140, 1827.

LOEB, J. *The Mechanistic Conception of Life.* University of Chicago Press, 1912.

LONGET, F. A. Fait physiologique relatif aux racines des nerfs rachidiens. *Comp. rend. Acad. d. Sc.*, 8:881, 1839. Influence des nerfs de la sensibilité sur les nerfs du mouvement. *Comp. rend. Acad. d. Sc.*, 8:919, 1839. *Anatomie et physiologie du système nerveux de l'homme et des animaux vertébrés.* Paris, Fortin, Masson, 1842. 2 vols. Nouvelles expériences relatives à la soustraction du liquide céphalo-rachidien, et à l'influence des muscles cervicaux postérieurs et du ligament sur-épineux sur la locomotion. *Comp. rend. Acad. d. Sc.*, 20:1742, 1845.

LUCAS-DUBRETON, J. *Louis-Philippe.* Paris, Foyard, 1938.

LUTAUD, A. Les médecins dans Balzac. *Bull. Soc. fr. d'hist. de la méd.*, 14:373-381, 1920.

MACKINTOSH, J. Cruelty to Animals Bill. *Hansard's Parliamentary Debates*, 12:1005, 1825.

MAGENDIE, F. Essai sur les usages du voile du palais, avec quelques propositions sur la fracture du cartilage des côtes; présenté et soutenu à l'École de Médecine de Paris, le 24 mars 1808, par Magendie de Bordeaux, aide d'Anatomie à l'École de Médecine de Paris; membre de la Société anatomique. Paris, Didot jeune, 1808.

Quelques idées générales sur les phénomènes particuliers aux corps vivans. *Bull. d. Sc. méd. de la Soc. méd. d'émulation*, 4:145-170, 1809.

Examen de l'action de quelques végétaux sur la moelle epinière. *Bull. Soc. philomat.*, 1:368, 1809.

Expériences pour servir à l'histoire de la transpiration pulmonaire. *Bull. Soc. philomat.*, 2:252, 1811.

Vomissement. *Procès-verb. Acad. d. Sc.*, 5:152, 1813; 5:174, 1813.

L'epiglotte et ses usages dans le déglutition. *Procès-verb. Acad. d. Sc.*, 5:192, 1813; 5:205, 1813.

Mémoire sur les images qui se forment au fond de l'oeil et sur un moyen très simple de les apercevoir. Paris, 1813.

L'influence de l'émetique sur l'homme et sur les animaux. *Procès-verb. Acad. d. Sc.*, 5:244, 1813.

L'action de l'oesophage. *Procès-verb. Acad. d. Sc.*, 5:252, 1813; 5:447, 1814.

Déglutition de l'air. *Procès-verb. Acad. d. Sc.*, 5:596, 1815. (Footnote) *Bull. Soc. philomat.*, 4:199, 1815.

Précis élémentaire de Physiologie. Paris, Méquignon-Marvis, vol. i, 1816, viii, 326 pp.; vol. ii, 1817, viii, 473 pp.; 2ᵉ éd. 1825; 3ᵉ éd. 1834; 4ᵉ éd. 1836.

Note sur les gaz intestinaux de l'homme sain. *Bull. Soc. philomat.*, 4:129, 1816.

Mémoire sur propriétés nutritives des substances qui ne contiennent pas d'azote. *Bull. Soc. philomat.*, 4:137, 1816.

Note sur un individu qui peut avaler sa langue. *Bull. Soc. philomat.*, 4:157, 1816.

L'action des artères dans la circulation. *Procès-verb. Acad. d. Sc.*, 6:155, 1817; 6:175, 1817.

L'acide prussique. *Procès-verb. Acad. d. Sc.*, 6:236, 1817; 6:489, 1819.

Physiological and chemical researches on the use of prussic acid or hydro-cyanic acid in the treatment of diseases of the breast, and particularly in phthisis pulmonalis. Translated from the French, with notes, etc., by James G. Percival, M.D. New Haven, Howe & Spalding and A. M. Maltby & Co., 1820.

Note sur l'emploi de quelques sels de morphine comme médicamens. *Bull Soc. philomat.*, —:54, 1818.

Reflexions sur un mémoire de M. Portal, relatif au vomissement. *Bull Soc. philomat.*, —:107, 1818.

Recherches physiologiques et médicales sur les causes, les symptômes et le traitement de la gravelle; avec quelques remarques sur la conduite et le régime qui doivent suivre les personnes auxquelles on a extrait des calculs de la vessie. Paris, Méquignon-Marvis, 1818.

Note sur les nerfs mésentériques du Pic-Verd. *Bull. Soc. philomat.*, —:119, 1819.

Note sur l'anatomie du cigne. *Bull. Soc. philomat.*, —:135, 1819.

Mémoire sur plusieurs organes particuliers qui existent

chez les oiseaux et les reptiles. *Bull. Soc. philomat.*, —:145, 1819.

Le méchanisme de l'absorption chez les animaux à sang rouge et chaud. *Procès-verb. Acad. d. Sc.*, 7:109, 1820.

Formulaire pour l'emploi et la préparation de plusieurs nouveaux médicaments, tels que la noix vomique, la morphine, l'acide prussique, la strychnine, la vératrine, les alcalis des quinquinas, l'iode, etc. Paris, Méquignon-Marvis, 1821.

Mémoire sur les organes de l'absorption chez les mammifères. *J. de physiol, expér.*, 1:1, 1821.

Expériences sur les fonctions des racines des nerfs rachidiens. *J. de physiol. expér. et path.*, 2:276, 1822.

Expériences sur les fonctions des racines des nerfs qui naissent de la moelle épinière. *J. de physiol. expér. et path.*, 2:366, 1822.

(Verbal communication on discovery of functions of dorsal and ventral spinal nerve roots.) *Procès-verb. Acad. d. Sc.*, 7:348, 1822.

(Note on Flourens' paper on cerebellum.) *J. de physiol. expér. et path.*, 3:95, 1823.

Note sur le siège du mouvement et du sentiment dans la moelle épinière. *J. de physiol. expér. et path.*, 3:153, 1823.

Note sur les fonctions des corps striés et des tubercules quadrijumeaux. *J. de physiol. expér. et path.*, 3:376, 1823.

Histoire d'un hydrophobe traité à l'Hôtel-Dieu de Paris, au moyen de l'injection de l'eau dans les veines. *J. de physiol. expér. et path.*, 3:382, 1823.

Le nerf olfactif est-il l'organe de l'odorat? Expériences sur cette question. *J. de physiol. expér. et path.*, 4:169, 1824.

De l'influence de la cinquième paire des nerfs sur la

nutrition et les fonctions de l'oeil. *J. de physiol. expér. et path.*, 4:176, 1824; 4:302, 1824.

Mémoire sur les fonctions de quelques parties du système nerveux. *J. de physiol. expér. et path.*, 4:399, 1824.

Effets qui proviennent de la lésion de la grande commissure du cervelet au-dessus du passage de la cinquième pair. *Procès-verb. Acad. de Sc.*, 8:57, 1824.

Observations faites sur un sourd-muet de naissance guéri de son infirmité à l'âge de neuf ans. *Procès-verb. Acad. d. Sc.*, 8:231, 1825.

(Note on goitre.) *Procès-verb. Acad. d. Sc.*, 8:281, 1825.

Mémoire sur la liquide qui se trouve dans le crâne et l'épine de l'homme et des animaux vertèbres. *J. de physiol. expér. et path.*, 5:27, 1825.

Sur l'insensibilité de la retine de l'homme. *J. de physiol. expér. et path.*, 5:37, 1825.

L'application directe du galvanisme aux nerfs de l'orbite, et sur l'emploi de ce moyen pour le traitement de l'amaurose. *Procès-verb. Acad. d. Sc.*, 8:395, 1826; cf. *J. de physiol. expér. et path.*, 6:156, 1826.

An Elementary Compendium of Physiology; for the Use of Students. Translated from the 2nd edition (of the *Précis élémentaire de Physiologie*) by E. Mulligan, M.D. Edinburgh, John Carfrae & Son, 1826.

Mémoire sur le liquide qui se trouve dans crâne et l'épine de l'homme et des animaux vertébrés. *J. de physiol. expér. et path.*, 7:1, 17, 66, 1827.

Ligature de l'artère carotide primitive. *J. de physiol. expér. et path.*, 7:180, 1827.

(Reply to Lefort's attack on Magendie's work on cerebrospinal fluid.) *Arch. gén. de méd.*, 15:140, 1827.

Mémoire physiologique sur le cerveau. *J. de physiol. expér. et path.*, 8:211, 1828.

Lectures on Experimental Physiology. *Lond. Med. Gaz.*, 1: 1828.

(Note on Bell's attitude towards animal experimentation.) *J. de physiol. expér. et path.*, 10:190, 1830.

(Note on Bell's attitude regarding Bell-Magendie controversy.) *J. de physiol. expér. et path.*, 10:1, 1830.

(Letter to the President of the Academy of Sciences.) *Gaz. méd. de Paris*, 2:444, 1832.

(Letter to English Ambassador.) *Moniteur universel*, Jan. 20, 1832.

Leçons sur le choléra morbus. Paris, Méquignon-Marvis, 1832.

(Verbal communication on continued abnormal growth in a woman 34 years old.) *Procès-verb. Acad. d. Sc.*, 10:462, 1834.

(Verbal communication on use of ammonium nitroprusside.) *Comp. rend. Acad. d. Sc.*, 1:80, 1835.

M. Magendie présente à l'Académie un jeune officier polonais. *Comp. rend. Acad. d. Sc.*, 2:447, 1836.

Traitement de certaines affections nerveuses par l'électro-puncture des nerfs. *Comp. rend. Acad. d. Sc.*, 5:855, 1837.

(Note on treatment of amaurosis by galvanism.) *Comp. rend. Acad. d. Sc.*, 5:856, 1837.

Mémoire sur l'origine des bruits normaux du coeur. *Mém. Acad. d. Sc.*, 14: 155, 1838.

Quelques nouvelles expériences sur les fonctions du système nerveux. *Comp. rend. Acad. d. Sc.*, 8:865, 1839.

Lettre de M. Magendie. *Bull. Acad. méd. Paris*, 3:965, 1839.

Leçons sur les fonctions et les maladies du système nerveux, professées au Collège de France. Paris, Ébard, 1839-1841.

(Comments on Breschet's memoire on glanders.) *Comp. rend. Acad. d. Sc.*, 10:223, 1840.

Rapport fait à l'Académie des Sciences au nom de la

Commission dite *de la gélatine*. *Comp. rend. Acad. d. Sc.*, 13:237-283, 1841.

Phénomènes physiques de la vie. Leçons professées au Collège de France. Paris, Baillière, 1842.

Recherches physiologiques et cliniques sur le liquide céphalo-rachidien ou cérébro-spinal. Paris, Mequignon-Marvis, 1842.

Communication relative à un cas de cow-pox, et à l'inoculation de la manière de pustules sur plusieurs enfants. *Comp. rend. Acad. d. Sc.*, 18:986, 1844.

Étude comparative de la salive parotidienne et de la · salive mixte du cheval, sous le rapport de leur composition chimique et de leur action sur les aliments. *Comp. rend. Acad. d. Sc.*, 21:902, 1845.

Note sur le présence normal du sucre dans le sang. *Comp. rend. Acad. d. Sc.*, 23:189, 1846.

(Comments on ether.) *Comp. rend, Acad. d. Sc.*, 24:134, 1847; 24:258, 1847.

(Reply to Flourens.) *Comp. rend. Acad. d. Sc.*, 24:320, 1847.

Note sur la sensibilité récurrente. *Comp. rend. Acad. d. Sc.*, 24:1130, 1847.

De l'influence des nerfs rachidiens sur les mouvements du coeur. *Comp. rend. Acad. d. Sc.*, 25:875, 926, 1847.

Leçons faites au Collège de France par M. Magendie. Sur le chaleur animale. *Union méd.*, 14:183, 1850.

(Comment on toad.) *Comp. rend. Acad. d. Sc.*, 33:115, 1851.

MAGENDIE, F., and DUMÉRIL, A.-M.-C. Traitement des maladies scrofuleuses à l'Hôpital Saint-Louis par les préparations de l'iode. *Procès-verb. Acad. d. Sc.*, 9:562, 1831.

MAGENDIE, F., and PELLETIER, P. Recherches chimiques et physiologiques sur l'Ipécacuanha. *J. univ. d. sc. méd.*, 4:322, 1816.

Extrait d'un mémoire intitulé recherches chimiques et physiologiques sur l'Ipécacuanha. *Bull. Soc. philomat.,* —:60, 1817.

Suite du mémoire de MM. Magendie et Pelletier sur l'Ipécacuanha. *Bull. Soc. philomat.,* —:71, 1817.

Des recherches chimiques et physiologiques sur l'Ipéca-cuanha. *Procès-verb. Acad. d. Sc.,* 6:156, 1817; 6:166, 1817.

MARTIN, R. Cruelty to animals bill. *Hansard's Parliamentary Debates,* iv s., 12:657, 1825; 12:1002, 1825.

MAYO, H. *Anatomical and Physiological Commentaries,* 2:10, 1823.

McCAY, C. M. Was Magendie the first student of vitamins? *Science, N.S.,* 71:315, 1930.

MENETRIER, M. P. Documents inédits concernant Magendie. *Bull. Soc. fr. d'hist. de la méd.,* 20:251-258, 1926.

MILCENT, A. *Jean-Paul Tessier, esquisse de sa vie, de son enseignement, de sa doctrine. Suivi d'une lettre sur Magendie, Récamier, J.-P. Tessier par le docteur De-vasse.* Paris, Baillière, 1863.

MÜLLER, J. Bestätigung des Bellschen Lehrsatzes. *Frorieps Notizen,* No. 646,647.

Nouvelles expériences sur l'effet que produit l'irritation méchanique et galvanique sur les racines des nerfs spinaux. *Ann. d sc. nat.,* Sér. 1, 23:95, 1831.

Handbuch der Physiologie des Menschen für Vorlesungen. Coblenz, J. Hölscher, 1835.

NORDENSKIÖLD, E. *The History of Biology, a Survey.* New York, Tudor Publishing Co., 1935.

OLMSTED, J. M. D. "Medical Classics." *Science, N.S.,* 86:520, 1937.

Claude Bernard, Physiologist. New York, Harper, 1938.

A letter from Felix Pascalis of New York to François Magendie in 1826. *Ann. Med. Hist.,* 3rd ser., 2:371, 1940.

French medical education as a legacy from the Revolution. *Essays in Biology in Honor of Herbert Evans.* University of California Press, 1943.

The Aftermath of Charles Bell's famous "Idea." *Bull. Hist. Med.*, 14:341, 1943.

ORFILA, M. J. B. *Traité des poisons tirés des règnes minéral, végétal et animal, ou toxicologie générale.* 2ᵉ éd. Paris, Crochard, 1818.

PELLETIER, P.-J. and CAVENTOU, J.-B. Nouvel alcali végétal, la vanqueline, trouvée dans la noix vomique et la fève Saint-Ignace. *Procès-verb. Acad. d. Sc.*, 6:392, 1818; 6:412, 1819.

RICHERAND, A.-B. *Nouveaux éléments de Physiologie.* Paris, Richard, Caille et Ravier, 1801.

ROBINSON, V. *The life of Jacob Henle.* New York, Medical Life Co., 1921.

Pathfinders in Medicine. New York, Medical Life Co., 1929.

ROLANDO, Expériences sur les fonctions du système nerveux. *J. de physiol. expér. et path.*, 3:95, 1823.

ROUSSEAU, J.-J. *Émile ou de l'éducation.* Amsterdam, Jean Neaulme, 1762.

SAINT-ANGE, M. *J. hebdom. de méd.*, Jan. 23, 1830.

SCHÄFER, E. A. *Textbook of Physiology.* Edinburgh, Pentland, v. i, 1898; v. ii, 1900.

SHAW, A. *Narrative of the Discoveries of Sir Charles Bell in the Nervous System.* London, Longmans, Orme, Brown, Green & Longmans, 1839.

SHAW, J. An account of some experiments on the nerves by M. Magendie. *London Med. and Physical J.*, 48:343, 1822.

(On the occasion of Magendie's visit to England in 1824.) *London Med. and Physical J.*, 52:95, 1824.

A manual for the student of anatomy, 1821. (First American from the last London edition, Troy, J. Disturnell, 1825.)

TRIAIRE, P. *Brettoneau et ses correspondants*, Paris, Félix Alcan, 1892.

P. Récamier et ses contemporains. 1774-1852, étude d'histoire de la médecine aux XVIII° et XIX° siècles. Paris, Baillière, 1899.

VULPIAN, A. *Leçons sur la physiologie générale et comparative du système nerveux*. Paris, Baillière, 1866.

WALKER, A. New anatomy and physiology of the brain. *Arch. Univ. Sc.*, 3:172, 1809.

The nervous system, anatomical and physiological: in which various parts of the brain are for the first time assigned, and to which is prefixed some account of the author's earliest discoveries, of which the more recent doctrine of Bell, Magendie, etc., is shown to be at once a plagiarism, an inversion, and a blunder associated with useless experiments, which they have neither understood nor explained. London, 1834.

WALLER, A. D. Charles Bell and the motor and sensory functions of spinal nerves. *The Lancet*, 180:614, 1911.

Sir Charles Bell and the functions of the fifth nerve. *The Lancet*, 180:1719, 1911.

The part played by Sir Charles Bell in the discovery of the functions of motor and sensory nerves (1822). *Science Progress*, 6:78, 1911.

INDEX

Abernethy, 141
Absorption, 37-42, 78-9, 124
Academy of Medicine, ix, 88, 154, 158n., 181, 192, 197, 214
Academy of Sciences, ix, xiii, 19, 20, 35, 37, 41f., 44, 45, 48, 51, 58, 65n., 69, 75, 86, 89f., 152, 160, 162, 177, 181, 183, 186, 190, 195f., 207, 209, 225, 244, 246, 257, 258, 259f.
Action currents, 259
Anaesthesia, 244-47
Andral, 85, 262
Animal heat, 46, 233, 259
Arago, 226
d'Arcet, 225f.
Aristotle, 25
Auenbrugger, 17
Auscultation, 85, 92, 208

Barreswill, 237
Barthez, 20, 21, 22f., 205
Baudin, 36
Beaumont, Wm., and Alexis St. Martin, 196
Béclard, 49, 56, 81
Becquerel, 233, 259
Bell, Charles, 85, 93f., 126, 135, 143, 147, 149, 179, 180, 220
    Exposition of the Natural System, xii, 179
    The Nervous System, xii
    Pamphlet of 1811, 104-11
    Letters, 94, 96, 99-100, 109n., 113-14
Bell, John, 111
Bell-Magendie Controversy, x, xi, xii, 85, 93-122, 130, 134, 165, 210, 215, 218, 248-49

Bell-Magendie Rule, 122, 211, 212
Bérard, 196
Bernard, Claude, ix, x, 30, 40, 41, 44, 46, 120, 129, 155, 158n., 178, 179, 182, 190, 191, 198, 204, 206, 211, 212, 213, 215f., 218, 227f., 250, 256, 260, 261, 262
Berthelot, 152
Berthollet, 35, 87
Berzelius, 65
Bichat, Xavier, x, 10, 15, 20-1, 23-7, 38, 49, 54, 63-5, 66, 79, 82-3, 105n., 174, 175, 177, 202, 262
    concept of tissues, 23-4
    doctrine of vital properties, 24-7, 63, 178, 202-3
Bichat's Fissure, 167-69
Bichat's Law, 169
Bleeding, 155f., 239, 259
Blood, 204
    propulsion of, 69-71, 205
    pressure, 204-8, 250
Boilly, Jules, lithographer, 158n.
Borelli, 27
Boussingault, 235
Boyer, 9, 11, 14, 15, 49, 81
Bretonneau, 151, 159
Breschet, 82, 84, 133, 156, 192, 219, 222f., 226, 228, 233, 254
Byron, Lord, 157

Caillard, 130
Caroline, Queen, 140
Carrel, A., and Lindbergh, C. A., 203n.
Castaing, trial of, 133
Cave of the Dog, 241

Caventou, 38, 71f., 84
Cerebellum, 123, 124, 125, 128, 150, 170, 197, 216, 217
  Bell's view of, 106-9, 121
Cerebrum, 125
  Bell's view of, 106-9, 121
Cerebro-spinal fluid, 148, 163, 165-70, 219, 230, 232-33
Charles X, 173, 176, 177n., 251
Chaussier, 9, 47, 48, 89, 133
Chevreul, 66, 69, 225
Cholera, 181-94, 196, 224, 253-54, 255, 257
Chomel, 208
Chorda tympani nerve, 197-98, 213
Chossat, 130
Circulation time, 207
Circus movements, 128-29, 150, 170, 216
Cloquet, 67, 81
Collège de France, ix, xi, 13, 89, 158n., 160, 174, 177f., 189, 192, 202f., 209f., 216, 220, 226, 228, 230, 231f., 237, 241, 256, 258, 259
Committee on Equine Hygiene, 222, 234-36, 252
Committee on Public Health, 253-56
Contagion, 181, 184, 186, 191, 224, 254-56, 257
Corneal ulcers, 129
Corpora striata, 127, 217
Corvisart 17, 81, 89
Cotugno, 148
Cretinism, 150
Crossed circulation experiments, 40

Dalton, 28
David d'Angers, 158n.
Davy, Sir Humphrey, 135
Decerebrate rigidity, 126
Delille, 35f., 42, 51, 66
Deperey Delaunay, Marie Nichole, 3, 4, 5, 12
Depuisay, Dr. Charles, 212, 261

Descartes, 167
Desmoulins, 112, 149
Dessault, 10
Determinism, 27, 30, 33, 83
Devasse, J., 229, 230
Devay, J., 158n.
Diabetes mellitus, 238
Digestion, 235, 237
Dubois, Antoine, 173
Dubois, F., 261, 262
  Eulogy of Magendie, ix, x, 3n., 54, 154, 225, 254, 258, 266
Dubois-Reymond, 259
Duchenne, 148
Duhamel, Georges, 165n.
Dumas, Alexander, 189
Dumas, Jean-Baptiste, 73, 235
Duméril, 75, 88, 89, 124, 146, 170, 181, 196, 198, 257
Dupuy, 95
Dupuytren, 11, 15, 16, 39, 40, 47, 49f., 66, 75n., 84, 88, 176, 181, 191, 226
Dutrochet, 88, 180

Écoles de Santé, 9, 11, 16, 17, 47
Edwards, 66, 88
Ellerby, Dr. J., 150
Elliotson, 119, 134, 134n., 137, 208n.
Emetics, 48, 52, 53, 55, 71, 127
Emetine, discovery of, 71-73

Faculty of Medicine, 3, 17, 18, 19, 45, 47, 50, 81, 159, 160, 183
Fedora, 124, 127
Ferrand, 243
Ferrus, 12, 151
Flint, 119, 119n.
Flourens, 119, 123-27, 165, 170, 196, 218, 219, 226, 238, 246, 247, 249, 257, 261
  Eulogy of Magendie, ix, xii, 3n., 49, 86, 89, 90, 112, 153, 182, 254, 261

Folie des Animaux, 235
Formulaire v. Magendie's *Works*
Fourcroy, 9
Fourier, 163
Fourquier-Tinville, 58
Frayssinous, l'Abbé, 159, 173
Fulton, J. F., 104n.

Gall, 117, 123
Galvanism, 85, 147, 197, 213, 229
Garibaldi, 194
Gaudichaud, 206
Gay-Lussac, 28, 35, 76, 88, 190, 234, 258
Gelatine, 225-28, 257
de Gembloux, Pierquin, 234
Genty, 50
George IV, 140
Gerdy, Dr., 236
Glisson, 26
Gmelin, 66, 85, 88
Goitre, 150
Goly, 222
Graves, 150
Grisolle and pneumonia, 155
Guérin, 13, 158n.
Guillot, Dr. Natalis, 183
Guizot, 14
Gull, 150
Guy's Hospital, London, 144

Haemodynamometer, 85, 205-8, 250
Hale, Dr. E., 145
Hales, Stephen, 206
Hall, 32, 112
Hallé, 87, 89, 91, 160
Haller, 26, 51, 149
Harvey, 86, 112, 143
Hauriot, Dr., 158
Hawkins, Caesar, 98, 112, 113
Heart sounds, 204, 208-10
Henle, 71, 180
Home, Sir Everard, 141
Hope, James, 208-10
Hospitals in Paris
  Bicêtre, 158

Hospitals in Paris (*Continued*)
  Charité, 9, 11, 76, 148, 155, 208, 236, 246
  Hôtel-Dieu, 9, 10, 11, 50, 130, 144, 151, 155, 159, 176, 179, 187, 188-9, 195, 197, 199, 202, 220, 226, 229, 232, 243
  Saint-Louis, 16, 198
  Salpetrière, 12, 37, 75, 79, 151-52, 159, 166
  Vénériens, 16
von Humboldt, 36, 51, 142, 180, 201
Hunter, John and William, 38, 38n., 65, 117
Huxley, Aldous, xiii
Hydrophobia, 84, 130-32, 144

Immobility in horses, 163, 217

Jackson's discovery of ether, 244
Jacob, medical illustrator, 233
James, Constantin, 179, 202, 210, 212, 217, 228, 241, 246, 257
Journal of Experimental Physiology,
  v. Magendie's *Works*
Jussieu, 37

Kant, 21
Keil, 27
Keith, Sir Arthur, 107, 120
Kergaradec, 85
Koch, 193
Krogh, 70n.

Laennec, 85, 88, 91, 133, 151, 158, 204, 208-10
Lafayette, 201
Lamarck, 21, 35
Lancet, The, 132, 137-38, 167, 168
Laplace, 19, 35, 46, 58, 87, 135, 152, 162, 201
Lavoisier, 19, 27, 46, 58, 201, 233
Lawrence, Thomas, 135
Leaches, 251
Leconte, Dr. Charles, 261

Lectures on Cholera, v. Magendie's *Works*

Lectures on the Nervous System, v. Magendie's *Works*

Lectures on the Physical Phenomena of Life, v. Magendie's *Works*

Lefort, Dr., 163

Legallois, 56

Legion of Honor, 3, 193, 240, 259

Lemare, 11

Leroux, 81, 83

Leschenault, 36, 37, 43

Liebig, 235, 244

Longet, 112, 119, 211-19, 232, 238, 248

Longevity in toads, 257

Louis XVIII, 159, 176

Louis-Napoleon, 251

Louis-Philippe, 176, 177, 181, 188, 251

Lugol, Dr., 198

Lymphatic system, 38-40, 78, 146

Mackintosh, Sir James, 141, 155

Magendie, Antoine, 3-9 *passim,* 12, 16, 51, 240

Magendie, François
Life and Thought:
birth and parentage, 3
early education, 4-5, 7
medical studies under First Republic, 8-12
prize for "republican virtue," 7-8
pupil of Boyer and his prosector in anatomy, 9
poverty relieved by legacy, 11-13
classical studies, 11, 161
early lectures and demonstrations in anatomy, 10, 11, 19
early interest in surgery, 12, 51
exemption from military service, 3, 14, 16, 57-58

Magendie, François
Life and Thought: (*Continued*)
completion of medical studies under the Empire, 16-18
interneships, 16
aide in anatomy, Faculty of Medicine, 16-17, 19, 45
doctorate of medicine, 18, 19, thesis for, 17, 3n., 18n.
election to Société Médicale d'Émulation, 20; president of, 81-82
reaction from Bichat's views, 21, 27-34, 35, 38, 54, 63-65, 79, 82-83, 164, 177, 202, 262
already a scientific determinist although still a vitalist, 30, 33, 83
experiments on strychnine and its absorption, 35-44
crossed circulation technique, 40
father of experimental pharmacology, 44
prosector in anatomy, Faculty of Medicine, 47, 49
quarrel with Chaussier, 48
registration of medical diploma, 49
private lectures in experimental physiology, 49, 51, 62, 161-62
renunciation of surgery and anatomy, 49-51
experiments on mechanics of digestive tract, 51-52, 53-55, 56-57
retinal images, 53
medicinal use of tartar emetic, 53
election to Société philomathique and editorship of its *Bulletin,* 55-56
exemption from draft under Napoleon, 57-58

Magendie, François
Life and Thought: (*Continued*)
epidemic of typhus, 58-59
work on protein free diets, 67-69
work on arteries in circulation, 69-71
discovery of emetine, 71-73
growing reputation abroad, 74
development of private medical practice, xiii, 75-77, 79, 146f., 152-55, 162, 258
work on lymphatic system in birds, 78-79
lecturer at Athenée Royal, 81
founding of his *Journal of Experimental Physiology*, 84f.
connection with the Montyon Prize in Experimental Physiology, 86-88, 90, 99, 124, 130, 196, 215
membership of Royal Academy of Medicine, 88-89
election to Academy of Sciences, 89-91
relations with John Shaw, 95f.
experiments on the functions of the roots of the spinal nerves, ix, x, xii, 93, 100-03, 111-12, 124, 180
dispute over priority with Bell and Shaw, 103-4, 112-21, 165, 179-81, 215, 220
claims as his own discovery of functions of spinal nerve roots, 103-4, 117-18, 149, 210, 248-49
contemporary sentiment against Magendie in France, 119, 130, 217, 218, 249; in Germany, 119, 180; at first for, later against, in England, 118-19, 120-21; in America, 120

Magendie, François
Life and Thought: (*Continued*)
review of evidence supports Magendie's claim, 122
work on central nervous system, 123-30, 149-50, 210, 215-16
rivalry with Flourens, 89, 123f., 130, 165, 218-19
decerebrate rigidity, 126
olfaction, 127-28, 217
circus movements, 128-29, 150, 170, 216
experiments on the 5th cranial nerve, 129-30
treatment for hydrophobia, 84, 130-32, 144
direct injection into veins, 144-45
first visit to England, 134-37
attack in Parliament on his vivisections, 138-42
insensitivity of the retina, 146-47, 245, 259
specific nerve energies, 147
galvanism, 85, 147-48, 197-98, 213, 229
cerebrospinal fluid, 148-49, 163-64, 165-70, 217-18, 219, 230, 232-33
Magendie's foramen, 166, 168
observations on goitre, 150
hospital connections, 16, 79, 151-52, 155n., 159, 176, 188-90, 195, 199, 229, 243
clinical instruction, 151, 176, 195, 229
opposition to 'bleeding', 155-56
marriage, 172f.
residence, 86, 172, 199, 200, 201, 243
appointment to Chair of Medicine at Collège de France, 177; earlier rejections, 91-92, 158-61

Magendie, François
Life and Thought: (*Continued*)
visit to England to report on cholera, 182-85
services in cholera epidemic in Paris, 188-93; in Dunkerque, 253-54
country life, 199-201
work on blood pressure with Poiseuille apparatus, 205-208, 250
heart sounds, 204, 208-10
affair of Longet and recurrent sensitivity, 211-18, 249-50
new laboratory at Collège de France, 220
collaboration—with Delille, 35, 38, 42, 66; with Pelletier, 71; with Caventou, 71; with Chevreul, 66, 69; with Breschet, 84; with Dupuytren, 66, 84, 199; with Duméril, 198; with Andral, 85; with Fedora, 124, 127; with Desmoulins, 149; with Poiseuille, 205-08 (blood pressure, haemo-dynamometer); with Bernard, 206, 211, 212-13 (5th & 7th cranial nerves), 215-16 (recurrent sensitivity), 217 (site of cerebellar injury), 227, 231 (*préparateur*, Collège de France), 232 (cerebrospinal fluid), 233 (animal heat, seat of oxidation), 234 (madness in horses), 236 (saliva, pancreatic ducts), 237 (pancreatic juice), 237, (blood sugar), 240, 243 (*suppléant*, or deputy, at Collège de France); with Ferrand, 243
sugar a normal constituent of blood, 237-38, 243

Magendie, François
Life and Thought: (*Continued*)
work on committees, 162, 181 (Cholera), 225-27, 257 (Gelatine), 222-24, 234-36, 252 (Equine Hygiene), 253-56 (Public Hygiene)
views on contagion, 181, 184-86, 224, 254-56
opposition to use of anaesthetics, 244-47
attitude to vivisection, 143, 174, 222
attitude to medical profession, xi, 77, 85-86, 90, 153-57, 229-31
political sympathies, 18, 91-92, 157, 160, 173-75, 202, 251-52
philosophical views, 29, 30, 33, 64, 79, 83, 174, 202-03, 203n.
characteristics as a man, 18, 56, 90-91, 149, 157, 162, 202, 228, 229, 241, 257, 258; as a scientist, x-xiii *passim*, 32, 40-41, 54, 144, 167, 210, 215, 236, 237, 238-39, 244, 259
appearance, portraits, 13-14, 158n.
failing health, 259
death, 261
contemporary estimates, ix-xiii, 90-91, 142, 151, 173-75, 221, 229-31, 239
Works, discussed or referred to:
Thesis for M.D.: *Essay on the uses of the soft palate*, 3n., 17-18, 18n., 271
First published article, *Some general ideas on phenomena peculiar to living bodies*, 10, 20, 21, 27-34, 271
Study of action of certain vegetable poisons, 35, 36-38, 271

Magendie, François
  Life and Thought: (*Continued*)
    Experiments on pulmonary transpiration, 45-47, 271
    Vomiting, 51-52, 271
    Epiglottis and its function in swallowing, 52, 271
    Memoir on retinal images, 53, 271
    Influence of emetics, 53, 271
    Action of the oesophagus, 53, 271
    Swallowing of air, 60, 271
    Précis (Text-book of Physiology), 62-69, 149, 272; quoted, 62, 63, 66; referred to, 28n., 29n., 63, 65, 69, 79
    English translation of, 125n.
    Note on intestinal gases, 69, 272
    Memoir on protein-free diets, 67-69, 272
    Note on tongue swallower, 75, 272
    Action of arteries in circulation, 69-71, 272
    Prussic acid, 76, 272
    Note on prescription of morphine, 77, 272
    Comment on Portal on vomiting, 57, 272
    Physiological and medical researches on urinary calculi, 77, 272
    Note on mesenteric nerves of woodpecker, 78-79, 272
    Note on the anatomy of the swan, 78-79, 272
    Memoir on divers organs in birds and reptiles, 78-79, 272
    The mechanism of absorption in warm- and cold-blooded animals, 79, 273
    Formulary, 72, 73, 79-80, 133, 199, 229, 273

Magendie, François
  Life and Thought: (*Continued*)
    Memoir on the organs of absorption in mammals, 84, 273
    Experiment on functions of spinal nerve roots, 85, 100-03, 273
    Note on Flourens' paper on cerebellum, 125, 273
    Note on seat of movement and feeling in spinal cord, 111-12, 273
    Note on functions of corpora striata and quadrigemina, 127, 273
    Account of hydrophobic patient at Hôtel-Dieu, 130-32
    Is the olfactory nerve the olfactory organ? 127-28, 273
    Influence of the 5th cranial nerve on the eye, 129, 273
    Results of cutting the cerebellar peduncle, 128-29, 274
    Observations on a deaf mute, 130, 274
    Note on goitre, 150, 274
    Memoir on cerebrospinal fluid (1825), 148, 274
    Insensitivity of retina, 146-47, 274
    Galvanism in treatment of blindness, 147-48, 274
    Memoir on cerebrospinal fluid (1827), 148-49, 274
    Ligature of carotid artery, 152, 274
    Reply to Lefort's attack on cerebrospinal fluid, 163, 274
    Memoir on the brain, 165-69, 274
    Note on Bell's attitude to animal experimentation, 118, 275

Magendie, François
Life and Thought: (*Continued*)
*Note on Bell's attitude regard-
ing Bell-Magendie contro-
versy*, 117, 275
Letter to President of Academy of Sciences, 183-85,
275
Letter to English Ambassador,
187, 275
Lectures on cholera, 189, 196,
275
Report on abnormal growth,
197, 275
Report on Polish officer, 197-98,
275
*Treatment of certain nervous
affections by galvinism*, 198,
275
*Note of treatment of blindness
by galvinism*, 198, 275
*Memoir on origin of heart
sounds*, 209, 275
*Some new experiments on func-
tions of nervous system*
(1839), 212, 275
Letter to Academy of Medicine
(regarding Longet), 214,
275
*Lectures on the Nervous
System*, 210, 275; quoted, 93,
123, 136, 146; referred to,
12, 67, 129, 197, 210, 212,
217, 254
Comments on glanders, 223-24,
275
*Report for Gelatine Commis-
sion*, 227, 275
*Lectures on Physical Phenom-
ena of Life*, 202-05, 203n.,
276; quoted, 34, 35, 45, 59,
74, 153, 172, 189, 195, 203,
220, 243; referred to, 58,
178, 185, 206, 207, 209, 244,
255

Magendie, François
Life and Thought: (*Continued*)
*Physiological and chemical re-
searches on cerebrospinal
fluid* (1842), 232-33, 276
A case of cowpox, 200, 276
Study of saliva in the horse,
236, 276
*Note on the normal presence of
sugar in the blood*, 237-38,
276
Comments on ether, 245, 248,
276
Reply to Flourens (regarding
Bell), 248-49, 276
Note on recurrent sensitivity,
249, 276
*Influence of spinal nerves on
heart movements*, 250, 276
Lectures on Animal Heat, 233,
276
Comment on toad, 257-58, 276
(With Duméril) *Treatment of
scrofula with iodine*, 198, 276
(With Pelletier) *Researches on
ipecacuanha*, 71-73, 276-77
Magendie, Jean-Jacques, 5, 8, 8n.,
173
Magendie, Mme (Henriette Bas-
tienne de Puisaye), 172, 199,
201, 240, 246
Magnus, 235
Maingault, 56, 57
Manni prize, 190
Marie-Louise, Empress, 3
Martin, Richard, 138f.
Materialism, 21
Mayo, Herbert, 112, 113, 118, 137
Mechanism, 22, 203n., 206
Medical education in France—Post-
revolutionary, 8-9; in Napo-
leonic times, 14-18; tendency
toward practicality, 15; pres-
ent Faculty of Medicine
founded, 18

Medico-chirurgical Review, 132, 137-38

Mirbel, 258

Montalivet, 58, 176

Montpellier, 9, 20, 22, 151, 204, 230

Montyon, 87, 88, 90
    prize in experimental physiology, 90, 99, 124, 130, 196, 206, 215, 249

Moreau-Jones, 186

Morton's use of ether, 244

Müller, Johannes, 105, 109n., 147, 180, 219

Naples, 241

Napoleon, 3, 9, 14, 15, 17, 57, 58, 59, 251

Newton, 20, 22, 64

Nicholas I, 181

Olfaction, 127-28

Orfila, 44, 81, 188, 219

Pancreas, 66, 236, 237

Pariset, 158, 255

Paracelsus, 155

Parry, 150

Pascalis, Felix, 150

Pasteur, 191, 193

Pattison, 118

Payen, 235

Peel, Sir Robert, 141

Pelletier, 38, 71f., 76, 84, 88

Pelouze, 199, 244

Percy, 52, 87

Perier, 188

Permeability, 79

Pharmacology, beginnings of, 44

Physical Phenomena of Life v. Magendie's Works

Physiological and chemical researches on cerebrospinal fluid (1842), v. Magendie's Works

Physiologist
    attitude of, to Bell-Magendie controversy, 122
    Magendie as, 75, 95, 152, 159, 167

Physiology
    Bichat's domination of, 33, 177
    early text-books of, by Richerand, 16, 66; by Magendie, v. Précis, Magendie's Works
    Magendie's examination in, 16
    experimental, x, 49, 51, 161, 178; Magendie's Journal of, 84-86; Magendie's laboratory for, 220, 228, 231; Magendie's lectures in, 49, 51, 62, 161-62, 178-79, 195, 197, 202-05, 210, 237, 241, 256, 258-59; Magendie pioneer of, xiii-xiv; Montyon prize in, v. Montyon

Pineal gland, 166, 167, 217

Pinel 35, 37, 41, 42, 43, 52, 87, 89, 152, 164, 218

Poiseuille, 85, 204, 205f., 222, 250

Portal, 57, 181

Protein-free diet, 67-69

Prussic acid, 76

Quarantine, 158, 184-87, 255-56

Rayer, 222f., 228, 234, 254

Réaumur, 65

Récamier, 88, 159-61, 176-78, 191, 191n., 220, 226

Recurrent sensitivity, 211-16, 249-50

Restoration of monarchy, its effect on medicine, 157-61

Retina, insensitivity of, 146-47, 245, 259

Retinal images, 53

Revolution of July, 1830, 173, 175-76, 251

Richerand, 16, 50, 66

Robespierre, 6

Rodents as laboratory animals, 69
Rollando, 85, 124, 126
Rousseau, J. J., 4, 7, 174
Roux, 49, 81, 198, 213, 219, 220, 244, 246f.

Saint-Hilaire, G., 35
St. Thomas Hospital, London, 134, 137-38
Sainte-Ange, Dr. Martin, 168
Saliva, 236
Salons, post-revolutionary, 12, 14
Sannois, 199-201, 243, 261
Serres, 181, 196, 246, 261, 262
Shaw, Alexander, 110n., 115
Shaw, John, 93f., 115, 137, 210
Sherrington, 32, 126, 126n.
Silliman, Benjamin, 76
Société Médicale d'Émulation, 20, 33, 81-82
Société philomathique, 55-56, 236
Society for Prevention of Cruelty to Animals, 138, 141
Specific nerve energies, 105, 147
Spurzheim, 96, 117, 123
Stethoscope, 85, 92, 151, 208, 208n., 209
Strychnine, 35-44
Sugar in the blood, 237-38
Swallowing, 52

Tartar emetic, 43, 53, 127
Tenon, 75
Thénard, 72, 88, 190, 226
Tiedemann, 65, 85, 88, 169
Trophic nerves, 129
Trousseau, A., 151, 159
Typhus, 58, 255
Thyroid, 150

Upas antiar, 42, 43
Upas tieute, 38, 39, 43
Urinary calculi, 77

van Tieghem, 228
Velpeau, 219, 244f.
Viellermé, 261, 262
Vitalism, x, 20-27, 29, 30, 33, 64, 79, 83, 174, 202-03, 236
Vitamins, 68
Vivisection, 138, 140-44, 174, 221-22
Vomiting, 43, 51-52, 53-55
Vulpian, 119

Walker, Alexander, 112, 119
Wallaston, 134f.
Waller, Augustus, 107, 120
Williams, C.T.B., 208n.